In the past twenty years every county in Britain, from Caithness to Cornwall, has had recurrent sightings of 'big cats' – described as being like pumas or panthers.  These anomalous big cat sightings are now running at an estimated 1,200 a year.

Farmers, gamekeepers, ornithologists, policemen and even parents on the school run have all been thrilled – or terrified – to see what they assume is a big cat escaped from a zoo. Yet these big cats are neither escapees from zoos nor, as this book conclusively argues, the descendants of pets released into the countryside by their owners in 1976 when the Dangerous Wild Animals Act made it too expensive to keep big cats.

The questions therefore remain, what are they and where have they come from? With the orthodox explanations overturned, Merrily Harpur searches for clues in the cultures of other times and places. She discovers our mystery felines have been with us for longer than we imagine, and throws unexpected light on the way Western civilisation looks at the world.

*Mystery Big Cats* is the first serious and comprehensive book on the subject. From the drama of eyewitnesses' verbatim accounts to the excitement of new perspectives and insights into a strange and often terrifying experience – it gets to grips with what is now the commonest encounter with the unknown in Britain.

**Merrily Harpur** is a cartoonist and writer. She has published three books: *The Nightmares of Dream Topping, Unheard of Ambridge* and *Pig Overboard.* She divides her time between Dorset and Ireland, where she founded the Strokestown International Poetry Festival.  www.harpur.org

# Mystery Big Cats

## Merrily Harpur

**Heart of Albion**

**Mystery Big Cats**

**Merrily Harpur**

Cover illustration by courtesy of
Exotic Felines Breeding Center, Rosamund CA.

ISBN 1 872883 92 3

EAN 978 1872 883 922

Published by

**Heart of Albion Press**
2 Cross Hill Close, Wymeswold
Loughborough, LE12 6UJ

albion@indigogroup.co.uk

**Visit our Web site: www.hoap.co.uk**

Printed in England by Booksprint

To John Michell, who so kindly set me on the right track.

# Acknowledgements

I am grateful to everyone who shared their experiences and data with me. There are too many of these generous donors to name individually, but a few deserve special mention:

Di Francis, the intrepid enthusiast, whose book *Cat Country* provided the first inspiration - and much information - for this one; W. Ritchie Benedict in Canada, the arrival of whose letters bulging with clippings was always a thrilling event; Mark Fraser who has been extraordinarily generous with his time and information and whose vast archive, together with his insights into the big cat phenomenon, amounted to a complete education in the subject; Nigel and David Spencer who provided information, help and hospitality; Paul Screeton who passed on his personal anomalous big cat archive; my god-daughter Katie Leonard for calculating how many leopards could theoretically result from a single breeding pair after fifty-nine years (16,310,042!); and Paul Sieveking whose regular round-ups of sightings in *Fortean Times* and witty, concise summaries have succoured mystery big cat literature for several decades.

In addition I wish to thank that magazine's founder and present co-editor, Bob Rickard, for so kindly unearthing boxes of archived newspaper clippings for me to browse through. His books on anomalous animals and events, co-authored with John Michell, had already showed me the tools necessary to grapple with rebarbative subjects such as mystery big cats and I have tried to imitate their good humour and deftness of touch in this one.

Most crucial to the emergence of this work was the writing of my brother Patrick Harpur whose exquisite exegeses of Neoplatonism and traditional wisdom, and their application to the present time, was available for me to commandeer and roughly treat for my own purposes. In that sense I hope this book may serve as a footnote to his.

Merrily Harpur

October 2005

# Contents

# Chapter 1

# Big cats in Britain – the three mysteries

Kim Welsh is a teacher and a wife and mother, and on a bright morning in May 2001 she was driving her twelve-year-old daughter home from a riding lesson near Ringwood, Dorset. They had gone only about two hundred and fifty yards out of the village when they had an experience which Kim described as 'completely bizarre':

> 'We came round a slight bend to see a big, jet-black cat – the size of a panther – emerge from the left hand side hedge, and stop in the middle of the lane. I braked but it didn't move so I then had to stop the car. It stood there only a few feet from the bonnet. The car is a Nissan Serena of just over five foot six inches wide – and it was at least the whole width of the car. It had huge paws, a long tail looped up at the end, a panther-like domed head, and amber eyes. It stayed completely still in front of the car looking at us for about thirty seconds I should think, though it seemed like an eternity, and then it sauntered – with a typical feline gait – off to the right, and disappeared into the hedge. My daughter and I looked at each other in stunned silence; it was quite frightening, and I know it was silly but I locked the car door. You just don't see something like that.'[1]

There is something odd going on in Britain's green and pleasant land that no one can explain – increasing numbers of people are encountering big cats at large in the countryside. They are people like Kim – normal, sensible people going about their daily business and as shocked as you or I would be to see an African or Asian panther in the lanes of England.

Kim had certainly not expected to see an anomalous animal, and, she told me, would previously have dismissed the idea that she might – 'I just have never really been interested in that kind of thing.'

Paul Traynor was driving along the A442 in Shropshire when, he said:

> 'I was amazed to see a large black cat jump over the central reservation directly in front of me. I can say without any doubt that it was a large panther. I had to brake very hard to miss the

animal and ended up sideways on the road. I would estimate I
stopped around twenty feet from the animal… The animal
recoiled for a second or two. It then watched me briefly before
trotting off to my left into the trees. I would estimate the animal to
be three to three-and-a-half feet tall and about five feet long. It
was jet black with a long tail carried in a long curl.' [2]

Both Kim and Paul immediately rang the police. Through such official reports fleeting encounters such as these often make the local press. Emboldened by others' experiences more eyewitnesses often come forward to report their own sighting and the ensuing spate of reports has been wittily dubbed a 'cat-flap'.

There had been a cat-flap in Gloucestershire in the 1990s. Like most people I had vaguely seen the reports, but not knowing what to make of them had forgotten them.

I was certainly not thinking of big cats on the summer's evening I turned down a Gloucestershire lane and, about eighty yards ahead, a peculiar animal loped across it. I ran through the familiar possibilities and dismissed them. It was clearly not a dog, nor a deer, nor a calf. It was the height of a roe deer but longer, and its head had a blunt, feline profile. It had a long tail that swept down towards the ground and up again in a loop. It was black and smooth-coated, and it moved gracefully, vaulting easily up the steep bank with the sinuous ease of a cat.

Puzzled, I drove forward as fast as my dilapidated car would go and stopped at the place where the animal had disappeared into a cornfield, but could see no further sign of it. Gradually it dawned upon me what I could have seen – the panther-like animal written about in the local newspapers. It was what they had named, in tabloid style, the 'Beast of Gloucester'. I got back into the car hastily.

I went on my way thinking about the event. It was an event both trivial in one way and shocking in another. Indeed it was in the slightness of the event that its alarming quality lay. Something odd had managed to insert itself fleetingly between the predictable lines of normal life.

My curiosity piqued, I searched out back copies of the local newspapers when I returned home, to see if my sighting matched those of other people. I read their testimonies from a new perspective: what had formerly seemed lifeless, silly-season reportage now glittered with incidental detail and rich drama. Most had had far more interesting encounters than I. For instance Mrs Margaret Jones had been walking near the village of Dymock when she saw 'a black animal' strolling down the road towards her. She said:

'I had a very full view. It was about as high as a sheep but it had
the swaggering roll of a cat. It turned totally sideways and I was
amazed to see a very long tail which touched the ground and
curled up at the end for about nine inches. It was a muscley sort
of animal, pitch black with a small head and this massive tail...
I was watching it for a couple of minutes as it came towards me
then it jumped ten or twelve feet up the bank and disappeared.' [3]

What had she seen? And indeed what had I seen? It was then that I decided to research the subject of big cat sightings in Britain from scratch, determined to get to the bottom of these intriguing experiences.

I turned first to a unique resource which I already had in my possession – a file full of first-hand reports of big cats sighted from 1948 onwards. They had gathered dust on my shelf for years, although I had always kept them safely on the off-chance they might one day prove useful. Now, it seemed, was that day.

I had acquired them almost accidentally some years before. Like most people I had not taken big cat reports seriously until one afternoon in 1983. I was drawing in my studio when I heard the eerie half-roar, half-cry of one of these animals and literally sat up, the hair creeping upright on my arms. It was on a radio programme and had been recorded by Di Francis, the first person to publish a book examining exclusively British big cats.

I had grown up with the Surrey Puma – spotted regularly during the 1960s and 70s when I was at school. At that time I vaguely felt it must be some kind of psychological effect – a spectre projected on to their over-suburbanised landscape by the repressed bourgeoisie. I was a teenager and those were the times we were living in. But the sound of Di's recording alerted me to something I had not considered before, that these animals might have an independent physical existence – that, in short, they could be real.

It was as exciting a thought as it was problematical. If they existed in some numbers, as she believed, what were they and what were they doing here? Did Di Francis have a theory, I wondered, and if so what was it? I rang the radio station and tracked her down to ask.

It turned out that she had the most audacious – and therefore most engaging – theory I could have imagined. She claimed these big cats were a relict pre-Ice Age species, native to this country and living undiscovered by science until now.

She generously included me in some of her expeditions in which she roamed Devon looking for evidence to support the theory – which was where the problem began. It was not that there was insufficient evidence – there was too much. It was doubtful whether one kind of big cat could have remained concealed in the landscape since primeval times; but when reports of different types and colours of mystery feline flooded in it became necessary to postulate more than one hide-out species – two at least. Then three… then the idea became untenable and collapsed.

Without an explanation – however *outré* – for these anomalous big cats my interest lost focus. I relegated the mystery of the big cats to the pigeonhole marked 'Perhaps' and forgot about them again.

However after she published her book *Cat Country* in 1982 Di had received a deluge of letters from people detailing sightings from as far back as the 1940s. They had, it seemed, been bottling up vivid accounts of sightings of big cats, waiting for a sympathetic researcher to tell. When she went off to live in Scotland she donated this file of letters to me, and it had remained unopened on the top shelf ever since.

So it was, nearly two decades later, that I fetched it from its place with great anticipation. The hide-out theory – as a literal representation of the facts – had never been a possibility; yet as a metaphor its echo remained – there was still an unresolved enigma lurking within the familiar landscape of everyday life. So it was that, puzzled and intrigued all over again, I opened Di's file of letters and sat down to see what, if anything, it had to tell me about this weird phenomenon.

I was not disappointed. The experience was like taking the cork out of a venerable bottle of wine – the room filled with the incense of confided secrets. Each writer had laboured to do justice to incidents they experienced as bizarre or incredible.

I read that something just as unexpected as my own experience – and that of Paul Traynor and Kim Welsh – had happened to Sarah Priestly, of Sandgate in Kent. She had been walking her collie in nearby Encombe Woods one sunny morning in the April of 1984. 'I had emerged from the ruins of Encombe House', she wrote, 'when I saw a strange, cat-like creature about eight or nine feet – the width of my living-room – away. It was half lying, half sitting up the way cats do, sunning itself.

> 'I studied it for about two minutes before it saw me, looked at me for a moment, and then leaped up with a very powerful, cat-like leap, revealing powerful hind quarters, and disappeared into the undergrowth. It was the size of a Great Dane, tan in colour, head slightly darker, and its stomach was whitish. It had tiny pointed ears, rounded cheeks, square jaw, and a small head in comparison with its body… I thought, "What on earth can that be?" But I knew at once – and I remain adamant – that it was some kind of cat.' [4]

Then there was what Mrs J. Bagley described as a 'startling experience.' It took place in South Croydon, Surrey, in the late summer of 1978. Mrs Bagley wrote:

> 'The time was around 4:30 p.m., and it was a warm, sunny, still afternoon. I had been to visit my mother who lives in a flat, and was just leaving. There is a driveway at the side of the flats which leads to a courtyard at the back. This is bordered by a grassy embankment leading up to a railway line. As I walked towards my car, with my Scottie dog on a lead, a large cat-like animal ran up the driveway, straight past my dog and me and within about twelve feet of us. It was about three feet high and five feet long, a slim build with long legs and a long tail. It had a leopard-like head without the spots, with small rounded ears lying flattish on the head. It took no notice of us, made no noise, and there was no odour from it. It had mid-beige colour fur, and a very graceful gait, with long strides. My Scottie dog froze to the spot but didn't growl or bark. It ran up the embankment, and disappeared over the railway line… '

Her sighting was corroborated, not just by the reaction of her dog, but by her mother. 'She also saw this as she stood at her bedroom window, two floors up, waving me goodbye. Although my mother and I had both seen it, from different viewpoints, I didn't report it to the police, assuming they would think us foolish or over-imaginative.' [5]

As I read more reports I found that these two women's meticulous attention to detail and straightforward, restrained language was typical of all the eyewitnesses who had written to Di. All strove to describe their experiences as honestly as possible, concerned to pass them on to someone they believed would be interested, in a spirit of shared scientific enquiry. Few felt qualified to make any assumptions about the species they were looking at. 'A cat-like animal' and 'some kind of big cat' was all most witnesses were sure of. The more real and immediate the experience, it seemed, the more a clear, unembroidered description of it ensued.

I skimmed on through the pile of letters hearing the conviction in the writers' voices:

> '… it was on a hot summer day in 1979 that I saw it, I can even recall the dress I was wearing at the time… '

> '… Then this creature went up a large tree just like a cat does… My dog still goes to have a look at that tree.'

> '… I searched all through our books to find something that resembled it but there was nothing the right size… '

> '… My husband pulled back the bedroom curtains, and stood looking at the fields beyond, at the rabbits, pheasants, and occasional fox – a thing he did every morning. He suddenly shouted at me to come to the window. The tone of his voice made me leap out of bed… '

> '… It was about fifteen feet away from us when it noticed us and stopped. He lifted up his head and just stared at us. We were amazed and just stared at him… '

> '… I can assure you this is the truth of what we saw… '

> 'I have decided to write to you to put on record my sightings of a cat-like creature which I will call a puma, as this is the closest animal to which it has a likeness… '

> '… For a split-second I froze with fear, then the animal sped away into the surrounding forest at a tremendous speed… '

> '… The shiny sleekness of the animal and long, thick tail made a great impact on us. We could hardly believe what we were seeing and stopped because it was a little scary… '

> '… On returning home I telephoned the police. I have frequented these woods for years, and have never encountered anything like this before… '

On and on, the same story was repeated through dozens of individual variants from all parts of the country.

The immediacy of the writers' stories invited some response. I did not know what they were seeing, but their descriptions intrigued me enough to try, at least, to make sense of what had clearly been a distinct, unusual, baffling – and shared – experience.

The letters dated mainly from the 1970s and early 1980s. Of course I immediately wondered whether comparable numbers of anomalous big cats were being seen today – two decades later – and if so what modern eyewitnesses were saying about them.

I therefore set about collecting more recent incidents to add to the file. The first thing that surprised me was the sheer volume of reports. It seemed that in the fifteen or so years since Di's correspondents put pen to paper sightings of big cats had snowballed.

There had been cat-flaps in every county, but because these were mainly confined to reports in the local press, the national picture did not emerge until I totted up the total. In the year 2001 approximately 484 sightings of big cats were reported by local newspapers alone.[6]

Scotland topped the league for sightings published in the press that year, with 78 from various parts of the country. Gloucester came next with 55, closely followed by Cornwall with 52. Sussex, Devon and Wales each had between 41 and 45 reports during that period. Kent and Norfolk each had 36 sightings. That year the people of Leicestershire saw 32 big cats clearly enough to notify the police and the press, as did the inhabitants of Buckinghamshire. Northampton newspapers carried reports of 25 sightings, and Essex of 10.

By 2003 the annual number of press reports had doubled, with three times as many sightings again reported to other agencies, such as the Web sites of big cat enthusiasts who had begun to collect and publish sightings in this way.

The most assiduous investigators had, it turned out, large archives of personally reported sightings on file. Nigel and David Spencer (www.bigcats.org.uk) had logged reports of big cats in the Leicestershire/Rutland area for many years. Mark Fraser has systematically collected and published sightings of these animals in Scotland, (www.scottishbigcats.co.uk) and nationwide (www.britishbigcatgroup.com) investigating most claims personally, for more than a decade. He had recorded well over three hundred sightings in Scotland alone during 2002.

Yet amazingly these outlandish numbers seemed to be but the tip of the iceberg. Mark, along with the other long-term investigators, had found that at least four out of five sightings went unreported or remained within the witness's family circle.

Thus it was possible to say that at least 1,500 people saw an anomalous big cat in the years 2001 to 2002 combined, with an estimated upper total of possibly 4,500. In 2003 the estimate grew to somewhere between 2,000 to 4,000 sightings of big cats for that one year alone.

## The first mystery

The first mystery I encountered was that despite these large numbers, and despite the best efforts of the authorities and private individuals over many years, none of these big cats had been caught, trapped, shot, treed by hounds, or even killed on a road. There were persistent rumours of bodies by the side of motorways which subsequently disappeared; and of farmers who had shot and buried a big cat. But no one had ever produced the requisite puma or panther body – or even a clear photograph of one. This was odd because there would be a lot of money to be made out of the discovery of such a corpse, quite apart from the zoological interest it would generate.

There was a steady trickle of amateur photos and videos showing blurred black blobs, some of them tantalisingly like glimpses of big, cat-like animals. There were livestock kills and incriminating big cat footprints. But what is generally termed 'hard' evidence remained annoyingly elusive, given the huge numbers of animals seen.

While many reports could have been of the same animal seen serially, the vast geographical spread of them – from Sutherland to Cornwall – still suggested a disturbingly large population. In fact the numbers seemed so preposterous that I began to wonder if people might not have been entirely mistaken about what they were looking at – on a huge scale. Could it be, for instance, that most witnesses were townies, for whom the brief glimpse of a deer or fox constituted a sighting of the big cat they had perhaps read about?

I returned to my files to recheck them for signs of possible misidentifications. Crucial details were uncertain in only a handful of these – the vast majority of closely-observed, first person accounts reported in the press and which I subsequently investigated stood up to scrutiny. In some ways this was not surprising. Most press stories are derived from the alarmed witness's call to the police, and no one wants to make an official report that might make them look foolish unless they are certain of what they saw.

In fact the more I delved, the more impressive the eyewitnesses' evidence seemed. It was mainly knowledgeable country people – farmers, shepherds, bird-watchers, gamekeepers, field sports enthusiasts – who were seeing these big cats in every conceivable part of the country.

Ornithologist Roy Neville from Berkshire made no guesses about what species the creature he spotted might have been – he simply observed its striking appearance.

> '… At noon, I went to the lake which is hidden among thick rhododendrons on a large country estate, for the purpose of checking the water level and also looking at the wild Canada geese which visit it. When I cautiously crept up to peer through the shrubs, I was shocked and amazed to see a large, beautiful, jet-black, cat-like animal drinking at the clearing. It was a very powerful looking beast, around four to five feet in length, with

raised shoulders, a thick neck and a beautiful, shiny, black coat. It appeared to be aware of my presence at once as it glanced in my direction. I saw it had large yellowy-green eyes. Suddenly it dashed off through the bushes and left me astounded and as scared as the animal itself!' [7]

Norvie Berry is a gamekeeper in Suffolk. He related:

'I was out night-shooting rabbits near St Felix School in October 1999, and met a puma. At first I thought it was a dog, as it was very light in colour and the size of a Labrador. But I could see whiskers and rounded ears, and it was plodding along in a furrow with a long thick tail that looked just like a hockey stick… I was only eight yards away from it and I've got a good scope on my gun. I was excited and the adrenaline was going but I wasn't frightened. I was thinking "Should I shoot it?" but there was no reason to kill it – it was doing no harm… After I reported it I had twenty-three calls from people telling me they had also seen a big cat. People are too embarrassed to tell anyone at first because they think they will get laughed at.' [8]

Like Kim Welsh, the witness is often so close to the animal that a mistaken identity can be safely excluded. Mark Hill was also forced to stop his car when driving over the Mendips in Somerset one night he saw a large cat-like animal on the road ahead. It crossed casually in front of him, no more than six feet from the car, and brilliantly illuminated by the headlamps which were on full beam. It then clawed at and ate from a discarded food wrapper by the side of the road for a few minutes while Mark sat and watched in amazement, in no doubt that:

'It was a large, black cat, about four foot long, and two foot high. It had a small head compared to the size of its body, feline features, and a long tail. I edged up to about one metre away and was looking at it over the bonnet of the car. This enabled me to gauge its size accurately, and also the fact that it took up about half of one carriageway of the road. I watched it for about two minutes. It did not seem fazed by the car at all.' [9]

Three of the sightings I have quoted so far were of fawn or sandy-coloured animals. It seemed this colour was typical of the majority of anomalous feline animals seen in Britain in the early decades of big cat sightings – from the 1950s to the 1970s. Many of them roughly approximate to an American cougar or puma.

However, as the reports I collected turned from dozens into many hundreds, I noticed that the predominant colour of these anomalous big cats had gradually changed over the decades. Black ones had been regularly spotted throughout the years, but from the 1980s big cats of this colour began to be seen more often, and finally to predominate. In the last ten years approximately three or four black animals – such as the ones Kim Welsh and Mark Hill met – are seen to every fawn or sandy-coloured one.

## The second mystery

This puzzled me, for the most popular candidate for the identity of these animals had hitherto been that of the American puma or cougar. But pumas are never black. They may range from fawn through ginger to dark tan, but there are no certain records of black pumas either here or in their native America.[10]

The only big cats which have a melanistic (black) form are leopards (and their New World equivalent, jaguars). Black cubs occasionally crop up among litters of conventionally-spotted leopards, and such animals are popularly termed 'black panthers'. (I also use this term, or simply 'panther' to denote a black leopard.) They are valuable exhibits in zoos precisely because they are uncommon. Yet it seemed from my daily increasing records that hundreds of these rare, black leopards are apparently at large in our island.

In the face of this statistic it was natural to wonder – once more – if witnesses could have been mistaken. However, with their usual fastidiousness, witnesses either detailed colours as accurately as possible, or where they were unsure explained why they could not be specific. Distance, or back-light, was the most often-quoted reason for a small minority of animals appearing only 'dark' rather than a specific colour. Those who were in no doubt usually gave very clear descriptions of the animals' colour and appearance.

Colin Booth, a landscape gardener in Wiltshire got a very leisurely look at a big cat. He reported: 'I was cutting back a hedge at Rowden Hill, Chippenham, and had the shock of my life when a black panther strolled out of it! The cat walked towards me until it was only about twenty feet away.'

Mr Booth was shocked but not afraid, and studied the animal closely before it glanced at him and walked back into the undergrowth. 'I have two German shepherd dogs and it was a good six inches longer than them, but not taller. Its ears were flat against its small head, and it was very muscular. Its coat was jet-black, and shone as it walked.'

He added: 'It was a beautiful creature, and had a profound effect on me I will remember it for the rest of my life. It was such a privilege to be there and I hope people will leave it alone – but I informed the police because I thought they might want to warn people.'

A woman strolling in a country lane in West Sussex was similarly entranced by the sight of 'a large, jet-black cat'. This one was 'standing – posing almost – high on the bank'. She described the encounter in graphic detail: 'I stifled a gasp of wonder as the sun rippled its early-morning light right across the sleek and glossy back… positively shimmering with health!' Like Colin Booth she was able to judge the size of the cat from a comparison with her own dog, an Old English mastiff called Lovely. She estimated 'it was roughly the size of Lovely, but with enormous paws, quite out of proportion to the rest of him. His tail, longer than his own body length, was held straight out, with a little curl at the end. His face seemed square from his profile, with pointed, erect ears. Without turning once in my direction, the majestic animal clambered down the bank and loped across the lane, hips rolling with a loose-limbed, easy gait, before leaping effortlessly up the bank the other side and out of sight'.[11] The witness was the actress Sarah Miles, and the sighting took place near her home in West Sussex in 1998.

Dramatic sighting of 'jet-black' big cats like these are often confirmed by more than one witness.

Gary Nisbet was driving with a group of friends 'when' he said, 'I noticed what at first I thought was a very large, black dog on the roadside verge, walking in the direction of Grangemouth:

> 'It was clear and sunny that day and as we got closer we saw that the animal wasn't a dog after all. It had a long, thin, black tail and a square-ish head rather than snouted like a dog's. It was tall and slender and, judging by the height of the fence it was travelling beside, must have been three feet high and four to five feet long. We all agreed that it was a big cat – similar to the panthers I have seen on television. It was completely black. We slowed the car and watched for two to three minutes as the cat moved along the top of the road verge. My colleague, who is a policeman, then called the police to report the sighting… '[12]

At the other end of the country Joan Hatch, her daughter Anne and son Robert – wildlife experts who regularly go out to photograph the native birds and animals of Dorset – were driving at walking speed along a woodland lane one afternoon, expecting to see deer. 'Suddenly,' Mrs Hatch related, 'a large, cat-like creature slid down from a bank on the right of the road and crossed no more than about three metres in front of us – ever so close – I almost had to peer over the bonnet to see it. It was a glossy black, and about the size of a Labrador but longer.' The Hatches are experienced observers of animals 'but what we saw that evening was something quite new.' [13]

All these animals were seen unexpectedly in broad daylight by reliable people, and studied closely, and there seems to be no mistaking their species or colour. 'Completely black', 'jet-black', 'sleek' and 'glossy' – the words used by these witnesses are endlessly repeated in the annals of big cat sightings. Whether these mystery black felines are leopards or not, they are certainly not pumas.

**The third mystery**

At the same time as I was uncovering the reports of anomalous big cats around the country I was coming across the routine explanation for their presence. It was quoted uncritically in all the media. It was that anomalous big cats are the offspring of big cats set free when the Dangerous Wild Animals Act was passed in 1976. This Act required big cats to be licensed – a costly process – and it was generally assumed that, rather than pay the money, unscrupulous owners simply released the animals into the wild to fend for themselves.

However I could not help noticing that – quite apart from the fact that there is no evidence for numbers of these irresponsible big cat owners having ever existed – this apparent 'explanation' did not account for the types of animals seen.

If these black big cats are rare melanistic leopards which have escaped or been set free by their owners, I reasoned that there should obviously be reports of their common spotted brothers which had found freedom by a similar process.

Accordingly I searched anew and found that animals sporting a variety of differently-coloured pelages – dark grey, light grey, white, dark brown, dark brown and black, tawny – had very occasionally turned up. Yet oddly enough no normal, spotted leopard had ever been reported by a witness.

**The three mysteries**

These were the first three major anomalies in the British big cat phenomenon that I ran up against: firstly that despite exhaustive searches these animals are never found, dead or alive; secondly that the conventional releases/escapes explanation for the presence of anomalous big cats among us did not seem to account for the overwhelming preponderance of apparent leopards (black animals) over apparent pumas (brown animals); and thirdly – given the hundreds of *black* leopards apparently at large – the complete lack of reports of leopards with spots.

What else I discovered when I started delving into these mysteries, how the picture of these strange animals developed, and how I unearthed some unexpected answers, is what this book is about.

# Chapter 2

# Witnesses: the big cat experience

I am going to start by amplifying two points a little more: firstly the positive feline identity of these dog-sized animals (to which I shall henceforth refer acronymically as ABCs – 'anomalous big cats' and *not*, I should stress, *alien* big cats – they are very much at home here) and secondly the authenticity of the witnesses' experiences.

Trevor Bartle had worked late on the evening of 4th February 2000 and set off at about ten o'clock for a well-earned pint at the local pub:

> 'I am used to seeing animals in the road so I wasn't surprised
> when I picked up two brilliant eyes – like two lights – in the
> headlights about a hundred and fifty yards away. I slowed and
> then stopped as whatever it was walked into the headlights
> towards me. When it got to within six or seven feet of the bonnet I

*Trevor Bartle at home near Mylor Bridge. 'If the window had been open I could have touched it'.*

could clearly see it was a black cat roughly the same size as an Alsatian, but lower to the ground. Its shoulders stuck out from its body and you could see all the muscles rippling, in that beautiful way they do on big cats.

'I had Jimi Hendrix's rendering of *The Star-spangled Banner* turned up to ear-splitting volume but this did not seem to frighten the animal because it calmly moved around the front of the car to the driver's side, stretched up and looked in at me. If the window had been open I could have touched it.

'It was magnificent, I must admit. Its fur was jet-black, sleek and shiny, in wonderful condition. It was a fabulous, fabulous animal. I thought at the time "I'm not going to tell anyone about this"; but next day I decided I should tell the police. Meanwhile the one friend I did tell rang the local newspaper, so it got out. I had to endure a year's mickey-taking!' [1]

Trevor's sighting is one of many recorded for Cornwall, but it was in Devon that Claire Blick, strolling on a sunny August evening in 1999 along the bicycle track that runs alongside Chivenor army air base, saw to her horror an animal 'so obviously a cat and not a black Labrador… with a long tail which swept the ground, emerge from

*Claire Blick saw a panther-like animal cross her path fifty yards ahead.*

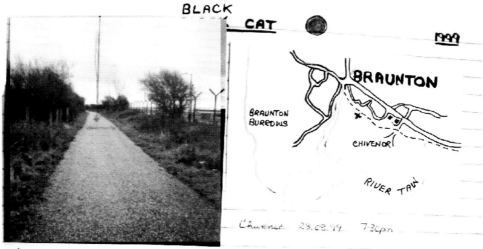

**BLACK CAT 1999**

BRAUNTON

BRAUNTON BUROWS

CHIVENOR

RIVER TAW

Chivenor 23.09.99 7:30pm

I was taking a walk alone, along the cycle bicycle trail from Chivenor army. air base towards Wrafton. I felt safe walking next to the Marines in the lovely sunny evening. I walked for about 35 mins and decided to turn back home before it was dark. About 7.50 pm I had not seen any other people and as I turned round I saw a very big black cat come out of the bushes at the edge of the track. It seemed to me to be so obviously a cat and not a black labrador. I was used to seeing dogs around and this animal was shorter than a dog with a long tail which swept the ground and its movements were different to a dog. It made slow sort of like stealthy movements not like a bouncy dog. It did not appear to have seen me, so after a few seconds I turned away and walked very fast not running so as not to draw attention to myself because I was frightened. It was about 50 yds away. I turned occasionally as I paced away but did not see it again. It was very shiny black with thick fur, a small head, very long tail and brown patches on its hind quarters.

← Photo of "cat" five months after.

path 4½–5 ft wide

Claire Blick's report.

*Sam Cooke stands at the spot where he and his dog watched a big cat bounding through long grass into the forest.*

the trackside bushes. Its movements were slow, snake-like, stealthy movements – not like a bouncy dog. It was very shiny black, with thick fur, a small head, very long tail and brown patches on its hind quarters. I turned and walked away very fast because I was frightened… ' Claire is an artist and drew what she had seen, wrote down the details, and photographed the spot where the big cat had crossed the path.[2]

Further north, in Wiltshire, Jacqueline Cooke was alarmed to observe from the bathroom window, in the light of dawn one March morning, a black, panther-like animal walking along the garden wall. Her son Sam had poo-poohed the incident, but more than a year later, in June 2005, he unexpectedly saw something that changed his mind.

> 'It was 8.30 p.m. last night. I went outside to call my dog, and found her sitting on the edge of the lawn looking tensely towards the forest. I, too, looked down the bank and saw bounding along through the rushes and tall grass what I at first thought was one of our neighbour's black Labradors – but then realised was a slightly bigger animal with a much, much longer tail. It was about twenty-five metres away, and moving in a cat-like way – more elegant than a dog – but it was obviously not a domestic cat. I was amazed. My dog was just sitting there looking at it as if amazed too… '[3]

Tim Maydwell farms on Burrough Hill in Leicestershire and, as one of that county's three senior park rangers, has a comprehensive knowledge of local wildlife.

*Tim Maydwell, a Leicestershire farmer and park ranger, has seen panther-like big cats on three occasions.*

'I was on my quad bike looking after my cattle one mid-morning in 2000 when a black animal, bigger than a collie, ran across the path about ten yards in front of me. I assumed at first it was my own dog – but quickly saw it was something else – feline, with a lovely, sleek, svelte tail. My impression was confirmed when, with all the grace of a big cat, it jumped clean over the hedge.'[4]

Like Tim, Linda Compton, a nurse, and her daughter Clodagh, a student, are country people and typically down-to-earth, unflappable witnesses. Both were shocked by an event in June 1998. Clodagh recalled:

'It was a warm, sunny evening and I was relaxing on the patio behind the house. Suddenly this ugly thing – an animal, dark in colour – appeared on the right hand side of the lawn and walked across it about forty feet away. I yelled for my mother to quickly come and look.'

Linda continued:

'Hearing Clodagh call I went out on to the patio to see what the matter was. I can see it now as well as ever. It was a big animal – bigger than at any sort of dog I've seen, slightly taller than a sheep – very dark brown or black, with a long stringy tail curving downwards. But it didn't look like a dog – it had a round face like a big cat. It was walking with a slow rolling gait, at a slow pace. As I studied it in amazement I thought "that's what's been taking our lambs!"

'It continued walking across the lawn as though it didn't see us, as though it was doing its own thing – concentrating on something. We just stared at it incredulously – wanting to look at it as long as possible – until it disappeared into the hedge on the other side. I

*Linda and Clodagh Compton, who watched a cat-like animal stroll across their lawn, pointing to the hedge into which it disappeared.*

rang my husband who arrived within fifteen minutes and searched the area, but there was no further sign of it.'[5]

Many witnesses of ABCs are trained observers of wildlife and at pains to dispel the obvious doubts they feel will greet their story. Particularly meticulous was one Scottish gamekeeper:

'My passenger and I both agreed that it most certainly wasn't a dog. I have six gun dogs of various breeds and know a dog's shape and movements in all lights and distances...The body length of the cat plus its head was about four to five feet; its tail was a further two to three feet long, carried low to the ground in a lazy curve up at the end. A Labrador, by contrast, holds it tail up when moving, as do most dogs. A Labrador also has an 'otter' tail going from thick to thin, whereas this tail seemed to maintain equal thickness throughout. It had a short snubbed nose or head. The animal's body came along more or less parallel to the ground, if anything slightly angled down from front to back, starting from approximately the inside of the front elbow... '[6]

A Staffordshire couple turned their car round to get another look at a strange feline animal by the roadside. They stopped and watched it for a minute – time enough for them, too, to go through a set of detailed comparisons:

'It was cat-like, very smooth, and very shiny, and appeared to be black with short hair. Its eyes were far apart, and very round. It looked very muscular and was moving its shoulders and neck around to get a better view of us!

'It had its mouth open for the whole duration, and I could quite clearly see its tongue. It was not anywhere near as long as a dog's tongue and the face appeared very blunt and squat. It was much stockier and longer than a German shepherd (we have three and often see them from the front at night in the dark as we come home). After a minute or so it turned and we saw its legs were very muscular and thick as it moved smoothly away into the field.

Two of our dogs are jet black, and we saw them half an hour later when we got home. By comparing it to their size, weight, shape and the way they moved, it was obvious that we had not seen a loose dog. It was far bigger than any fox or badger – we are used to seeing these and would not even consider its being one of them.'[7]

Another acute observer was Mike, who has been deer-stalking all his life. It was after one such occasion – this time further south, in Dorset – when he and his co-stalker saw something so strange that he recorded it in his diary:

'10th August 1995. A fruitless evening stalk on the south-east side of Bulbarrow Hill... Once in position we waited in long and agonising silence and expectation, until the light faded to such a degree that it was time for us to make our way back to the vehicles.

'As we were walking uphill on the last two hundred yards to the road, I saw my car and, rather oddly, a bulky item on the boot. Who had dumped a bag on my boot, and for what reason? At about one hundred yards away a head came up, the 'bag' slowly unwound and languidly lowered its front feet to the ground – whilst the rear of the animal, for such it was, remained on the boot. A sizeable beast. I immediately chambered a round in my rifle, and looked at the apparition through my telescopic sights which gave me a clear view of the animal.

'By then it had all four feet on the ground. It looked at us, its eyes glinting with a faint yellowish tinge. It looked for all the world like a black panther. It was hard to believe that such an animal was there right in front of us, but my co-stalker and I agreed, with eyes firmly fixed on the cat, that that was the reason why we had seen no other animals during our evening.

'I was ready to shoot the beast if it approached us, but when we came to about fifty yards of it, it turned, showing the curved tail characteristic of big cats, and walked away slowly up the hill alongside my car – silhouetted on the horizon and no longer a safe shot – and into the woodland out of sight.'[8]

Or what about Don Humphreys? He was driving back from shopping with his wife one Thursday morning, and had almost reached their village near Diss in Norfolk, when he saw what he knew was a big cat trotting across a field, less than a hundred yards away: 'You know – a gentle lope. A terrific sight.'

He is better-qualified than most to know what he was looking at: 'I used to work at London Zoo as assistant Head Keeper of elephants, and am very familiar with big

*Don Humphreys, retired zoo keeper: ' I'd never believed this big cat business, but now I'm convinced.'*

cats. It looked to me like a leopard-type – it wasn't a puma. Apart from being black it hadn't got that thick tail. The body would have been about four feet long excluding the tail; and then there was the beautiful motion of it. I'd never believed this big cat business, but now I'm convinced.'[9]

Time and again informants describe how they ran through the checklist of possible native animals in their minds and discounted them. One Dorset driver, Peter, told a typical story:

> 'A yellowy-brown, big cat ran out into the road in front of me,
> between my car and the car in front. It was about five feet long
> and two and a half feet high. It ran bounding across the road with
> a fluid movement, and through the hedge. I have lived in the
> country all my life and am certain it was not a deer, dog, fox or
> anything like that. It was definitely a cat, and the long rounded
> tail, arched up, distinguished it beyond doubt. I didn't mention it
> to anyone at first in case they thought I must be mad... '[10]

Dave Rickards, one of a group of builders on a building site in Bishop's Cleeve in Gloucester who were stunned to see a black cat, about four feet long and about two feet tall casually sauntering past them, explained similar feelings: 'Two other guys saw it so I know I'm not going mad. I just couldn't stop staring at it... It's not really something you see every day, is it?'[11]

Peter and Dave articulate the dilemma in which eyewitnesses find themselves. They know that the utterly concrete experience they have just had is going to sound fantastical, if not mad, when they recount it to someone else. It is so strange they hardly know how to believe it themselves. Indeed their fears are well grounded – Trevor Bartle 'had to endure a year's mickey-taking!'

This difficulty of having to reconcile something so outlandish with the expectations of everyday life is one reason why many are reluctant to come forward to report sightings. What kind of perspective can accommodate the prodigious and the quotidian at the same time – an English country lane and a wild animal from Africa? Such events may be only momentary, but they imply some long-lasting questions.

*Steve Evans was checking his sheep when he saw an Alsatian-sized cat and two cubs.*

Not only have witnesses to cope with the immediacy of the experience, they have to contend with the question it provokes: how can one believe the unbelievable?

The more I read the more I found it impossible to dismiss the honest accounts of reliable people such as those I have quoted. Nor were they isolated incidents but typical of literally thousands of similar stories. It therefore became obvious that nothing of any interest would come of attempts to diminish them, or alter them to suit easy explanations. Serious research, as I conceived it, must be an attempt simply to make sense of them as they stood.

It was therefore experiences like that of Karen Rees and Steve Evans – both engaging, straightforward country people – that perforce became the central focus of my investigation.

Steve is a shepherd and was checking sheep one morning in March 2004 on his quad bike. Glancing down into a small coombe, he saw what he thought was a black Labrador. 'Then another one appeared, and I realised – no, they are cats. I stalled the quad and sat there watching them as they circled a patch of brambles, as though they were after a rabbit in it or something.'

Then, to his amazement 'a third cat appeared out of nowhere and stood there watching them'. He realised he must have been looking at a pair of cubs, for the third animal was bigger still – 'Alsatian-size in height, but longer. She was black and glossy as though the coat was shining'. He watched them for fifteen minutes before coasting down the hill on the quad with the engine off to try to get closer to them; but when he arrived at the spot they had gone, leaving only a pungent odour he did not recognise.[12]

*Karen Rees and Sunny. The ABC was lying just the other side of the barbed wire.*

Karen Rees is a wife, mother, and the administrator for a boat-building school – and on a summer's morning in 2003 she had one of the most startling encounters I came across.

Every morning at 5.30 she takes her dog, Sunny, a large, black Labrador-lurcher cross, for a walk in the meadows. She often meets her mother there, walking her black Labrador, Mia, and the two women circumnambulate the meadows together. 'Mia is very, very shiny' Karen explains, 'because my Dad used to be a Metropolitan police dog-handler and buffs her up with chamois leather.'

'That morning I set off towards our usual meeting point – a thicket midway. I was marvelling at the beautiful morning and just thinking vaguely about the day's work ahead.   Then about thirty yards away, behind the barbed wire fence at the edge of the thicket I saw what I thought was Mum's dog – a hind leg with a really glossy, glossy black coat. It looked as though she might be lying injured, and I went towards it thinking "Oh God – that's Mia", but as I got closer I realised it was much too big to be Mia.

'It was lying completely motionless, but when I was within a few feet of it and just beginning to call "Mia", it sprang up – and I saw it was a panther-like big cat. It went from lying down to up on all four paws in the blink of an eye.

'I was almost near enough to have touched it. As it sprang up it bared its teeth at me and made a peculiar noise which I took to mean "Bugger off and leave me alone". I was more than happy to oblige!

'The two things that most struck me were its eyes and teeth. The canines were about two to three inches long. Its eyes were a smoky amber colour – as if an orange had a grey veil over it; or – although it sounds clichéd – the same colour as the light vein of a piece of polished Tiger's Eye gem stone. The noise was blood-curdling – neither a hiss nor a growl, but a very guttural noise, difficult to describe.

'It then turned and made off into the thicket, and I estimated its size as being three times the size of Sunny. The tail was very long and hooked up at the end.   Sunny had not seen the cat at he was chasing rabbits some distance away, but when he got back to me he stayed very close beside me, which was most uncharacteristic of him… '

Karen rang the police as soon as she arrived home, but their subsequent search failed to find the animal.[13]

Every day my files grew fatter with powerfully compelling testimonies like these. People who see anomalous big cats range right across the social spectrum, are of all ages, and live in every part of the United Kingdom. In short it seemed they have nothing in common except that none was expecting to see an exotic feline animal at the time of the sighting – and each of them was adamant that what they observed was some kind of big cat.

There are many other kinds of evidence for these creatures, and much of it persuasive; but it is the honest anecdotal evidence of individuals – the kind, after all, on which our law courts depend – that makes the apparent presence of big cats amongst us a case to answer.

# Chapter 3

# The hunt for the British big cat

During the spring of 1983 a mysterious predator was killing sheep in an area of Exmoor, Devon, centring on Drewstone Farm, the home of Mr Eric Ley, his wife Ruth, and their young family. Each morning for two weeks Eric had found the half-eaten carcass of a ewe or lamb – regular kills adding up to a mass slaughter without precedent on his farm or any other of the neighbouring farms. Finally he called in Brian Stevens, a crack shot with a rifle, to help him shoot the elusive sheep-killer which was raiding his farm at night.

> 'The two men settled down at dusk in the hedge bottom, concealed by a holly bush, and, with Brian's rifle sighted and in position, prepared to watch and wait. As it grew dark, several red deer hinds passed within feet of where they lay, quite unaware of their presence. Later, from the woods in the background, owls hooted to each other and the small flock of sheep in the far corner of the field in front settled down for the night.

> 'When darkness fell everything went silent, so silent that one could have heard a pin drop. The following morning as dawn broke, Brian shifted from the cramped position in which he had spent the night and made out the shapes of the sheep still lying down in the same positions as they had been in the night before. His eyes then travelled to the shape of a water-trough lying along the hedge behind them, and beyond that he saw something he instinctively recognised – the carcass of a sheep lying on its side. The mysterious killer had struck within two hundred yards of where they had watched and waited. Yet all that night neither man had heard the slightest sound of an intruder, nor had they heard a bleat from the remaining sheep in the field to indicate that they had been disturbed at any time.' [1]

The plains of Africa and the jungles of India are very large and wild places, but their native felines are trapped, or shot, or photographed regularly by tribespeople, foreign hunters, zoologists and wildlife photographers. Yet if the same animals really are

*The Shooters Hill 'cheetah' hunt of 1963. (Fortean Picture Library)*

naturalised in the small, densely populated, domestic landscape of Britain, as some people suggest, they seem bafflingly hard to photograph and, as Brian discovered, even harder to kill.

The stake-out at Drewstone Farm having proved a failure, the worried farmers then decided to draw the woods with the local foxhounds. At the same time they surrounded the covert with a cordon of armed farmers, gamekeepers and others to ensure that the killer could not slip away unnoticed. This was done; the woods were thoroughly searched; but once again no predator was found.

More effort and expense than ever went into Imperial tiger hunts has been expended in the hunt for ABCs. The majority of sightings in the first stages of a cat-flap are investigated by the police. The first thing they do is to contact all the local zoos, menageries and private owners, and ask them to check that all their animals are locked up – which they always are.

The search then intensifies as sightings continue, the police being persuaded by the sincerity, good sense, and often real fright of the witnesses. The police officers called to the scene sometimes see the animal themselves. Guns with night-sights, helicopters with surveillance equipment, along with Army marksmen may then arrive at the scene. But however intensive the hunt it always has the same result – nothing is captured. Dispirited, the police then wind down the search, sometimes claiming, perhaps to save face, that what people were seeing was in fact a dog/fox/deer/a plastic bag etc. and that the search has ceased because the mystery has been solved.

### Essex police fail

The most labour-intensive hunt was for an animal dubbed by the press 'The Shooters Hill Cheetah'. On the 18th July 1963 David Beck, driving through Shooters Hill in south-east London, saw a large animal lying by the side of the road. Assuming it to be an injured dog he approached it, and then realised it was in fact a large cat with a long, upward-curling tail. It ran off into Oxleas Wood. The same night police officers were amazed to see a 'large golden animal' jump over the bonnet of their patrol car. A check with zoos and circuses confirmed that no animals had escaped,

It was a magnificent affair. It covered 850 acres and involved 126 policemen with twenty-one dogs, thirty soldiers, ambulance men and RSPCA officials. No sign of a big cat was found – except for some spoor. These were huge – some seven inches across, the size usually associated with a lion or a tiger; yet they showed claw marks, the characteristic not of a lion's but of a cheetah's paw print. The 'cheetah', however was never caught and the hunters dispersed.

## Soldiers fail

There had been around sixty big cat sightings recorded from Bodmin Moor in Cornwall when, in 1999, the RAF reservists decided to get to the bottom of the matter. Equipped with night-vision sights which intensify existing light, and seismic-intruder devises which detect vibration, they decided to try to capture a photograph at least of the 'Beast of Bodmin' as a training exercise. One of the reservists was a chef and he even provided chicken offal as bait to attract the animal. But to no avail – the big cat did not turn up for dinner.[2]

Not merely reservists but also the cream of the professionals has had its chance. The hunt for the so-called 'Beast of Exmoor' – the animal accused of killing more than a hundred sheep including Eric Ley's – famously involved the Marines who spent more than five weeks in 1983 determined to kill the large, black feline animal seen in the area.

The nightly contingents of soldiers with L42 sniper rifles and expensive night-sights, the same crack troops who had defeated the Argentineans at Port Stanley, were in turn defeated by the Beast. While some of them claimed to have seen the animal they could not fire their ultra-powerful rifles unless they were certain where a bullet that missed might land. However a large, black dog was rumoured to have been dispatched, and did its duty by saving a certain amount of face, and the Marines retired.[3]

Not only did the sheep kills continue, but it seemed the hunt had not even frightened the animal. Reports continued of its undisturbed existence in the area. Not long after the hunt Mr Lewis of Barnstaple was sitting in his car enjoying a break in his working day when a large, black panther-like animal strolled along the lane towards him. He was able to observe it perfectly clearly as he ate his sandwiches. The animal jumped from the lane into the fields, and he watched it wandering into the valley heading towards the woods.[4] Another woman met the creature face-to-face while she was mushrooming.[5] A day or so later a Mrs Huxtable saw the same animal run across the fields to disappear among the masses of Himalayan balsam growing by the river.[6] Although it remained a mystery to the well-armed agents of the Crown, it seemed the unpredictable Beast of Exmoor continued to appear to ordinary people, in daylight, going about its normal business as they went about theirs.

In the twenty years since then, more sophisticated technology for hunting people and animals has become widely available, notably the use of thermal-imaging equipment. This is usually fitted in police helicopters and can pinpoint a living creature by its body heat, even if it is concealed in undergrowth. Such equipment was employed to track down another ABC – apparently quite at home in suburbia –

*Charles McGuinness of Monaghan, Ireland, saw a large cat-like animal cross his field and as he approached it with binoculars his wife, Helen, captured a few seconds of video footage. (Charles McGuinness)*

which two members of the public separately reported to Barnet police in September 1998. When two police officers in the adjacent London suburb of Potters Bar also spotted the big cat, 'bigger than a Labrador dog', a major hunt got underway and the helicopter was called out to help search teams consisting of police, representatives from London Zoo, the RSPCA and the Royal Veterinary College. But the technology, expertise and manpower was all to no avail; despite searching for three days, and despite the populous nature of the area, they found nothing.

### Welsh police fail

Welsh police have fared no better. In September 2002 when two of their officers saw a reported 'black panther' they launched a full-scale hunt including the use of a helicopter with thermal imaging equipment; but they found no sign of the animal. Two years later, when farmer Paul Gash, of Tyddyn Bach, Llanddona, spotted a big cat as he was driving his tractor, an armed response unit came within ten minutes or so and a helicopter half an hour later, along with a posse of local farmers and shooting men. The ABC was not an easily-overlooked animal, Mr Gash confirmed: 'It was black and big – I mean big. Taller than the biggest Labrador dog and four to five feet nose to tail end. It sloped across the field, backed up to a tree and sprayed to mark its territory, just like a domestic cat would do. Then it walked on, quite leisurely, and disappeared into undergrowth. It was really alarming and there is no way I would have gone towards it without a gun in my hand.' But the extensive search was to no avail, the creature had apparently disappeared into thin air.[7]

### Irish police fail

The police forces of Northern Ireland and Co. Monaghan, on the Irish Republic's side of the border, have on occasion thrown every device that those security-conscious police forces could muster into the search for a variety of big cats seen by numerous members of the public. A cat-like creature was even photographed by a Dublin GP, Dr Brendan O'Donnell, during the cat-flap on the Antrim coast in the autumn of 2003, but the local police never located it.

In June 2004 sightings of a black 'panther-like' cat in West Monaghan over several months, were corroborated by 'proof' when a herd of calves was attacked and one half-eaten. Police staked out the farm overnight in an attempt to capture or kill the beast, but no trace of it was found. The search was intensified and police flew a helicopter and a fixed-wing plane both with thermal imaging equipment over the area for two days in an attempt to locate the cat, while the Army provided trained marksmen at ground level. The hunt proved fruitless.

## Traps and trips

These are a tiny handful of the large-scale hunts instigated by police in every county during cat-flaps, but it would be tedious to describe any more.

After documenting the endless failure of police forces to round up ABCs, I naturally began to wonder if it was the very intensity of the hunts that had caused their failure. Could it be that the rather flat-footed, noisy, technology-intensive approach of the official agencies was counter-productive?

Big cats are famous for their stealth and cover large distances. Pumas, for instance, are reputed to roam over territories of up to two hundred square miles in their native America. It was reasonable to think that by the time the police searches got underway the ABC could have been miles away.

I wondered if what was needed was equivalent stealth: solitary naturalists and trackers, who know and can blend with the natural environment, and who use discreetly placed, baited traps.

In fact expert trackers of this type, often from abroad, are attracted to cat-flaps, rather in the manner of the stranger who rides into town to clean it up in cowboy films.

During the period of sightings of the 'Wrangaton Lion' in South Devon police received a string of calls from 'experts'. Suggestions ranged from equipping officers with large nets to erecting loudspeakers that would play animal noises and attract the lion into the open where it could be captured. One man who claimed to have captured lions and tigers around the world faxed his curriculum vitae to police headquarters and offered his services.

Such individuals confidently offer to dispatch the marauder, but those who have tried have also failed. Bryan Hughes, for instance, who claimed formerly to have been a ranger on a game reserve in Africa, arrived during the depredations of the Exmoor Beast and spent several nights of vigilance on his own inside a hen-house. This had been moved into a likely firing position, close to a disused railway line running down the valley. Despite his patience and experience he had no more luck than anyone else.

Needless to say other methods of catching, killing or photographing big cats have been used by ABC hunters in this country. Different kinds of lures and baits, such as urine-soaked wood shavings from local wildlife parks, have been tried in combination with trip cameras, or cameras with infra-red sensors, and so on, in areas where ABCs have been seen or killed livestock. Although their efforts have turned up unexpected amounts of native fauna, so far no big cat has been photographed.

*The door of this trap is electronically wired to a computerised alarm system which alerts the owner if it shuts.*

More frustrating for them is that they often seem to suffer from unusually bad luck. 'I set-up a concealed video camera ten metres away from what looked like a carcass concealed by a big cat, but the estate had a pheasant shoot on the Sunday and I swear this drove the killer away... ' complained one.[10] The County Antrim marksmen blamed the arrival of sightseers on the failure of their bait to lure the 'puma' into the open. Whatever the reason, forty years of hunters' and trackers' determination has never resulted in the capture of their quarry's body, alive or dead. [11]

*CCTV cameras attached to a barn at a farm where panther-like ABCs have been sighted on several occasions.*

*Christopher Johnston from Lancashire with one of his trip cameras. Every kind of wildlife has showed up on his films, but no big cat yet.*

## Cats that can be caught

The failure of anyone to catch an ABC, even on film, was doubly puzzling when, as I learned, the system of attracting big cats with various lures is a highly successful method of trapping them in their native countries.

As early as the 1840s in British Guiana a trap was designed specifically for catching pumas. It apparently consisted of a large box, reinforced with iron, and baited with a goat or sheep. Twenty to thirty pumas were captured in it every year. [12] In 1938, Tappan Gregory of Chicago led an expedition to the Carmen Mountains in Mexico and was successful in obtaining for the first time self-taken photographs of a puma using catnip oil as a lure.[13]

The distinguished and resourceful ABC hunter, Nigel Brierly, tried the same trick on Exmoor, with catnip oil he had distilled himself – but without the same success.

Pumas are systematically shot for sport in some states in the USA. They are tracked and chased up trees by dogs where they present an easy target. African and Asian big cats, such as leopards are also routinely trapped – by poachers for their skins, or zoologists to tag and release for their research programmes. Whatever the reason for

*Andy Williams from Buckinghamshire demonstrates the night-sight on a camera. He saw an ABC in broad daylight, but has not yet caught one on camera.*

acquiring live or dead bodies it is not considered an unduly difficult exercise by professionals.

It is not too difficult to photograph big cats in the wild in their native countries, as television documentaries show. Admittedly more cunning is required to catch wild leopards on film, since their jungle habitat affords more cover than the plains favoured by lions and cheetahs. Nevertheless miles of footage have been shot of wild leopards. British big cats, on the other hand, seem to be as proof against guile as they are against strength or technology.

# Chapter 4

# Where have they come from?
# Are they released pets?

A self-styled former lion-tamer, Leslie Maiden of Cradley Heath, near Dudley, West Midlands, known locally as 'One-eyed Nick', appeared on a BBC regional news programme in 2000 proclaiming he had released two big cats into the wild. 'I released a panther twenty-six years ago on to the moors on the Pennines at Snake Pass near Sheffield in Derbyshire,' he said. 'It was miles from anywhere. It was a couple of days after releasing a cougar.'

There are many theories about where ABCs come from and what they are, but one theory is routinely presented as fact in the media. It is the belief that there were many people like Mr Maiden who, when the Dangerous Wild Animals Act of 1976 (henceforth DWAA) came in, simply released their big cats rather than incur the cost of licensing them as the Act required.

This view is that all ABCs seen are pets released in considerable numbers by possibly hundreds of irresponsible or impoverished owners, or else are the descendants of such animals which continue to breed in the wild. It was a reasonable-sounding idea, and in the initial stages of my research I, too thought it would probably be able to account for the big cats seen. To my surprise I could find no evidence for it.

Captive big cats have enlivened private zoos and menageries since the Middle Ages, but such establishments were exclusively the property of the rich and aristocratic. Even when big cats became more available – and fashionable – in the 1960s and 70s their ownership was confined, as historically, mostly to the new rich. Gordon Mills, the manager of various pop stars, kept tigers in his large garden at St George's Hill in Weybridge in Surrey. Owners such as Mr Mills would have had no trouble in complying with the DWAA, or, if they wanted, flying the tigers first-class back to India.

Amongst ordinary mortals it is true to say the kind of person who would indulge in 'status' or 'fantasy' pets would most likely also be the kind of sentimentalist prone to releasing them into the wild if times got hard. Mr Maiden explained his irresponsible releases with the words: 'I've always been an animal lover. But people came to me with animals, saying they would have to put them down. I had no option'. His friend Lewis Foley, who shared the menagerie with Mr Maiden, claimed that a friend of his in Coventry had also set a panther loose in Nottinghamshire in 1974, saying: 'He knew about the new laws and didn't want it put down.' [1]

I assumed that Mr Maiden's well-publicised confession would prove to be the tip of the iceberg; that many other well-meaning sentimentalists would come forward with stories – even uncorroborated ones – of releasing big cats. It was not illegal to release exotic species into the wild at that time, and therefore such people need have had no fear of retrospective prosecution. Yet only one other couple, David Carter and Tony Cripps, have claimed to have released big cats – two young pumas – into the wild, and I return to their story later in the chapter. Search as I might I could find no first-hand evidence of other releases.

Nor have other investigators had much more success than me in trying to prove a link between sightings of big cats and the 1976 DWAA. Despite the fact that there is news mileage and financial gain to be made in selling such dramatic stories, no one has come forward – even anonymously – to help out with some real-life details. Makers of television documentaries in particular have appealed publicly at various times for liberators of big cats to come forward, along with assurances that they cannot be prosecuted and presumably would make some money, but to no avail.

### The black leopard mystery

Whilst there may have been a number of pumas around in Britain in the 1970s[2] and the DWAA could – in theory – have been responsible for some of them being released into the countryside, leopards were always rarer and more exotic, not to say more dangerous. (As I have explained, the animals popularly known as 'black panthers' are simply leopards exhibiting genetic melanism – i.e. which have black fur.) Pumas are easily tamed whereas the much more powerful leopards always remain dangerous. Of all the big cats leopards are reckoned to be the species most likely to attack humans, perhaps because of their likeness to the leopard's common prey – monkeys.

Black panthers are much rarer than their spotted brothers. Melanism is almost never reported among African leopards, though it crops up more frequently in the dark, dense, forest habitats of Java and the southern part of the Malay peninsula. As a result such animals have always been valuable zoo exhibits. An animal dealer in Birmingham had a black panther for sale for £500 in 1976 which was a considerable sum of money in those days – the price of a small car.[3] There would consequently have been a huge incentive for an owner simply to sell an unwanted or unruly pet, rather than release it into an uncertain future. It is reasonable therefore to make two assumptions: firstly that conventionally spotted leopards would have been more numerous in private ownership than black ones, and secondly that – if someone wanted to release their leopards – the spotted ones would have been released in preference to their valuable black siblings.

Of course not every pet-owner is motivated by common-sense or money – Mr Maiden and Mr Carter both claimed to have released theirs out of sentimentality, and there always remains the possibility that there were more people similarly moved.

Mr Maiden's action notwithstanding it is difficult to imagine more than a minute number of potentially lethal leopards being released so irresponsibly or contrarily, and yet the stubborn fact remains that the majority of present day sightings, spread over the whole geographical range of Britain, are apparently of that species. Moreover *all* of them are of black panthers – none are of leopards with normally-spotted pelts.

In any case, if pumas, leopards and other big cats had been released in the required numbers in 1976, a high proportion would have been immediately trapped, rounded up, killed – or at the very least, photographed. After all these captive big cats would be tame or at least accustomed to receiving food from humans. They would be inclined to hang around human habitation looking for free lunches. But the numbers of sightings did not increase immediately after 1976, nor was there a rash of captures as might have been expected if hundreds of semi-tame animals had been suddenly disgorged into the countryside.

**Mascots**

I discovered that another rumoured source of released big cats – primarily pumas, since they are native to America – was wartime GIs who allegedly kept them as mascots, setting them free in the countryside when they returned home.

Interestingly the same rumour circulates in both Australia and Afghanistan – wartime GIs being held responsible for releasing regimental mascots.

An ABC researcher based in Cambridge, Terry Dye, has taken a long-term interest both in the American units based in his area during World War II, and the mascot theory. However, although his research turned up a clutch of lovable mascots, none of them were pumas. This is what he found:

> '456 Bomber Group had a black and white collie called Elmer who rode on the jeep, and was left behind in the UK. B17 B24h-20 had a small terrier called Gertie. The B17 was missing in action over Europe in June 1944. The crew were killed in action and it is not known what happened to the dog.

> 'One crew had a terrier named Homer. One had a small black cat called Hypo. Then there was "Recon" who was with the Reconnaissance Unit. He was bitten by a rattlesnake when taken home to Alamogordo but survived, only to be killed during fighting in Casablanca.'

The only big cats that Terry was able to turn up were from the First World War, in France. 'Some Americans in the French Foreign Legion persuaded the authorities to form an Air Squadron for the Legion  named the 'Escadrille Americaine'. They had two lion cubs as mascots, called Whisky and Soda, but I could not find out what happened to them.'[4]

Another ABC researcher, Jeremy Holford-Miettinen, also looked into mascots as a possible source of escaped pumas, but was also unable to find any USAAF units with puma or panther mascots.

He did, however, speculate wittily about the fate of the French lion cubs that Terry had unearthed: 'Shifting back to WW1 and the lion mascots Whisky and Soda, I have read that an American ex-serviceman living in Paris in the 1920s kept a lion that had been raised by his unit. Could this be one of the pair? The man was in the habit of taking the lion into bars and cafés with him, which must have made for interesting chat at the bar. It is alleged that Ernest Hemingway once threw a man and a lion out of a Parisian cafe. But you know the stories that get told for self-publicity – probably half the lions in Paris claimed Hemingway picked on them in the 1920s... '

Despite the colourful picture it suggested, in the face of no evidence I was forced reluctantly to consign the mascots theory also to 'foaflore'.[5]

## War stories

A ninety-two year old Dorset woman told me that a big cat came to eat food put out for badgers at the local big house during the war – 'the feeling was that because of rationing someone had turned it out.' Another rumour concerned Dartmoor where people were said to have released their exotic pets because of wartime stringencies.[6]

Other wartime legends centre around bombings – one claims that Chessington Zoo in Surrey was bombed and ten pumas escaped. Untraceable stories of releases and escapes during the war years made me pause to wonder whether new folklore self-spawned as people searched for a way to acclimatise to the unbelievable; or perhaps catastrophes in nature were summoned up to help illustrate the social catastrophe. At any rate such rumours and beliefs from another era seemed to add to the strong whiff of urban legend which hung about the modern Releases Theory.

Although it is both unproven and unlikely the Releases Theory remains popular by default – simply because it is the only 'explanation' on offer. Most ABC enthusiasts assert – although with increasing desperation – that it is only a matter of time before the 'hard' evidence for it, such as a convincing number of suitable bodies, turns up.

So far there have been only two: a dead puma which a family stumbled upon while hiking in Scotland, and a live one which became known as Felicity. This latter, celebrated case, far from providing unambiguous proof for the Releases Theory, has always remained controversial. Rather like the Bible, the case of Felicity has been quoted to support almost any theory.

## Felicity

In the six months up to October 1980 there had been numerous sheep and deer killed by an unknown predator on the Cannich Estate at Ardross, Easter Ross, in Scotland. Big cats had been reported in the area, as I have already mentioned, since the 1940s, and Ted Noble of Kerrow Farm who had lost stock had an idea of what might be responsible – he was sure he had seen what resembled a lioness in the hills. He made a steel cage-trap and baited it with a sheep's head. On the 29th October he and his son Julian checked the cage. They heard growling, and found a puma snarling and lunging at them from behind the wire in the sprung trap.

Throughout the day a tarpaulin cover was kept over the cage as the puma spat and snarled, and villagers arrived at the scene to catch a glimpse of the puma. The Kincraig Wildlife Park near Aviemore agreed to give the puma a home and its director, Mr Eddie Orbell, arrived at the scene armed with tranquilliser darts, but in the event he did not need them: the puma was smoothly transferred from its cage-trap to a specially designed animal carrying case.

Once safely ensconced in the zoo, the puma underwent a personality change. Perhaps she only 'spat and snarled' for newspaper reporters, because she and her new owner, Eddie Orbell, got on famously. Within a day he had declared: 'I am certain the puma is used to captivity. I think she was dumped in the area only days or perhaps hours before being captured.' He found he could put his hand through the bars of the cage and stroke her. He said: 'She has been rubbing her body against the bars and purring. Her coat is in flabby zoo condition, not what you would expect of an animal on the loose for years. She is overweight, which she should not be if she had been living wild. I gave her a dead rabbit and she let it lie for hours before she touched it. I'll try her with some Kit-e-kat later. I think the farmer has been hoaxed… this is definitely a put-up job, it's the work of a prankster.'

Next day the puma did eat its dead rabbit. Rebutting accusations that the animal's domesticity could be attributed to some form of sedation, Mr Orbell said the beast had never been sedated since its capture. The puma was christened Felicity, and the zoo was inundated with visitors to see the new celebrity.

A short time later Ted Noble received a curious letter. It purported to be from a prisoner incarcerated in Winchester Jail, Hampshire, far away in the south of England. The prisoner, David Carter, said he had released two pumas called Rooster and Jen in the Highlands the previous year (i.e. 1979). He said the pumas had come from a friend who could not keep them because he was moving back to Germany, and that they were quiet and would answer to their names.

He wrote 'I love all wildlife. I knew if and when I would be put in prison the cubs would be put down or end up in a cage. I could not think of that.' He claimed that he had decided to free them 'where there would be no people to harm them. What better than the Highlands where they could live free?'

Doubt was cast on Felicity's status as the prisoner's former pet by a vet, George Rafferty, who had examined the animal shortly after its capture. Carter had referred to the animals he had released as 'cubs', but Rafferty commented: 'I think the captured puma is about six years old.'[7] At this Tony Cripps, a photographer from Fareham in Hampshire, contacted the press to back up David Carter's claim. Cripps said he had helped Carter release the animals and was sure the captured puma was one of them.[8] Unfortunately, despite being a photographer, he did not seem to have taken a photo of the remarkable event.

A week after her arrival at the zoo the results of the tests designed to determine the nature of Felicity's lifestyle, arrived from the Institute of Terrestrial Ecology. The analysis was carried out by Dr Hans Kruuk, the principal scientific officer at the institute, on two samples of droppings taken about one-and-a-half days after she was captured.

He noted: 'One dropping was 95 percent deer hair – probably roe deer, with 4 percent rabbit remains and 1 percent sheep. The second dropping was 99 percent sheep, with 1 percent rabbit. 'It certainly suggests that she has been surviving in the wild, and making a pretty good living,' he said.[9] George Rafferty, the vet from Grantown-on-Spey, consulted his reference books and concluded that she had not been living wild for very long, because 'she is definitely overweight for a female puma'.

He also remarked on what everyone noticed about the new captive: 'There is also no doubt she has been used to contact with humans. She loves to have her ears tickled, and comes straight over to the bars of the cage when you approach.' And yet at the same time she showed some features consistent with a life of freedom: 'Her teeth are in remarkably good condition, although yellow with age. There is no tartar on them, which suggests she had been living on a natural diet, as opposed to processed food.'

Mr Rafferty also examined Felicity's claws. I had come across the controversy (which I will refer to later) about the fact that the supposed pugmarks from ABCs often show claw marks uncharacteristic of big cats, (which, with the exception of the cheetah, retract their claws when walking). Felicity's claws were in keeping with all the other ambiguities of her existence. He reported: 'The claws on the animal's back paws are very worn, but the front ones are normal,'[10] which implied she kept the front claws retracted, but not the back claws. Was Felicity just eccentric, or could this shed light on the walking habits of other big cats?

Felicity became the zoo's most discussed resident, and the various facts about her physiology and behaviour used to support widely differing theories about her provenance and past life. 'The capture has certainly raised more questions than it has answered,' concluded Sergeant John Cathcart.[11]

For Mr Noble, the capture had ended an eighteen month hunt. 'People were beginning to think I was nuts the way I was so obsessed with capturing this animal,' he said. 'I'm glad I have been proved right, but at the same time it is a pity to see such a nice-looking animal in captivity.'

'But that may not be the end of the story', *The Scotsman* added presciently in its final report on the saga. 'Mr Noble and others who have seen more tracks in the area, think the puma may be one of two.' If David Carter was to be believed another puma was indeed still at large.

Certainly sightings of ABCs, and associated sheep kills, continued. Five years after Felicity's capture, in the summer of 1985, James Smith and his parents were staying at a remote campsite near Inverness and had set out on a walk, heading for the beach. He recalls:

> 'We must have been going for a good two hours when we came to the edge of a large wood, and to the right we saw in the long grass what we thought to be a dead dog. However when we approached the animal it became very clear that this was a cat. I remember my parents both realising at the same time – and my

Mum saying "That's a lion!", and my Dad not being quite as subtle (I won't tell you what he shouted).

'I still have a very clear picture of this cat in my head. The top half was badly decomposing and the bottom half was in reasonable shape. The most noticeable things were the size of the head which, compared to the body, was very small; and its paws which were enormous, as were the teeth; the fur was a darkish-tan colour. The animal had no noticeable disfigurement and was nowhere near a road of any sort, so I can only presume this cat died of illness or natural causes. We were all in agreement that this was a puma – of that there is no doubt. I would bet my house on that.' [12]

Could this have been, perhaps, Felicity's alleged comrade, demonstrating that a puma can live at least six years in foreign terrain? Curiously, Felicity died the same year. It seemed that hard evidence to support Carter's claim to have released two pumas in the Highlands had – uniquely – emerged: two were subsequently found – one alive, one dead.

## Where are the others?

Perhaps the only definite thing to be said of Felicity is that being easily captured she demonstrated what should have been the fate of hundreds of other released big cats, had they existed – but to this day she remains the solitary trapped specimen.

Likewise corpses such as that which James Smith and his family came across should be commonplace on farmland and roadsides. But that, too, remains the only body available to serve as a possible connection to a claimed release.

The testimonies of the four men I have quoted – Leslie Maiden, Lewis Foley, David Carter and Tony Cripps – are still the only first-hand reports of big cats being deliberately released, and the latter two stated that it had been circumstances other than the DWAA which had prompted the release of the pumas. So as my files grew fatter, this explanation for the presence of ABCs among us grew thinner.

Even if there were a number of pumas released as a result of the DWAA of 1976, it is difficult to picture enough of them being released to constitute a healthy breeding population, let alone a breeding population that is so extraordinarily widespread. And if that is difficult, the idea of rare black leopards released in such numbers as to form an even bigger breeding population was infinitely more so. I had to conclude that the Releases Theory tells us more about the inertia of theorists than the provenance of ABCs.

# Chapter 5

# Escapes: early explanations for ABCs

'A Circus passed the house – still I feel the red in my mind... '

Emily Dickinson (1830–86)

Another obvious drawback to the 1976 Releases Theory is that plenty of ABCs were being seen regularly before that date.

Felicity was captured in the Cannich area of Easter Ross in 1980, but men who worked on the hydro scheme in that locality had seen a large, black, cat-like animal as early as the 1940s. [1]

There were also early sightings of a fawn-coloured big cat in Scotland. In 1957 Mrs Bridget Mackenzie, the warden of Achinvar Youth Hostel near Achiltibuie in Sutherland, and a group of hostellers heard:

> '... a sudden great agitation among the sheep and we went outside to see what ailed them. They were all baaing and snorting and dashing out of the mist as if a strange dog were at them.
>
> 'Then we saw that it was not a dog. It was a bigger animal, a cat – very like a cougar I had seen in British Columbia. It was a bright sand colour all over with no markings. Its ears were rounded rather than pointed and set close to its head, which was broad and shaped like a lioness's. The tail was longish and sandy, the same colour as the body, with a tuft at the end.
>
> 'It passed twenty-five to thirty yards from us, moving in a sort of feline slink, with its head thrust forward and totally ignoring or unaware of us. We were standing in a group in front of the house and the six of us watched it follow the galloping sheep across the slope of the field and over a rise in the ground. It had not caught any by the time it went out of our view and we certainly did not follow it. In fact we all bolted back into the house and shut the door very firmly. It was very menacing, and we all admitted to finding it rather alarming. It was broad daylight when we saw it, and we were all sober, young and keen-sighted and were all agreed on what we saw.'[2]

England had its share of big cats too. On a sunny spring morning in 1959 Joan Jewitt set out for a ride in country on the outskirts of Sheffield:

> 'We trotted through a wooded copse and came out alongside a field. My pony suddenly stopped dead in fright and I must say that I too felt scared, as straight ahead of me was a creature I had never seen the like of before.

> 'It was a species of cat, that was obvious, but as big as a sheep – easily – golden fawn in colour, fairly shaggy, with a 'big cat' head – but pointed upright ears! The tail was shaggy. He, or she, did not immediately see us – I can always remember it most clearly – he was prowling around sniffing at the thistles. After a few minutes he looked up and saw us and froze – we too were standing perfectly still – my pony was terrified and, I think, too frightened to bolt – and I was afraid but fascinated.

> 'He was only about fifteen or twenty yards away. He continued to stare, malevolently I thought, with large eyes, and made no move to go away. In the end our nerve broke – my pony spun round and we careered back the way we had come, leaving, I suppose, the cat staring after us.

> 'I told my parents and several other people of my experience – but I don't think anyone believed me. I fully expected the papers to be full of "big cat escapes" stories – but they weren't – and no-one else reported a sighting.' [3]

## 1760s and 1960s

In the south of the country the first chronic cat-flap – sightings of animals collectively dubbed the Surrey Puma – took place in the 1960s. The Godalming police logged 342 sightings between 1964 and 1966, and the reasonable conclusion they drew was that an escaped puma or pumas were managing to live wild – indeed thrive – in the well-wooded parts of rural England.

However a sighting of a strange, large cat-like animal in Surrey had been reported long before – in the 1760s. The great radical writer, William Cobbett recalled in his *Rural Rides* [4] how, as a boy, he had seen a cat 'as big as a middle-sized Spaniel dog' climb into a hollow elm tree in the grounds of the ruined Waverley Abbey near Farnham in Surrey. Later, in New Brunswick, he saw a 'lucifee' (North American lynx – *Felis lynx canadensis*) 'and it seemed to me to be just such a cat as I had seen at Waverley.'

In the 1960s Mike Davis was warned about a black, big cat regularly seen on the hill overlooking the railway at Maiden Newton in Dorset by a railway worker. 'He said "don't go up there – there's a big cat up there". I said what do you mean? and he said "there it is now" – and pointed it out to me on the hillside. We never went up there after that.' Similar cats were filmed there in 2002. [5]

*Jim Miller, fisherman, of Lulworth in Dorset. He and his crew watched a black, panther-like big cat pick its way along the white cliff in the 1960s.*

Also in Dorset, Jim Miller saw 'a bloody great cat' picking its way along Whitenothe cliffs near Lulworth in the 1960s. 'It was black and near enough the size of a donkey in length but shorter legged, with a tail as long as its body.' He and his crew were in a fishing boat at the time and watched it for twenty minutes, clearly visible against the white cliffs, as it jumped two crevasses before disappearing over the cliff top. Twenty years later he saw it – or rather, another – racing over the sward in front of his cliff top house.[6]

## 1970s

There were multiple reported sightings of ABCs in Hampshire, Dumfriesshire, and Devon between 1970 and 1974.

In West Lothian a housewife, Mrs Hall, looked out of the kitchen window 'and', to her surprise 'I saw what I believe was a puma walk through our farmyard. It was bigger than an Alsatian dog, and light brown in colour.' She was more fascinated than frightened. 'I ran out and followed it for a mile over the country. I thought it may have escaped from a circus van… '[7] A South Molton businessman had the same thought when he and his wife saw a black, panther-like animal walking the railway area close to Hacche Moor in Devon. He recalled, 'I said at the time that it had probably escaped from some zoo or circus.'[8]

## Escapes from circuses

That was the orthodox explanation before the 1976 DWAA supplanted it – that ABCs must have escaped from zoos or travelling circuses or menageries. It was a common-sense idea to account for an otherwise inexplicable occurrence. Many witnesses, like Mrs Jewitt, were surprised when no circus could be found nearby, and no corroborating reports of escaped big cats were announced in the press.

Forty years later this idea has re-emerged as a way of accounting for the improbably large quantity and different species of ABCs seen today. Many ABC investigators had concluded – as I had – that the DWAA 1976 alone could not account for our population of ABCs. They therefore suggested that released pets could perhaps have topped up an already existing population of big cats, which could hypothetically have been escaping from run-down menageries, circuses, or private owners for decades or even centuries.

Like the Releases Theory, the Escapes Theory has always had popular following by reason of its convenience. During the Harrogate cat-flap one woman assured Andy Roberts: 'They all come from Knaresborough Zoo, you know', despite the fact that this had never been publicly suggested, the police having checked that collection of big cats at least twice during the scare and found them secure.[9]

## Roman circuses and mediaeval menageries

How probable is the idea? How many circuses and zoos did Britain have in past centuries? What proportion of them had big cats? Could they have escaped and what happened when they did?

It is assumed that the Romans would have imported big cats into Britain for their circuses, but the first documented wild animal collection was installed by Henry I (1100–35) in his park at Woodstock, near Oxford. Here the king kept animals presented to him by other monarchs, including lions, camels and a porcupine. Later medieval English kings kept their animals at the Royal Menagerie in the Tower of London.

By the mid-eighteenth century many large country estates in Britain also had menageries, but the word was applied equally to collections of birds. The garden historian Sally Festing has identified a total of at least forty-three menageries in British country estates – using historical records, paintings and similar evidence.

From the Elizabethan period circuses had occasionally travelled around Britain, but in the 1800s with the expansion of the British Empire exotic animals became more accessible as well as popular, and entrepreneurs like the Fossetts, Chipperfields, Barnum, Bailey and the Ringley brothers formed portable menageries and circuses.' [10]

An Exeter biologist and ABC researcher, Chris Moiser, has collected local evidence to show that those showmen were trundling big cats around Devon and Somerset from the late eighteenth century at least.

He reasoned, therefore, that big cats could theoretically have been escaping from their vans to settle in the countryside, from then until the 1930s, when travelling shows largely ceased. [11] A poster advertising the arrival in Plymouth in 1855 of George Wombwell's menagerie promised among the 'novelties' it was exhibiting: 'Lions of all ages, sizes and species, Tigers, Panthers, Leopards, Pumas, Bears and Wolves.' [12] Presumably that is the order of value of the animals on show; and therefore the inverse order in which they would have escaped.

Not that this seems actually to have happened. Despite this considerable number of exotic animals being exhibited in Britain, there are no historical records of animals – least of all the exciting ones – escaping into permanent freedom. Mr Moiser concedes, 'not many are recorded, and those that are usually resulted in the animal being shot.' [13]

### Escapes from zoos

There is no firm evidence, either, that more modern, static zoos were the source of fugitive big cats. Researchers have, therefore, had also to infer surreptitious escapes from those establishments. 'Of the thirty-eight collections that had pumas in the 1970s,' Chris Moiser notes, 'at least seventeen are now closed; many as a result of financial recession... It is possible to imagine a scenario where the puma escapes from a zoo currently fighting for survival, and the owner, hoping to avoid the local authority's disapproval and consequent planning controls takes the view that the escaped animal will be back when it is hungry, expecting to have it back within two to three days. At the end of the week the animal has perhaps not been seen, and it is then too late to report an escape, because questions will be asked about why it hasn't been reported missing sooner.' [14]

I could indeed imagine it. What I found more difficult however, was imagining this scenario happening again and again, over many decades, all over the British Isles; and apparently involving many rarer, expensive, black leopards than common pumas. And how is it that black leopards must have necessarily escaped in large numbers while no spotted leopards escaped at all?

### Actual escapes

It is possible to winnow the few facts from the suppositions about escapes and releases.

What has happened, for instance, to the big cats known to have escaped in past times? The fate of one such panther is commemorated by a sixteenth century wooden cross[15] at Chillington Hall in Staffordshire, home of the Giffard family.

The panther had been given to Sir John Giffard who kept it at Chillington Hall, but one morning it escaped. With his son he tracked the beast towards a group of cottages about a mile away, where they saw the panther crouching ready to spring upon a women with a baby in her arms. As Sir John drew his bow his son exclaimed: 'Prenez haleine, tirez forte', meaning: 'Take breath, pull hard'. Sir John shot the panther as it leaped. The King, hearing of the gallant deed, granted him the crest of a panther's head with his son's urgent injunction as the motto.

In more recent times, too, a few big cats have discharged themselves from their cages. The fugitives were all re-captured or shot, although none in so dramatic a fashion as the Giffards' panther.

Perhaps the most bizarre re-capture was achieved – or should I say experienced – by PC Mike Gittus. He was on night duty in Leamington Spa when he received a brief message on his police radio that a lion had been sighted on Warwickshire Road. Somewhat nonplussed he drove there, and seeing a milk float in the street, shouted to the milkman 'Had he seen a lion about?' 'He looked at me rather strangely', recalled Mike.

'But the next thing I became aware of was a passing blur and a sudden weight in the back of the Talbot Horizon, the make of panda car we had then. In one fluid movement the lion had jumped through the back window on to the passenger seat, just like a circus lion. There was a tremendous smell – I hadn't realised lions had such bad breath.

> 'I sat there for a moment considering my options... I didn't want to run as I thought I might look like live food. I looked in my mirror and could see it had settled, so remembering how my daughter used to fall asleep in the back of the car I thought perhaps I'd drive off and recover the creature.

> 'I put the car into first and drove off gingerly. It was clunking because of the weight on the back axle, but the lion appeared comfortable. I drove it into the back yard at Leamington police station and ran into the secure area.

> 'It turned out to be a tame lion which its owner used in advertising, and had trained to jump into his own car to be transported.' [16]

The moral to Mike's remarkable story is that trained or tame animals do not particularly relish freedom; they are more often anxious and confused by unfamiliar terrain and eager to return to recognisable surroundings.

### Re-captures

Past reports of other known escapers illustrate the same point. On the 4th August 1975 a leopard cub with a blue collar was easily re-captured when it obligingly wandered inside a house in Fallowfield, Manchester. A puma escaped from Jeff Day's garden shed in Hampshire, and strolled aimlessly around the village gardens for a few hours before being recaptured.[17] Just as easy to capture was the pet puma which escaped at Blackley, Manchester,[18] while the lion that escaped from its cage in a Belfast theatre tasted freedom for only two hours before police and circus staff approached and tranquillised it.[19]

The following year three lions escaped from a circus in Epsom, Surrey. One attacked a horse, but all were soon recaptured. A few days later three lion cubs were soon recaptured after escaping at Stevenage, Hertfordshire.

*The recapture of a puma which escaped from a house in West Horsley in Surrey, circa 1900. (Fortean Picture Library)*

In 1975 a black panther cub was stolen from Colchester Zoo but was found and caught the next day on the banks of the River Medway, East Peckham, in Kent.

According to the Ministry of Agriculture, all but two of the sixteen big cats that escaped into the wild in the UK between 1977 and 1998 were recaptured within twenty-four hours. The remaining two were shot.[20]

The only record of a known escapee surviving successfully for a while in the wild was a clouded leopard, which got out of Howlett's Park near Canterbury. It lived for eight months at large in Kent, before being shot by a farmer whose lambs it had killed.[21]

### ABC collared

Evidence that big cats may have escaped unreported is virtually non-existent, but there is one report of an ABC wearing a collar, which I include as it is amusing. Ed Cose, a marine engineer and keen amateur naturalist, was walking up a path on the edge of a wood near Totnes in Devon 'on a filthy day, blowing a gale of wind and rain and suddenly found it right in front of me.

> 'I crept up behind it and when it turned round I saw it quite
> clearly. It was a large fawn-coloured cat with a long black tail;
> much too large to be a dog. It had a puma-like face with this quite
> wide collar around its neck. I realised I had nothing with which to

protect myself except a bag of bird nuts. I threw them, and it jumped over a clump of brambles, went through a hedge and disappeared... '[22]

In addition police did manage to capture a biggish 'small' cat that no one had apparently reported missing – alive. They descended on a garden in Barnet, North London, following the sighting of a young lynx. She was tranquillised and taken to the big cat enclosure at London Zoo.[23]

It seems that the police, vets, and marksmen manage to account for known escapees more or less efficiently. This success rate provides an obvious contrast with their failure to capture any of the many times more numerous ABCs. Four decades of fruitless expenditure of effort and money in the attempt seem to show that the British ABC may simply not be catchable by any of the currently-practised methods.

## The nail in the coffin

It seemed the obstacles to the Escapes Theory remained the same as to the Releases Theory: firstly there was no evidence that such events had taken place. Secondly the most recalcitrant facts – the ABCs' ubiquity over a long period of time and their extraordinary elusiveness, and the predominance of 'black panther' types and the absence of spotted 'leopards' – remained unexplained by either. However it was some fascinating evidence from Scotland that hammered the final nail in the coffin of both.

In 1985 Mrs G.W. Brodie described a surprising encounter:

'About seven years ago while on holiday, on a quiet, early morning, we were driving very slowly spotting wild birds when we met a big cat. At first we assumed he was a black Labrador dog – until he crossed the road and scrambled over rocks and on into the foothills of Ben More, when we saw he was unmistakeably feline. We had an excellent view of him. He had that slack piece between the lower ribs and hindquarters which enables them to leap. I assumed someone had abandoned one of the panther or cheetah family to fend for itself.

'I presume he had either been at the loch for a drink, or looking for mussels, but at any rate we watched him move for at least twenty-five to thirty yards.

'I have been there many times since then, and as yet I have never been fortunate enough to see that magnificent cat again. And cat he certainly was, and in the very best condition.'[24]

The Brodies' sighting was on the Isle of Mull off the west coast of Scotland. Mull is cut off from the mainland by a stretch of water that takes the ferry just under an hour to cross. There are no zoos on Mull for such an animal to escape from, and no menageries have visited it. It is doubtful that any terrestrial animal could swim the distance from the mainland to Mull, even if it wanted to. Moreover a person would have to be mad deliberately to release a panther there, with all the problems of transport over the water, when there is the equally wild but much more easily-accessible splendour of the mainland Scottish Highlands in which to let it go.

If this sighting strains the Escapes/Releases Theory, then subsequent events strain it even more. On the 15th September 2002 another couple were enjoying a holiday on the island. In the witness's own words:

> 'We were sitting by the stream whilst my partner recounted stories of her childhood memories of the house where her relations lived. She suddenly asked me to turn round slowly and when I did I saw a large black cat lying on small hill about a hundred yards away. I knew the distance and the height of the grass having walked over that area the previous day. It lay watching something (we saw its profile) and then slunk away out of sight. We had watched it for about two minutes and estimated the length of its head and body, but not including its tail, to be four feet... '[25]

The same autumn, three amateur naturalists arrived in Mull for a week's holiday. One of them wrote:

> 'While not claiming to be experts we do have a good basic knowledge of bird species and other animal life. I make this point at the outset, as what follows might provoke scepticism.
>
> 'On Thursday 24th October, at about 3 p.m., when we were returning from the Ross of Mull, we noticed a dark, or black, animal walking along the grass verge by the side of the road. We were about a hundred and fifty yards away and at that point we thought it was a dog. However, as we got nearer it turned sideways, crouched briefly, and leapt away into the trees. Immediately on seeing its profile we realised it was a large cat-like creature. It definitely was not a dog, domestic cat or deer... I am convinced what we saw that day was a big cat.'[26]

Three months later yet another witness saw a sleek, black, cat-like animal, walking across the road into ferns. It had a very long tail, and he estimated it to be about four feet in length and two and a half feet high.[27]

Either there must have been not one but *two* black panthers released on the island at the time Mrs Brodie saw hers – about 1978 – which subsequently bred, or else someone decided to carry out exactly the same, mad idea twenty-four years later, in 2002, for leopards live only about fifteen years at the most.

### The Surrey Puma

The Surrey Puma which, as I mentioned above, eluded the police from approximately 1962 to 1966, was not just the first cat-flap. It occasioned the first theory – that the 'pumas' were escaped zoo animals or pets. Yet despite the determination of officialdom to believe it, by the end of the flap this simple explanation was looking shaky. Too many different kinds of animals seemed to be involved, all of them apparently uncatchable.

Di Francis, in her book *Cat Country*,[28] quoted the testimony of an observant and reliable witness, Mrs Chrystal Arnold, who lived in Crondall and often walked near Bushylease Farm, the epicentre of the ABC sightings. Mrs Arnold had observed a large cat-like animal there on more than one occasion. She wrote:

> 'I think I have been closer to this animal than anyone, and my experience is on police records... I say the creature was not a puma. It was the width of Redlands Lane away, and I saw it face-to-face. I have never seen anything quite like it before or since, and we have travelled to look at circuses and zoos and seen heaps of pumas, big and small. This animal was not in the least like that.

> 'I got the stench of it from a long way up the lane and thought "fox or deer". When I came upon it, it had gone back towards the wood and left a half-eaten bird at a stile on my side of the road.

> 'I froze, and we just looked at one another – then it spat all the time. It had marks like a cheetah on its face and was greyish, browny-beige with spots and stripes. Its back was deep red-brown and massive at the back legs, which were striped black and red-brown right down. It had a white, beige, and grey front, and – this is the one thing that makes me say it wasn't a puma – it had a beautiful striped red-brown and beige, white-tipped tail. The stripes were as on the back legs, with black thin lines. Yellow slanted eyes, wire-like whiskers and tufted ears… It leapt the width of the lane and went through the hedge, stopping to drink water that had spilled from the cattle trough.

> 'Fortunately it seemed just as frightened of me as I was of it (I was petrified!). My legs just turned to jelly. Well, one doesn't usually meet up with such things on a country walk!

> 'I saw it on several occasions in the distance at the dew-pond in the same field, and lying on the air-raid shelter which used to be at Bushylease Farm. (My two dogs went mad when it was anywhere around and one day my husband and I saw five foxes sitting outside the wood – we guessed the creature was inside).'

Despite the puzzling appearance of the animal Ms Francis notes: 'A policeman informed me that Mrs Arnold's statement was the clearest description he had ever known a witness gave.'

In the early 1980s Ms Francis also interviewed Edward Blanks, who had been manager of Bushylease Farm, 'and,' she writes, 'a very different story emerged from that in the police files of his having seen the Surrey Puma over a number of years.'

> 'He and his family had indeed had a number of sightings, but not of the same animal. Mr Blanks, in fact, remembers seeing large cat-like animals from approximately 1962 until 1971. Over this nine-year period he and his family saw at least three distinctly

different animals, but only one was taken seriously by the authorities – the so-called puma, a large Great Dane-sized tawny creature with darker reddish-brown shading along its back. It was powerfully built with a long blunt-ended tail that curled at the tip. This animal appeared to show no aggression to humans, in fact it showed curiosity and the family was often conscious of being followed when moving around the farm at night. Sometimes a swiftly shone torch beam would reveal a flash of glowing red eyes. Although it appeared to prey on both sheep and deer occasionally, its main diet seemed to be rabbits and even wood pigeons; indeed it was once seen to snatch a group of dead birds that the farmer had shot. Its footprints were four inches long and it left claw marks on tree trunks.

'It made frequent trips into outbuildings, and appeared to use straw as bedding some nights when it denned up there. It was associated with a very strong scent, by which the family learned to recognise when it was in the area. Cattle and dogs showed fear when in the presence of this odour, which was described variously as "almost suffocating", "musty, like rotting wood" and "a strong smell with an ammonia tang". This animal was accepted by the authorities, at it fitted their belief that a feral puma was living in the area.

'However, they did not accept a second animal that was seen a number of times, though less frequently than the tawny one. It was similar to the brown cat in size and build, but its coat was either a dark grey or black.

'The third animal was slightly more like the creature described so well by Mrs Arnold, though far from identical: it was smaller than the tawny and dark animals, and Mr Blanks saw it only three times. It was about the size of a medium dog like a spaniel, ginger coloured with spots and stripes in a darker colour. It had a flat cat-like face with protruding fangs hanging over its lip. It was rather like a hybrid lynx as it had tufted ears – but it had a long tail.' [29]

The writers Janet and Colin Bord also noted additional details in the reports that make the appearances of the puma seem less easily explicable, but more in keeping with descriptions of other 'alien animals', such as bigfoot, lake monsters, winged creatures etc. which they discuss in their eponymous book.

For instance, Edward Blanks had reported that during the severe winter of 1962–3, when there had been some heavy snowfalls, there had been a complete absence of the footprints by which he had hoped to track the animal. When the animal was known to be around the property, the farm dogs, normally quite fearless, had been unleashed but had strangely refused to follow the scent and appeared to be quite terrified. Although its visits were usually made at night, sometimes it appeared during foggy days; it made screaming and yelling noises, usually when crossing open ground.

The dairyman's Mini van had run over 'a strange cat-like animal' with a loud thump as the creature hit the underside, and sustained damage, but the puma apparently did not – it leaped into a barley field; yet the Mini had a flat, solid bottom and a ground clearance of only five inches, not nearly enough space for a domestic moggy let alone a puma.

They note that strong odours 'almost suffocating', are not typical of a puma in its natural state, but are sometimes reported by witnesses of other types of alien animal, especially the North American 'bigfoot' or Sasquatch. One could add here a detail that Ms Francis picked up – the feeling of being watched. Likewise, glowing red eyes are a feature of many spectral creatures, but not of literal pumas.

At the time of the flap Charles Bowen, the editor of *Flying Saucer Review* magazine, had also interviewed Mr Blanks. He noted a curious detail that conformed to his area of interest, but which had not attracted the attention of other investigators: that lights sometimes shone upon the roofs of the farm buildings at night. There was no apparent source for them in this isolated area, and every time they were seen, the animal was observed in the area shortly afterwards.

Mrs Arnold corresponded with Di Francis both before and after the publication of the latter's book *Cat Country*, and in a letter of 1982 she describes yet another investigator determined to get to the bottom of the mystery: 'I expect you know a man from the zoo came and spent a lot of time with us one Sunday, and brought books and dozens of pictures, but we couldn't find the cat at all. He particularly wanted me to say it was a puma, but it just was not a puma'.

The zoologist, disturbed by the way her outlandish animal did not conform to his view that it should be a 'puma', hoped that she had been mistaken.

But on the matter of Mr Blanks's having seen an additional 'black or dark grey' animal, it is Mrs Arnold's turn to want *him* to be mistaken – 'I think maybe Mr Blanks account of this being black in colour could well be because it is very deep red-brown up on the top, with stripes and spots which merge, and, seen from a way off could look grey or black.' A misperception just as improbable as the sighting itself.

Even Di Francis, noting the spots and stripes of the animal, wondered if Mrs Arnold might have been mistaken about the tail, and that it might actually have been a lynx (lynxes do not have tails – or at least very short stubby ones). But Mrs Arnold was adamant: 'No, I was not mistaken. It was a full tail'.

Mrs Arnold gave much thought over the years to 'her' cat, reading and visiting zoos in the hope of being able to match one of their exotic felids with the creature she had seen, but with no success: 'The serval cats are of the same sort of colour but so much smaller. I saw one of these, in the zoo, catch a pigeon that had unfortunately got it in with them, in flight.' And then, surprisingly, she did see something like it again – on television. She reported the event to Ms Francis, writing 'Watching Arthur C. Clarke's programme on mysterious animals, and seeing the creature which he called a king cheetah, I must say that this is the nearest I have seen to the cat I saw.'

The reason perhaps that Mrs Arnold's cat had not featured in the zoologist's encyclopaedia was that it was not at that time recognised as a separate species from the normal cheetah, and the king cheetah's position as a possible subspecies is still controversial. Its distinctive pelage, with dark reddish-brown stripes and spots swimming together and merging, was at first thought to be merely a variant of the usual cheetah spots.

The sightings such as those I have quoted above illustrate a consistent feature of eyewitnesses' reports to the present day: not only are they always adamant that what they have seen is some kind of cat, but they are not inclined to adjust their description of the cat to suit even zoologists' views about what species is most likely – or rather least improbably – on the loose. Mrs Arnold's king cheetah remains both one of the most accurately observed and bizarre ABCs on record.

After a few years sightings of the Surrey Puma diminished, and editors lost interest in the story – or perhaps it was vice-versa. At any rate, by 1967 no puma or big cat had been caught or satisfactorily photographed, and no answers to the mystery of its provenance and nature had been provided. The 362 witness statements collected by Godalming police over four years were destroyed and their file was closed.

It was the first systematic collection of data on ABCs and the first divergence of opinion about what constituted evidence and how to interpret it. Investigators and commentators separated broadly into the several camps they occupy today. There are those who insist on a biological origin for ABCs – that they are zoo animals which must have escaped or been released and are now naturalised in some way. Then there are others who place ABCs in a wider context – among the other species of out-of-place animals found in our countryside and worldwide. Yet others see ABCs as belonging with the various spectral animal forms provided by folklore or experienced as paranormal phenomena.

Needless to say the 'puma', in its various forms and colours, continues regularly to alarm Surrey's sober citizens. John Pickhaven saw a strange, grey feline animal stalking low to the ground in a field one morning near Haslemere;[30] Mary Moore was stopped in her tracks by a black panther – 'It stood in my way, just watching me, not startled at all.'[31] Mike Attard, driving on the road to Chertsey, saw in his headlights a sandy-brown animal ahead which he first assumed was a deer. 'When I got within twenty yards of it', he said, 'I realised immediately "That's a bloody *lion*!"'[32]

Regardless of the ABC theorists and their ideas stands another group – the stolid band of eyewitnesses such as Mr Pickhaven, who declared: 'I don't believe in ghosts and I don't believe in pumas. I just know that I saw it'.

# Chapter 6

# Creatures which can't be caught:
# the black dog connection

When, in the early 1980s, sightings of black ABCs began to predominate over those of tawny coloured animals some commentators suggested that ABCs might be variants of the spectral ' black dogs' of folklore.

The ubiquitous and ancient black dog legends are found all over Britain.[1] They appear or briefly trot beside travellers sometimes as companions, guides, or occasionally death omens. Norfolk's black dog is known as Black Shuck, while it is called Galley-Trot or Scarfe in Suffolk, Barguest, Trash or Guytrash in Lancashire, and so on.

Some ABC investigators who believe ABCs to be escaped captives have speculated on whether the black dogs of folklore might not have been an ignorant peasantry's misperception of 'real', black, panthers all along.

Conversely, some students of black dog folklore wondered whether the cultural context of phantom black dogs could have changed, and the same ambiguous animal encountered in country lanes is now reinterpreted by a sophisticated, wildlife-documentary-viewing peasantry as a ' black panther'.

### Dissimilarities

Although their shared blackness and habit of frequenting roads makes them superficially alike there are vastly more differences between them:

- ABCs appear in the hard light of day – even bright sunshine – whereas black dogs are creatures of the twilight or night.

- Not all ABCs are black – there is a range of other colours reported as well as a large minority of puma-colours – whereas black dogs are usually black by definition.

- The coats of black dogs are usually described as shaggy or woolly, whereas ABCs' fur is usually noticeably sleek and glossy.

- Black dogs often brush against the human, allow themselves to be touched, follow or accompany the human sometimes as a guardian, or convey a personal presentiment of death –

whereas the ABC makes little or no contact, appearing either oblivious of or indifferent to the witness.

- Black dogs' eyes are often red and/or glowing; those of the ABCs usually green or amber.

- ABCs often remain at a distance, whereas black dogs approach the witness or appear rarely more than the width of the road away, and frequently trot alongside the spectator.

- Black dogs appear repeatedly along the same stretch of road – often for generations – whereas ABCs' appearances are unpredictable and short-lived.

- Black dogs usually confirm their quasi-spectral nature by vanishing into thin air, whereas ABCs generally walk into hedges.

## Pairs and cubs

The black dog is an essentially solitary creature whereas ABCs are sometimes seen together. Elizabeth Downes and her mother saw two large cat-like animals converging from different angles on unseen prey in a field as they drove past. Elizabeth noted 'they were definitely black panthers – I used to work in a zoo and am well aware what big cats look like'.[2]

Iain Pringle was driving just south of Newark on Christmas morning 2002:

> 'Dawn was breaking when my headlamps lit up four green almond-shaped eyes. I slowed right down to see what looked at first sight like a pair of black Labradors running south along the verge of the inside lane. It was not until I was passing them that I saw the unmistakable gait and physique of two large, black cats. No, I had not been drinking, and yes I am sure of what I saw!'[3]

Moreover different 'species', both brown 'puma' types and black 'panther' types, seem to occupy the same locality. A big, black, panther-like cat was seen twice on one Devon farm in the spring of 1983. During the same period the farmer was walking over a water meadow when out of the rushes in front of him a markedly different animal sprang into the air and disappeared into another clump of rushes at tremendous speed. 'He saw it was light brown and had a long tail which has almost the length of its body. Its head was rounded with short ears. He was in no doubt that it was a puma.'[4]

Another Devonshire farmer had regularly seen a huge black ABC crossing the fields and running close to a deep hedge bank, but one day he saw it had company – there were two ABCs chasing across the field together, one jet-black, the other smaller and brownish.[5]

The two species seemed almost to be interchangeable according to two shocked motorists. They saw – from a matter of twenty yards away – a very big, black cat, running at speed through the grounds of a hotel near Melrose into a clearing:

'It had a long, thick "muscular tail", and its back legs seemed to come higher then the body as it ran. As the witnesses approached the clearing where the cat disappeared they had another shock: standing there staring at them was not the panther-like animal they had expected but a fawn-coloured cat, slightly smaller than the black cat. This one was identical to a puma. After watching the witnesses for a few seconds it followed the path the black cat had taken seconds earlier and disappeared into woodland.'[6]

Every ABC investigator can also quote examples of ABCs not just keeping company with other adult big cats but apparently also with cubs. I mentioned in a previous chapter how Steve Evans sat on his quad-bike and watched an Alsatian-sized ABC with what looked like two, Labrador-sized 'cubs'.

### How black dogs and ABCs are related

As mystery animals go, therefore, ABCs and black dogs are apparently as different as chalk and cheese. However the matter does not quite end there. Their relationship might be considered an example of the binary classification by which – according to structural anthropology – traditional societies make sense of the world. The opposing characteristics may, by analogy, form a single pattern – may be two sides of the same coin.

For instance one could say ABC is to black dog as smooth is to rough; or as distant is to close. Formally expressed some of the analogies might look like this:

| **black dog** | : | **ABC** |
|---|---|---|
| rough | : | smooth |
| close | : | distant |
| engaged | : | indifferent |
| habitual | : | random |
| stare | : | glance |
| metaphorical | : | literal |
| red eyed | : | green eyed |
| matt | : | shiny |
| singular | : | plural |

Thus ABCs and black dogs might balance a range of polarities. But our normal, household cats and dogs do the same thing. W.H. Auden makes the point in an amusing poem[7] contrasting the aloofness of cats indoors, with the companionability of a dog out of doors, and so on. Some of the polarities he expresses are:

| **cat** | : | **dog** |
|---------|---|---------|
| introvert | : | extrovert |
| imagination | : | emotion |
| apartness | : | togetherness |
| pride | : | subservience |
| indoors | : | outdoors |
| wild | : | tame |

Auden suggests that the opposing characteristics of cats and dogs mirror our own dualistic natures. An amusing extension of this idea can be found on a website called http://iusedtobelieve.com Here visitors can read a huge variety of childhood beliefs on a wide range of topics, and contribute their own.

One belief in particular crops up again and again – that dogs and cats are male and female, respectively, of the same species. As one contributor put it: 'I used to believe that the cat was the wife and the dog was the husband'. Another confessed: 'Like many people on this site, I used to believe that all cats were female and all dogs were male. The weird thing is, my family had both cats and dogs, and my parents showed us kittens and puppies being born, and taught us how to tell the difference between girls and boys, but I still sort of believed it.'

As an adult that contributor was able to analyse the two different kinds of belief that commonly co-exist in all of us. She accepted what she had been told: that, biologically, cats and dogs are of both genders; but she remained instinctively loyal to the idea of gender as part of a duality inherent in the universe, which extends beyond individual, physical sexuality. She still felt that at some other level of reality cats do correspond with a feminine principle and dogs with a masculine principle – comparably perhaps with the yin and yang of Chinese philosophy.

But to return to people's experience of mystery rather than domestic animals, is it too fanciful to suggest that just as domestic dogs and cats each have their opposing, complementary places in the human psyche, black dogs and ABCs might have similar roles but in the wider, geographical landscape?

It is of course a nebulous notion. Yet there are distinctive landscapes associated with ABC sightings which suggest something along those lines, and I will delve more deeply into the topography of ABC appearances in Chapter 12.

## Liminal zones

ABCs seem to appear randomly anywhere from back gardens to motorways. Black dogs, however, are commonly associated with what are known as liminal zones.[8] These are the transitional zones between one area and another – the kind of no-man's-land traditionally regarded as magical. In the landscape they include streams, bridges, stiles, gates and churchyards – spots literally or symbolically at the point of transition over a boundary. Frontiers between culture and nature may also be liminal places, and latter-day examples include marginalised locations and communities such as caravan parks, tip-heads, industrial estates or sewage farms. Dusk and dawn are liminal times of day, as are noon and midnight.

Having said that ABCs appear anywhere, it is worth noting that some of these locations have included distinctly liminal places. The black ABC that Anne Coombs saw passed through an archway into the churchyard. 'I could gauge its height in reference to the arch.  It was about two feet six inches to the shoulder... '[9] Another witness was walking his dog past All Saints Church in Leighton Buzzard 'when something leaped down from the very high wall, and landed very easily as a cat would do.' This ABC behaved slightly more like a black dog: 'The creature only made one step forward after landing before standing still and looking sideways at me from fifteen feet away. She was huge, grey and had a tail like that of a panther. I was extremely quiet and so was my dog!' But with typical feline detachment the big cat then walked away as if, he said, having acknowledged him, 'it had to be off on its way somewhere.'[10]

A piece of Norfolk folklore emphatically links a black dog – and by inference an ABC – to one such liminal place, a literal gate and symbolic portal:

> 'A farm labourer and his wife were returning home one summer's night. As they walked towards their house they heard a dog running up behind them. They stopped and turned, but could see nothing and the sounds of running paws stopped. After a moment the couple continued on their way, when they heard the dog running towards them again.
>
> 'Frightened now, they ran for their gate and slammed it shut behind them. Feeling safe behind the gate, the man looked back cautiously for the dog, but saw nothing – when a hideous scream pierced the night air. There on top of the gate was the biggest dog they had ever seen, its eyes burning bright green in the darkness. The dog then turned and vanished, its paws padding away into the night.'[11]

The couple instinctively recognised that the gate – the kind of liminal place favoured by black dogs – was the psychic as well as the physical barrier behind which they would be safe. And indeed the animal remained poised between two worlds, standing on the gate. But this particular black dog may have had a dual nature in more ways than one, for its piercing scream and green eyes, and ability to leap up and balance on top of the gate make it very much more like an ABC than a dog.

An equally ambiguous cat terrified a fisherman in Ireland. Mr Martin was standing on the dry, gravelly edge of the river, casting into a small pool, when he suddenly felt constrained to look to his right along the river. He could not see far, as there was a bend less than a hundred yards away.

> 'But as he looked he saw a huge black animal come into sight, padding along in the shallow water. He could not at first make out what it was – whether dog, panther, or what – but he felt it to be

intensely menacing, so without wasting a moment he dropped his rod and jumped for the nearest tree on the bank, a youngish ash, and climbed till it bent dangerously with his weight.

'Meanwhile the animal continued padding steadily along, and as it passed it looked up at him with almost human intelligence and bared its teeth with a mixture of snarl and jeering grin. His flesh crept as he stared back into its fearsome blazing red eyes, which seemed like live coals inside the monstrous head. Even so, he could only think of it as a wild savage animal which had presumably escaped from some travelling circus. It passed on and was soon lost to view round the next bend.'

He ran home, loaded a gun and searched for it – but drew a blank. No one he met, including those who must have been in its path, had seen it.

'He started to make inquiries among the local people and found it had been seen over the years, usually standing in or by the river near the local bridge, but always in the gloaming. He was told too, that it was fifty or more years since anyone had claimed to have seen it in full daylight.' [12]

The animal was cat-like: the idea of a panther occurred to Mr Martin. It snarled – as ABCs occasionally do before they make off, whereas black dogs are usually silent presences.

It had the red, glowing eyes of a black dog and it had a typical haunt, by a local bridge. But it was so obviously corporeal – splashing along in the shallow water – that he assumed, as do so many witnesses of modern ABCs, that it was a big cat that had escaped from a circus. Black dogs do not always seem so solid, although it should be noted that they sometimes walk with a splashing noise as the onomatopoeic name of one of them – 'Trash' – suggests.

Although he had sensed its imminent arrival, feeling constrained to look up river even before it appeared, Mr Martin's encounter was impersonal: the creature saw him and snarled, but continued on its way, ambling into and out of Mr Martin's view with the vagrant, preoccupied indifference of an ABC.

### Impersonal *v.* personal

There is an intelligible, human dimension to black dogs' existence – they may come to guard or to warn, or simply to travel alongside us on our road in whatever capacity. Conversely it is difficult to make sense of the ABCs' brief, insignificant appearances as they cross your path in front of you. The type of experience Brian Bedford had is constantly repeated in the annals of ABC research. He was driving to work when a huge feline animal crossed the road in front of him:

'It was not in any particular hurry. It was browny-black, with a long curly tail. It was far too big to be a domestic dog or cat… I was absolutely dumbfounded'.

Top left: *Bench-end at Charing church.*
Top right: *Cat head at Boughton-Under-Blean church.*
Above: *Tiverton church capital. (All three photographs by Nigel Rushbrook)*

The same thing happened to Gordon Singleton, who explained: 'It just leapt out of the field, dashed straight in front of me. It was jet- black and had a long tail.... I couldn't stop thinking about it. Every time I turn down Martin Lane now I hope to see it again, but I suppose I never will... '

These are two examples typical of hundreds where the ABC casually, unconcernedly, briefly crosses the road in front of the witness. Despite the powerful effect it has on the witnesses the ABC does not connect with them personally. As a spectral companion the black dog, however, seems to take a personal interest in the traveller, and in his occasional role as harbinger of death he becomes more personal still – his significant gaze contrasting with the indifferent glance of the ABC.

A modern account illustrates the point:

> 'I used to have dreams of a "demon dog", medium size, black, with glowing red eyes, and within two weeks someone I felt closely bonded with would die. One evening I saw the dog with my physical eyes. He looked at me intensely, eye to eye. The following day my four year old daughter died. About eight years ago I saw him again with my physical eyes. Again there was this intense eye contact, but his eyes were glowing as yellow this time and not red. It turned out to be a warning – by telling her of the apparition I saved my daughter from a fatal car crash.' [13]

In the way they meet our eyes both animal forms resemble their domestic equivalents: dogs solicit attention, cats are withdrawn and aloof.

## History

Another difference between ABCs and black dogs is the lack of historical ABCs sightings, as we know them today. There are reports of personal encounters with black dogs which go back to medieval times, but a scant handful of ABC reports before the twentieth century. But although scarcely anyone in medieval times had seen a big cat, they were very familiar with the symbolic meaning of, say, a lion as kingly valour. For centuries big cats were exclusively heraldic emblems or motifs in medieval church decorations – where the ambiguous 'green cats', half-man half-cat, spews out greenery of carved stone.

However black dogs have changed their demeanour somewhat over time; and so perhaps have ABCs. Jeremy Harte has shown how black dogs were once identified with the Devil but in modern times are more generally thought of as ghosts – of animals loyal to their owners for instance. As such they have gradually become less threatening. In Lincolnshire, he points out, the legendary 'huge dog-like creature, with flaming eyes' recorded by earlier folklorists had, by the time Ethel Rudkin came to undertake her fieldwork in the 1930s, become the black dog 'to be wondered at but not feared. Indeed, she tells one story in which his presence was welcome…as a guardian to a traveller.' [14]

Could it be that when, in modern times, the legendary black dogs stopped being demons and started to resemble the inoffensive ghosts of people's pets, ABCs followed suit?

Have they also been turned from symbols into literal animals, also reputedly people's former pets, and also credited with having been translated into another order of reality – but this time by 'escaping' rather than dying?

## The reactions of other animals

Black dogs are a cultural phenomenon – they appear to humans and whatever their meaning it is essentially a human one. ABCs on the other hand are events independent of human perception and interpretation - they impact strongly on other animals.

It was a sunny summer afternoon in 1995 and Alan Taylor and his friend were out shooting wood pigeon on farmland near Angus in Scotland. They were walking along a hedgerow when, they noticed, some horses in the adjacent paddock 'started to get spooked by something'.

'Guessing it was us with the guns,' Alan recalls, 'we kept quiet and walked slowly away from them. Then, from the long grass by the hedge, there arose a large, black panther. It was about six feet in length, and three feet in height. It had a wide head, green eyes and a long tail. We assumed it had been cat-napping in the sun and had just woken, judging by its startled behaviour.

> 'It was only twenty yards away, and with us coming from a downwind direction it seemed as surprised as us. My friend and I looked in amazement straight at the beast for a couple of seconds. I even raised the twelve-bore shotgun and had it in my sights – but wasn't quick enough to get a shot off before the cat darted through the hawthorn hedge and into a field of high potato shaws. That was the last we saw of it, but there were several large paw prints left in the dust which confirmed the size of the cat.'[15]

Likewise it was Rosemary Wilson's pony which gave her the first indication that something alarming was in the offing – it 'suddenly stopped dead'. She was riding along a single-track road, near Hale in Westmorland, when her mount apparently became aware of something the other side of the hedge. She said: 'I booted it on – but it was then that I caught sight of a large, black cat.' She watched the animal walking in her direction for about ten seconds before it disappeared into the hedge. 'You read about things like that but you don't expect to see them,' she said.[16]

## Dogs tremble and flee

Horses are not the only animals to react dramatically to the whiff of an ABC. Mr Batchelor was walking his lurcher bitch in the forest near Wareham in Dorset one morning in October 2004. It was a quiet, clear and bright day. Suddenly he noticed that she had sensed something further up the track because, he said, 'she was looking fixedly ahead, her hackles had risen and she was making quiet barks'. Mr Batchelor explained:

> 'She spots deer before I do, so I looked to see what it was. Crossing the path ahead of us was a black, Labrador-sized, cat-like animal. What catches your eye is the gait of the animal – it was just strolling. It had the typical, very long, curved tail – the classic thing. I might have thought it was my imagination if it hadn't been for the dog seeing it first. It certainly stirred her up – and dogs haven't got any axe to grind have they?'[17]

Some of the most persuasive evidence that ABCs exist independently of human perception is the – often uncharacteristic – reaction of other animals to them. As

Mr Batchelor pointed out, dogs have not got any axes to grind. However the wary reaction of his greyhound was unusually restrained – most dogs cower, tremble or flee.

Shep, who belonged to one witness, Mr Lothian, was put on the trail of the ABC his master had just seen 'but his hackles went up and he refused to budge.' [18] Likewise Zoë, a terrier out rabbiting with two teenagers 'shot off in the opposite direction and tried to get back in the van' when they spotted an ABC. Mrs C's Westie suddenly crouched low 'as if it were going to stalk something. It never made a sound but stared straight ahead. Then a very large cat-like animal appeared from behind a tree… ' [19]

A man walking his dog was surprised to find the animal, which had sprinted off after a rabbit, suddenly run back and cower behind him. Looking up he then saw two panther-like, black big cats walking towards him. They all froze, the cats looked at him for a moment, then ambled off. [20]

I wondered whether the dogs might have been taking their cue from the fear of the humans, but actually I found the opposite to be true: usually the dogs' terror surprises their owners. Mary Moore was unfazed by the animal she described as 'a black panther' which she came across while walking her dog in Bourne Woods, Surrey, on a summer afternoon in 1991. Far from panicking she had time to admire the creature, noting: 'It was sleek, black and powerful. A very fine creature indeed. I love animals and wasn't a bit frightened, although,' she added, 'my whippet seemed very scared.' [21]

Certain brave dogs have been known to chase an ABC. One such was a collie named Bos. Perkin Bosworth and his father encountered a large, black cat while driving along a country lane near Much Wenlock in Shropshire. 'It was black, large and looked to me like a panther,' he said. 'When we stopped to take a closer look Bos jumped out of the car and chased after the animal.' The ABC 'easily out-distanced him', but the chase gave Mr Bosworth the opportunity of comparing the animals: 'It was quite a powerful creature – we could see its muscles rippling under its sleek coat as it ran – it was larger than Bos, and he's big for a collie.' [22]

Even braver was Lonely – a dog belonging to Wendy Peacock. He flushed a black panther-like cat out of an overgrown ditch near Shelfanger in Norfolk. Mrs Peacock at first took the animal for a black Labrador – until it jumped ten feet up into a tree. 'The cat's long, black tail was hanging down and it was flicking it. My dog was at the foot of the tree going mad!' [23]

## Cattle and sheep

ABCs are sometimes implicated in stampedes of cattle. In the case of Mr Brands, that was what drew his attention to an ABC in the first place. He wrote:

> 'One evening during the autumn of 1984 I arrived at my home in Compton village, near Paignton, and noticed that, in the very steep field opposite my house, the bullocks that graze there were very disturbed. They were milling around and staring at some

point higher up the hill. When I looked up there I noticed a large, white animal standing still and looking down on the cattle. I ran inside and got my binoculars and was amazed to see an animal belonging to the cat family. I was about two hundred yards away and I was able to observe the animal clearly as it walked away from the cattle… ' [24]

Richard Polley in Essex was repairing a tractor when his attention was drawn to the noise of cows running as if in an agitated state. Moments later he saw what was causing a commotion; it was a large, black cat which was running through the herd. It appeared the cattle were chasing the beast.

The same kind of chase by excited bullocks was reported from Scotland. Les Hester noticed cattle stampeding in a nearby field – 'they were going crazy. They were following an animal which was loping along the line of the fence in the next field. The animal was a big cat.'

An Ayrshire farmer was out shooting foxes and noticed sheep scattering away from a large black ABC crossing a field. 'He was treated to a lovely broadside view of the animal when it turned sideways and – in a single bound – jumped a fence, and was able to estimate the animal's length as about six feet long excluding its three-foot tail. The field the cat jumped into was full of cows which, like the sheep, scattered to the far corner – all that is except one large brown cow which stood its ground and stared at the cat. The cat paid no attention to the fleeing cattle and ran straight across the field, disappearing into woods.' [25]

With the exception of the odd bloody-minded animal such as that brown cow, cattle seem to be more readily frightened by ABCs than are sheep. It was the attentive curiosity – and not fear – of nearby sheep confirmed the belief of a tourist, staying at a guest house near Durness in Scotland, that they were watching as unusual an animal as she was. She was reading by the window at 5.30 a.m. when she was shocked to see from the window a strange creature walking down the road. 'It was a big, pure black cat-like animal with a long tail. The sheep in the field were startled by it, and were just standing and staring.' [26]

On other occasions witnesses are struck by the fact that farm animals seem oblivious of the intruder – almost as though it were invisible. One witness described how a panther-type creature walked lazily through a field of sheep, in broad daylight. It was so close to them she could gauge its size from them ('its body length was as long as the sheep, and its tail as long again') yet, she said, 'the sheep were unconcerned, and continued grazing.' [27] Ken and Denise Ashby saw a large black, panther-like animal trotting across a field amongst the sheep. 'Strangely the sheep did not appear to be alarmed by it,' they reported. 'They just stopped grazing and watched it cross the field.' [28] A Dorset witness spotted an ABC 'bounding through the sheep' which, to her incredulity, 'ignored it completely.' [29]

## Wild animals

Not only domestic animals but wild creatures and birds also react to the presence of an ABC. Mr Hooper of Exeter and a colleague were bird-watching when their attention was drawn to four or five crows making a fuss and harassing something. Through their binoculars they saw it was an ABC – what Mr Hooper described as 'definitely an escape from somewhere'. They saw the big cat swing at the crows once or twice, and then break into a fast lope across country.[30]

Sometimes the appearance of a big cat is preceded by the disappearance of other wildlife. Simon Scott-White was out stalking with a friend when he noticed 'it was suspiciously quiet.' The two men were lying in a field of wheat looking down a steep valley, which to their surprise was empty: 'There were no deer – there are usually fifty or sixty there – and no rabbits or birds'. They realised the reason for this when suddenly they saw a black panther-like animal 'running along the hedgerow', and they watched it through their binoculars as it took off up the valley towards the village.[31]

Maurice Wallis also witnessed the alarm caused by an ABC while he was out badger-watching in a wood in Devon. 'Some badgers were coming towards me when they suddenly pulled up and ran back to the sett,' he recalled. 'Then I saw this cat, about the size of a Great Dane... it was in a hurry and ran past me about twenty feet away.'[32]

Patricia Lawrence and June Oram were used to deer crossing the road and, when one jumped in front of the car, Mrs Lawrence braked, expecting more to follow. But instead a black panther-like creature emerged from a roadside copse. 'It crouched, turned and then sped off back into the woodland,' she said. 'I could not believe what I saw. It was about the size of an Airedale dog, black with a very long tail. It was going at great speed. It was definitely a big cat chasing the deer.'[33]

In contrast black dogs are not known for alarming badgers, chasing deer, or being mobbed by crows, confining their effects to humans. ABCs range over the countryside as if it were their own, creating a stir among its other fauna just as any major predator – such as a human, big dog or perhaps an escaped leopard – would.

## Getting back to earth

In this chapter I have scrutinised possible connections between ABCs and what have been supposed are their nearest relatives – the enigmatic black dogs of ancient and modern folklore.

I have noted how appealing it is to jump to the conclusion that they are from the same family – a family not of this world, spawning various spectral beasts. Such a provenance would explain the apparent uncatchability of ABCs.

Unfortunately this idea seems too simplistic. Perhaps the most striking inference to be drawn from the behaviour of ABCs as compared to that of black dogs is that they are very much of this world. Apart from frightening or chasing other animals they have also been observed eating, drinking, crapping, spraying, raiding dustbins, stealing from bird-tables, rooting in discarded chip wrappers – activities no black dog would be seen dead doing.

Indeed this capacity for being not only 'of this world', but so at home in the sprawl of human habitation is what gives succour to the more widespread belief that ABCs are not spectral beasts but zoological specimens – former captives and their descendants. And in contrast to the evidence for black dogs which relies wholly on anecdotal and written material, zoologically-minded ABC investigators can point to physical traces left by concrete, hungry, big cats to support their theory.

In the following chapter I will look at those physical traces to see what they can prove about the mysterious big cats amongst us.

# Chapter 7

# Hard evidence: kills, footprints, bodies, skulls

### Kills

There is much concrete evidence that ABCs are hungry big cats. Sometimes this takes the form of livestock kills. Testimony from vets and farmers shows that to a knowledgeable eye a carcass that has been killed by a predatory big cat looks very different from the remains left by a dog or a fox.

Dogs are the most usual culprits being the only native British animal capable of killing sheep, but the sheep carcass inspected by Graham Godbeer, a vet, in the Blackdown Hills in Somerset lead him to believe that a dog was not its killer.

Mr Godbeer explained his reasons: 'Dogs don't kill animals to eat, they do it for the chase. If it had been a dog, or dogs, there would have been several sheep injured. Dogs would not sit there in the open and eat an entire sheep. They also make a real mess. In this case, the bones had been licked clean and the end of the rib bones shredded.' [1]

An ABC, which one local resident described as 'completely black with pointed ears, golden eyes and a square chest,' [2] had been seen in the vicinity, and both Mr Godbeer and the farmer who owned it suspected that the sheep had been killed by such an animal.

In the same county, two months later, another sheep was killed by an unusual predator. It was found dead, lacerated by large claw marks, and with all the flesh on the shoulder removed down to the bone by a very large and powerful jaw.

The attack had occurred at the Heaven's Gate Farm refuge, near Langport, in a twenty-three acre field overlooked by the animal welfare centre's reception area. Whatever carried it out must have been extraordinarily swift and stealthy because, as Centre Manager, Kathrin Porter said: 'It's amazing that nobody saw or heard anything because it was in broad daylight.'

There was another reason for discounting a dog attack. She explained: 'There were no marks of a dog and no wool about the place which you would also expect to see,' but what clinched the matter was the fact that there was a six-feet high chain link fence all around the field – an enclosure it would have been impossible for a dog to get into.

*This sheep was killed and eaten by a powerful, methodical predator such as an ABC, near Warminster 2002. (Marcus Matthews)*

## More sheep kills

Reports of livestock killed in suspicious circumstances are regularly logged by ABC investigators Nigel and David Spencer.[3] In 1998 they were called to an unlucky sheep's demise, reporting:

> 'The latest sheep kill has the hallmarks of a big cat's work, with classic evidence of a side-on ambush to the throat of the unfortunate animal, against a fence.

> 'This was confirmed by the presence of large blood stains up the fence where it was killed, the blood being some two feet off the ground. This debunks the theory of some farmers that this was a previously dead animal, eaten by foxes. The only remains of the sheep were the fleece, the ribs and spine, and three legs. Again the head was severed and missing. The carcass had been dragged twenty feet from the kill through a hedge and ditch to another field. The kill, stripping, and consumption of the carcass had occurred overnight. The police have viewed the site and are as convinced as ourselves that it is the work of at least one big cat.' Claw marks which had pierced the hide so as to push the wool through from the outside in little loops, also indicated a feline predator.

## Deer kills

Deer have been found eaten in a similar manner. In January 2001, a Harrogate man out for a walk came across a freshly-killed deer. The deer had claw marks on it, and the man turned round to see, a short distance away, a big panther-like animal staring at him.[4]

Mrs Hilary Comer was walking her dog in a field between Holcombe and Coleford in Somerset when her Doberman, who had momentarily been out of her sight,

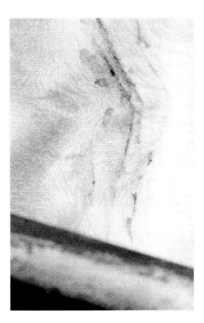

*Charles McGuinness heard his cattle milling around agitatedly way one night, and next morning found scratches he could not account for on the neck of a calf. (Charles McGuinness)*

appeared with the severed rear leg of a deer in its mouth. 'When I went over I was shocked to see a large, healthy, shiny cat turn away from the carcass of the dead deer and run up a tree. It had an elongated body about five feet long, not including the tail, and was jet black. I stood back in shock and, for a moment, thought it was going to pounce; but it just sat there, still and silent.' [5]

## Carcasses found up trees

Whole carcasses have been dragged into or out of different fields, sometimes over fences and up trees – feats far beyond dogs, foxes or badgers but well within the capability of leopards, which in their native countries drag carcasses up trees to keep them away from other predators such as lions and hyenas.

Nigel and David Spencer have logged several instances in Leicestershire, while in Devon Nigel Brierly noted that very often the fore limb of sheep carcasses would be missing, and 'several times I found signs of this having been devoured on the lower branches of a nearby tree.' [6] A local woman 'while out riding had noticed a sheep carcass which had been eaten to the bone on top of a six-foot hedge. Further up in the same field she spotted a large, beige cat-like animal half sitting up, cleaning itself in the sun, by the side of a second carcass.' [7]

A decomposed deer carcass was found fifteen foot up an oak tree in a wood on Bulbarrow Hill in Dorset in 2002, and another fresher one eight feet above the ground in the fork of an ancient beech tree by the roadside. The owner of the wood confessed himself puzzled, commenting: 'Deer jump high, but not into trees, and certainly not eight feet high.'

Neither legitimate stalkers nor poachers would need to protect a carcass from other predators in this way. They disembowel the animal on the spot, and in the case of poachers, butcher it too, for easier transportation. If it has to be left for any length of

*When its hide is drawn back this Sika deer carcass shows claw holes in the flesh. (Jonathan McGowan)*

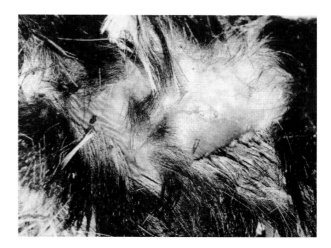

time a spent cartridge case by the body miraculously keeps foxes and other predators away. In any case neither stalker nor poacher would be inclined to fetch a ladder to stow their prize.

Was there an ABC in the locality which could have dragged its kills up the trees? The same wood had also provided one of the clearest sightings of such an animal – it was here that Mike, the stalker I quoted in Chapter 2, watched an ABC through his rifle sights as it uncoiled itself from the boot of his car and slunk off.

## Horses

Occasionally animals too large to be tackled by dogs, such as cattle and horses, have been found with lacerations consistent with being clawed by a large feline, as opposed to a canine, predator.[8] Melanie Macrow found slash and bite marks on her horse, Toffee, and believed the wounds could not have been caused by a dog, pointing out 'they are at the top of her legs and shoulders, too high up for a dog'. Unknown to Melanie a passing driver, Sarah Means, had seen a black ABC in the lane next to Toffee's field two days previously.[9]

## Dog kill

Early in 2003 it was widely reported in the Welsh and national media that a farmer had found a large, black, cat-like animal eating a pet whippet. Mr Mike Sheppard from Cwmgors had actually seen the animal on the dog's body at Llangadog, near Llandovery in Carmarthenshire,

> 'I went down the side of the stream and saw the dog lying there,
> with a big black animal right on top of it with blood on its mouth.
> It was about four feet long without counting its long tail and there
> was a smaller one, about half the size, right beside it.'

Mr Sheppard phoned for the police, who arrived, armed, within ten minutes. 'We went to have another look and the smaller cat was gone but the big cat was still there. They saw it on the other side of the fence, but could not get a shot at it before it disappeared.'

## Small prey

ABCs are occasionally seen with what looks like rabbits or similar small prey in their mouths. A Devon couple watched an ABC as it caught a rabbit, ate it in a leisurely manner and then washed itself. Mr Lewis saw an ABC in a field dash suddenly among a flock of wood pigeons feeding on clover, catch one and take it off into the trees.

Alan McNamee had a dramatic – and terrifyingly close – encounter with a big cat at a kill. He writes:

> 'I was working in my office, at home, at 11.15 p.m. when I heard a very strange sound coming from the side of my house. It was a sound that I had not heard before. At first I thought it was foxes or badgers fighting, but this sound was of some animal in great pain. I went downstairs and I could hear this awful sound getting louder as I got nearer to the side door. I switched the outside lights on and opened the door to the outside. Normally it would go quiet, and that would be the end to it. But it made no difference, whatever was behind the hedge went on making this noise. I then found a stick just outside the door, so I threw it in the direction of the noise, without any effect. By this time I can remember saying to myself, "What the hell is going on!" I then walked up the five steps up to the low hedge which was shaking as if it was being thrashed – and leant over. My God, less than one metre in front of me was a big cat!

> 'In its mouth was a badger, still alive and screaming in pain. The cat's tail was banging into the hedge less than six inches from my legs. Its head was facing away from me and its hindquarters were clearly visible. It was pure black and big! Just over a metre, with a tail as long again of about two inches thick. I estimated its size on the basis of the size of the hedge, path, and walls, and the fact I was so close to it. Its ears seemed to be pinned back and not visible.

> 'When it saw me it gave a growl which sounded deep and heavy, and chilled me to the bone.

> 'Within the time it takes to blink, it stood up, turned, and leaped a good four foot over a bank. I can't remember how I got back into the house, but I was scared to put it mildly.

> 'I ran back upstairs and rang the police, and reported what I had just witnessed. I'm a professional photographer, and at 11.35 p.m. I decided to photograph the area where I had seen the cat, which took a great deal of will power! I lent over the hedge and took one shot, then went quickly back into the house. At first I thought I had got nothing, but on looking more closely I saw what I thought could be lumps of flesh from the badger.' [10]

*The place where Alan McNamee saw a big cat at a kill, taken half an hour after the event. Ringed on the ground are what could have been lumps of flesh. Next morning they had gone.*
*(Alan McNamee)*

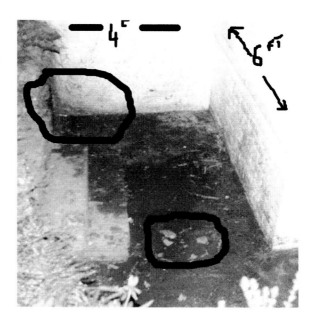

## Pawprints

The pawprints or pugmarks of ABCs are often found at or near the spot where the creature was seen.

There are several clear differences between the footprints of large dogs and big cats, the most obvious being that dogs usually show claw marks in their tracks. The received wisdom from the zoological world is that no cats' pawprints show claws because all cats walk with their claws retracted. They do this to keep them sharp, the better able to grab their prey or climb trees. The only exception to the rule is the cheetah, which does not retract its claws when walking; the reason for this is thought to be that because it runs at such high speeds it needs its claws to help it keep a purchase on the ground.

However cat tracks do show claw marks on occasion, but this is usually when the animal is climbing a slope or in slippery conditions, extending its claws to prevent itself from sliding. The hind claws of Felicity, the puma captured in 1980 by Ted Noble, were worn, implying that she must have used them to help grip the ground when necessary; whereas her front claws were sharp, implying she kept them sheathed for clawing.

Nevertheless as a general rule ABC investigators tend to discount padmarks which show claws, preferring to eliminate at least that area of confusion between canine and feline footprints.

This still leaves much persuasive evidence that big cats stroll over our countryside leaving footprints, from four to six inches wide, to bear witness to their passing. Nigel Brierly has examined hundreds of padmarks – both with and without claw marks – in places associated with sightings of a large, black, cat-like animal, but from which fences would have excluded dogs.[11]

*Above: Casts of tracks apparently left by big cats at Cwmcoch, the farm owned by Alan and Alayne Perrott near Felingwm Uchaf, Carmarthenshire, 1997–9. (Tony Healy/Fortean Picture Library)*

Left: *In the winter of 1985 Nigel Brierly found the tracks of a big cat in snow, showing its typical bounding motion. The distance between the sets of padmarks is fifty-four inches. (Nigel Brierly/Fortean Picture Library)*

*Marcus Matthews with plaster casts of pawprints of a Shaftesbury ABC.*

Devon police investigating sightings of the Wrangaton 'lion' made a cast of a large footprint with a pronounced rounded shape and asymmetrical pad marks, which was identified as that of a big cat by Robin Godbeer, keeper at Dartmoor Wildlife Park. He said he could not be sure which species it was 'but it is big enough to be that of a juvenile male lion which would weigh between fifteen and eighteen stone.'[12]

A paw print cast was taken in August 1998 from a series of prints in soft clay at the quarry of Castle Cement, Ketton, in Rutland. They were found after sightings of panther-like cats in the quarry by site employees and security staff over five years. Nigel Spencer reported:

> 'The print is very clear and has sunk into the ground some forty millimetres, indicating a heavy creature, yet there is no sign of claw marks as would occur with a dog. There is no public access to the quarry which is continuously staffed and subject to very tight security due to blasting – this again excludes the possibility of the footprint's being that of a dog'. Nigel took the cast to the local zoo for examination, and their experts 'confirmed it as being from a big cat of puma or panther type.'

Mr Chinchen of Stour Row, near Shaftesbury, saw a black big cat crossing a lane on the Dorset/Wiltshire Border.[13] He took two plaster casts of its pawprints, the size of a large dog's, which the Wiltshire researcher, Marcus Matthews, confirmed were consistent with those of a leopard or puma.

**Bodies**

In the United Kingdom five 'leopard cats' (*Felis bengalensis*) have been shot since 1981, and three 'jungle cats' (*Felis chaus*) have been found dead since 1988.[14] An African wildcat (*Felis Lybica*) was run over in Devon in 1991. None of these species are much bigger than a domestic cat – certainly not 'big cats' either technically or in actual size.[15] It would be reasonable to assume that since the bodies of small, non-native cats such as these are occasionally found, reported and identified without much difficulty, the same would be true of Britain's big cats. In fact their habit of

*Single leopard-like pawprint found on Pentridge Down in Dorset. The animal must have leapt two metres on to a dry bank ahead. (Jonathan McGowan)*

crossing roads should put them at greater risk of being run over, and their greater size should make their corpses more easily spotted, reported and collected.

This is certainly the case in other developed countries. The Florida puma (*Felis concolor coryi*) is an endangered sub-species of which the remaining fifty or so individuals occupy a range of approximately 6000 square miles of southern Florida. Sparse though this population is, road kills along state highways resulted in seven puma deaths between 1972 and 1985. Between 1979 and 1997, about forty-two percent of Florida pumas were killed by cars.[16]

And indeed, according to hearsay, panther-like cats have also been seen lying dead by British roadsides. The following report made by a puzzled employer in Lincolnshire on 20th April 2004 is typical:

> 'On Tuesday morning I was speaking to one of the drivers at work. He told me that the previous day he had set out early from work with a delivery when he saw what at first he thought was "a bloody great black dog laid dead in the road".
>
> 'As he drew nearer he noticed it wasn't a dog at all but a large black cat. He didn't stop, but the sighting played on his mind for the rest of the day until he returned to work later that afternoon.
>
> 'Upon returning he saw another of our employees, who he is friendly with, and said, as you would, "you'll never believe what I've just seen". To his astonishment the other lad said "a large, black, panther laid in the road".
>
> 'Apparently the son of one of our supervisors had also been driving out that way on his way to work. He, however, did stop – and got out of his car to cautiously have a look to confirm what he at first did not believe he was seeing. He described it as a large black panther or a puma. Excitedly he turned round and went back home for his camera. However on his return the beast had vanished. He had then rung his dad at our workplace and reported what he had seen.' [17]

Reports like this represent the most tantalising evidence for big cats, for as yet no-one has actually picked up – or even photographed – a panther or puma body. It should be remembered that such a body would be valuable – to ABC investigators, the press, DEFRA, the police and the media in general. A considerable amount of money could be made by anyone prepared to put such a road kill into their car boot.

In 2000, on the A1 dual carriageway in Rutland, a lorry driver saw the corpse of a very large black cat, the size of a big dog, about six feet from the road. He was able to spot it only due to the height of his cab – he said it would have been invisible to car drivers. He slowed right down on his trip the next day for another look and it was still there. The same night he informed Nigel and David Spencer of Rutland and Leicestershire Pantherwatch who visited the scene straight away. Nigel reported:

> 'With powerful lights we checked about a mile of the A1
> southbound at the location which the driver had given very
> accurately. However we found nothing, not even a badger.'
> Subsequent enquiries with the police and the council ascertained
> that there had been no removal of any kind of carcass from that
> stretch of road, and in fact they did a full search the next day as
> well. Yet the Spencers noticed that 'all [ABC] reports (of which we
> had many at the time) within five miles of the location ended
> abruptly for about two years.'

Another lorry driver reported a dead panther on the inside lane of the busy A14 dual carriageway just east of the M6 junction in Leicestershire – the police searched but found nothing. In 2003 a retired police inspector stopped at temporary lights for roadworks, near Coalville, and lying at the side was the body of what he believed to be a large panther, the back half having been squashed by a lorry but the front and head intact. He could not stop but rang the Spencers. 'However,' Nigel reports, 'calls on our behalf from the police to the council have not revealed anything, not even a dog.' A year later a passenger also travelling on the M6, but on the southbound side, in Lancashire, saw a big cat on the hard shoulder which he described as black, about two feet in height and with a long tail. He assumed it had been killed by a car. When he revisited the spot it, too, had gone.[18]

Maureen Pickup came to a short tail-back while driving near Frome, Somerset, one evening. She saw that about ten cars had slowed down to take a good look at a dead or unconscious cat by the roadside as they crawled by. She reported: 'It was about six feet long, jet black, and it was definitely a cat. I've spent a lot of time in Africa, and I know what a big cat looks like. This one seemed to be dead. I would have loved to get out and have a closer look, but I thought there was a chance it might just be stunned and could attack me, so I didn't stop.' Perhaps the animal had been only stunned, for no other drivers' reports came in, nor were there any of a recovered body.[19]

The story is always the same – the body has disappeared. This gives the roadside corpse the whiff of urban legend, particularly when it is accompanied by the idea that the animal has been taken by 'officials' from DEFRA, or the council, or the police, and that its removal has somehow, and for an inexplicable reason, been covered up. A Cambridge lorry driver, for instance, came across the body of a black cat long enough to stretch right across the hard shoulder. There were no other vehicles on the road, and he dared not leave the cab in case it was still alive. He reported it to the police at the next phone. Next day the body had gone and when he enquired he was told by police that there was no record of his phone call.[20]

## Shot cats disappear

ABCs are notoriously difficult to shoot. One Aberdeenshire vet had one in his sights but, he said, 'when I did go to draw a bead on this animal it was as if it was telepathic, as if it had read my mind – it just disappeared'. Where ABCs have been successfully fired at – even at close range – they seem to survive the bullets and disappear without trace.

Rabbit shooters near Little Ribston in Yorkshire were travelling along a road at night when a black ABC jumped out in front of them, over the hedge and into a field. When it stopped to look back at them they shot it. It jumped into the air and then vanished. When they went back in the morning to look for the body there was no sign of it.[21]

The big cat that Donald Mackenzie fired at spun round and fell down, got up again and limped off into the darkness [22] and a farmer at Greenfield near Oldham took a shot at an ABC as it attacked his sheep: 'People think you are nutty when you say you have seen a big cat, but I did. It was large and dark with orange eyes. I'm sure I hit it but it ran away towards some rocks.' [23] No trace of either body was found.

Stan Windsor is a retired gamekeeper and was the most nearly successful ABC hunter – he was only thirty feet from an ABC and he let it have both barrels. The event was in 1995 when, he recalls: 'I used to help a neighbour, Ernie Macleod, who farms near Gardenstown, Aberdeenshire.

> 'We'd lost two lambs, quite big ones, four or five months old. One had a bite hole on its jaw that the vet could put her finger down. The other lamb, one of twins, had disappeared completely.
>
> 'Ernie went on holiday and left me to mind the farm. He'd found a sheep which had been worried and part eaten, and he told me he'd pulled it off to one side, near some hay bales. I reckoned that if it was a rogue dog it would be back, so at three o'clock that morning I went up to the field with a gun.
>
> 'The clouds were down, it was a sort of hazy light, and as I went to the paddock I saw that the sheep were all staring in one direction. Then the mist suddenly lifted and I saw they were looking at three black forms feeding on the carcass of the dead sheep. Just as I was going to climb the fence to get closer to them one struck out at another and it ran off.
>
> 'As I climbed the fence my trousers got caught on it, and as I eased them off it twanged, and the noise made the remaining two creatures run off.

'They were cat-like but Alsatian-sized, black and long legged, and went like the clappers. I've never seen anything run as fast in my life.

'I then hid behind a bale, thinking they might come back. After a while I heard a thundering noise, as of a stampede. I reckoned they had gone down, round and back up.

'Meanwhile the one on its own came back – it jumped the fence, five strands of wire about four foot high – it went straight over the top and landed by the carcass.

'I shot it between the front legs – with both barrels. Its tail flew up over its back so I knew it had been hit – it went off down the hill staggering sideways. I followed it expecting to find it dead at the bottom, but there was no sign of anything. Nothing at all.

The police searched the area next day with a helicopter, but we never did find that cat. When Ernie came back from holiday he said "You're pulling my leg!"' [24]

Thus dead ABCs seem to be just as elusive as live ones. Mark Fraser remarks 'I could write a book about how many times I've been contacted by people who claim to have shot these cats and buried them – but not one of them has been able to produce a body or take me to the burial spot.'

The body of a panther or puma represents the evidential Holy Grail to those ABC investigators keen to prove the unambiguous presence of these animals, but so far their search has been in vain.

## Skulls

In 1993 the front portion of a big cat's skull was found on Exmoor, but like most such skulls, as the Natural History Museum confirmed, it showed signs of having been a mounted trophy.[25] Devon and Cornwall have furnished large feline skulls but they, too, have provoked more questions than answers.

In 1995 Barnaby Jones was walking on Bodmin Moor with his brothers and father, the Reverend Keith Lanyon Jones, the Chaplin of Rugby School, when in a fast-flowing stretch of the River Fowey he spotted what he thought at first was a large stone, but on fishing it out saw was the skull of a large feline animal.

Douglas Richardson, Assistant Curator of Mammals at London Zoo, examined the skull and announced that it was very likely the skull of the animal which was being seen frequently on the moor at that time, and which was being held responsible for sheep kills in the area. He said: 'I believe this is the Beast of Bodmin, or one of them.'

The zoo's confirmation of the existence of the Beast of Bodmin came less than two weeks after the Ministry of Agriculture had proclaimed the creature to be nothing more dangerous than a domestic pussy cat. Rosemary Rhodes, one of the many farmers on Bodmin Moor who claimed that a big cat had been preying on their sheep and cattle, said: 'This is the confirmation we have been waiting for. We never had any faith in the Ministry of Agriculture's Inquiry.'

However *The Times* of 8th August 1995 had bad news for Barnaby, Mr Richardson and the farmers of Bodmin, heralded by the announcement: 'Beast of Bodmin exposed as Piltdown Puss'. The skull had passed from London Zoo to the Natural History Museum, which had identified the skull as being from 'a young male leopard, which had died abroad, possibly in India a considerable time ago, and was most likely a hunting trophy.' Entomologists at the museum said they had found the remains of an egg-case of a large tropical cockroach attached to dried brain membrane in the skull's cranial cavity which meant that it had been abroad and 'in dry conditions for some considerable period' before it was placed in the river.

Mr Richardson conceded he had been misled into thinking the skull had come from an animal which had died recently by the softening effect of the water on tissue clinging to it.

The exposure of the hoax – if that was what it was – came as a blow to the farmers on Bodmin Moor who were convinced big cats were responsible for the outbreak of livestock kills. Everywhere else there was an outbreak of smugness, as science and theology united to scoff at those who had believed the skull to be evidence of a big cat at large on Bodmin Moor.

Barnaby's father said 'There is no doubt my lads genuinely found the skull in the river, but I was always very sceptical about its origins. How nice for a father to be proved right.' Barnaby's brother Sam said: 'I am absolutely gutted because Dad has been proved right after all. He will go on about it forever.'

The Ministry of Agriculture commented: 'We do not want to sound too smug, but we always said finding the skull begged a lot of questions.'

**The Lustleigh skull**

In January 1988 a big cat's skull was discovered near Lustleigh on the eastern edge of Dartmoor, in Devon. Simon Hopwood and his friend Sebastian Carnell had been walking along a lane near their village of Lustleigh, five miles from Newton Abbot, when they spotted it behind a thin hedge beside the road. The most significant item visible was the remnants of an old plastic bag in tatters nearby. They had found the jaw under this bag and a tooth in it, facts which obviously implied the remains had been dumped – but by whom? And why?

I took the skull to London where it was first examined by John Holmes, and Roy Hale of the taxidermy and model department of the Natural History Museum. They were the experts who reconstruct skeletons into lifelike models, had mounted numerous big cats for the museum, and were thus practised at estimating the species and sizes of animals from their skulls.

Roy Hale examined the skull with interest and thought by its large size it might be that of a young lion. I then contacted Daphne Hills at the Natural History Museum who decided that despite its size it was a leopard's skull, and showed me one of a similar size from the museum collection as a comparison. However she noted, with

*Simon Hopwood with a skull found near Lustleigh.*

some surprise, that the Lustleigh skull bore no holes or marks to indicate it had ever been mounted as a trophy or a rug.

## Scratches on trees

Where ABCs are seen climbing trees, scratches are sometimes found sufficiently high up to exclude the possibility of other animals having made them.

In June 2003 Mrs Betty Savory woke up in the night and noticed the security lights were on outside. Thinking it was probably a fox she looked out of the window and was amazed to see a big black animal clinging to the small ornamental crab apple tree outside, about fifteen feet away. The tree is approximately eight feet tall, and the branches start at about five and a half feet high. The animal's haunches were on the ground and its head was level with a small swinging bird feeder attached to the branch which meant that the animal was four to five feet long, excluding the tail. It was well-lit by the security light and Mrs Savory saw it was a big cat – and that had its paw raised as if about to claw at the bird box. She shooed it and it bounded off in big loping strides towards the field behind a row of garages. 'I hope it never comes back,' she remarked fervently.

Next day she found a fresh scratch four feet up the narrow trunk of the small tree which seemed to tell the same story – that something large with sharp claws had clung to it.[26]

**BRITISH MUSEUM (NATURAL HISTORY)**
Cromwell Road, LONDON SW7 5BD
*Telegrams : Nathisnus London*
*Telephone : 01-589 6323*

*Our reference:*     DMH/SO
*Your reference:*

3rd March, 1988

## SPECIMEN  IDENTIFICATION

Enquirer       Mrs. M. Harpur,
Address        25 Batoum Gardens,
              London W6 7QB.


Identification     <u>Panthera pardus</u>

Other information
or comment

Skull of leopard, condition good, some incisor teeth
1st upper premolars and last molars ($m^1$) missing.
Slight damage to mandible – coronoid processes gnawed by
small rodent.  Size and conformation are consistent with
the specimen being male.

       Enquiries, such as the above are answered, so far as is consistent with
the proper duties of the Scientific Staff, on the understanding that in the event
of litigation members of the staff of the Museum shall not be called upon to
give evidence in courts of law.

*S.W.Elliot*
p.p.    Secretary.

N.B.  This communication need not be acknowledged.
ID/Enq. No. 4.     1/6/73

690/1846L. D.234211 5M 8/73 T.P. Go 794


*Daphne Hills' identification of the Lustleigh skull.*

*Scratch on an ornamental tree where Betty Stocker saw a big cat reaching for a bird feeder.*

## Hair and DNA

Hair has been collected from places where ABCs have been sighted, but not much of it has proved suitable for analysis. DNA testing might prove what species of big cats are at large, but is expensive and official bodies are unwilling, so far, to spend money on it. Most testing on hair has been by microscopic examination, and the few occasions when this happened have provided inconclusive results: either the hair has been found to come from a native animal, or the scientists can find no match for it among the native animals they compare it to – which does not prove that a panther was the owner. Despite these difficulties Karl Shuker has reported at least one positive identification of a puma hair from Exmoor.[27]

Collections of hair usually go the way of many similar fragments of evidence. Without a co-ordinating body to collect and collate physical evidence for ABCs on a systematic basis, possible ABC hairs which interested amateurs occasionally gather have nowhere to go. They are put in an envelope, put in a drawer and eventually lost or forgotten.

That is what happened to the evidence Philip Bradley and his girlfriend collected in the November of 1993. Philip relates:

> 'I was travelling by car along the main road between Fort William and Mallaig, in Scotland, with my girlfriend at the time, a serving police officer I will call 'J'. She suddenly nudged me, pointed ahead and asked "What's that?"

'I looked to where she was pointing, and at the left hand side of the road and above on the crest of a ridge there was a large black shape. At first I thought it was a bin bag, but when I saw it moving I stopped the car, thinking by now it was a large dog of some sort.

'We were about a hundred and fifty yards away. As we watched, the animal raised itself on its legs and stood, looking straight towards us. I got out of the car for a better look, and from that distance the animal looked black, and its shape was feline. The face was broad, the ears erect. At this point, the animal turned around, and stretched slightly – and with this movement I knew it was definitely a cat of some description. It seemed completely unconcerned by my presence. It then moved over the ridge, through some gorse bushes, and out of sight.

'I got out of the car to examine the spot where the animal had lain and found a large patch of flattened long grass, circular in shape and about six feet across, where the cat had been lying. Reaching down I could feel a slight residual warmth from its body. There were also some small tufts of short, soft hair, which upon inspection, were not actually black but a very dark grey. I looked over the ridge but there was no animal to be seen. I watched for about ten minutes but saw nothing more.

'I kept the hair for a while, but has now lost it. So my report remains entirely anecdotal – no physical evidence at all.' [28]

## Where does it leave us?

These are only a few examples of the varied physical traces which regularly turn up to confirm the idea, so stoutly maintained by witnesses, that ABCs are solid, three-dimensional creatures and not mere fictions. Taken en masse they undoubtedly suggest the presence of big cats at large in our country. But suggestion is one thing and proof is another.

Unfortunately for their peace of mind, many ABC researchers feel that nothing less than a body would lead to ABCs' being officially recognised, protected and studied as a new British species. Yet even they concede that a single body may ultimately prove nothing. The bodies of big cats would have to be *routinely* found, and/or live ones routinely filmed, in order for them to be classified as naturalised British wildlife.

Until such repeatable evidence comes to light, such investigators must make do with bits and pieces – a footprint here, a sheep kill there – in the hope that it will eventually add up to something that will impress government bodies such as DEFRA. In the meantime they continue to follow the trail of small, individual 'proofs' of ABCs' existence occasionally heartened – like Philip Bradley – by the residual warmth left by the mysterious animal on the earth.

# Chapter 8

# Photos and films, roars, screams and growls

## Photographic evidence

At once the best and worst evidence for ABCs is the collection of photographs and films of them which have accumulated since the 1970s.

Many show simply a black blob in a landscape; others show animals that seem undeniably feline, but of indeterminate size; a very few do show that animals the size of a big dog and the shape of a big cat are at large in the landscape. None, however, shows a big cat of an identifiable species.

Unlike their African equivalents which often appear in television documentaries, it seems ABCs are unusually difficult to photograph because there have been no shortage of rewards offered by local and national newspapers to anyone who can do so. At the time of writing the *Huddersfield Examiner,* for instance, is offering £500 for a photo of the 'panther' currently causing their cat-flap.[1] None has so far been claimed.

ABCs' resistance to being photographed is legendary among enthusiasts whose ironic dictum is that if you want to ensure that you never see an ABC keep a camera at the ready.

Therefore the few existing photos of alleged ABCs have mostly been taken in haste by witnesses who had scarcely time to grab a camera let alone to compose the shot. The obvious problem is that few have the time or expertise to include a nearby object to act as a scale of size.

### Barbara Fryer

Typical of the genre is the photo Barbara Fryer took in 2000 while she was trying out her new camera. She and a friend, Philippa May were strolling towards Heanton Court, near Barnstaple. 'We were walking along the path beside the estuary looking for wildfowl for Barbara to photograph,' said Philippa. 'As we were coming back a peculiar sort of animal crossed the path about twenty yards away. We both simultaneously froze on the spot – we were transfixed'.

*Barbara Fryer photographed this ABC near Barnstaple.*
*(Barbara Fryer/Fortean Picture Library)*

Barbara confirmed: 'I had my camera and thought I'll just take a quick picture first. It was the size of a dog but it had the long tail and movement of a cat. It stopped and looked at us and then sloped off into the bushes. I wanted to go after it to get a better picture but Philippa was nervous and wouldn't let me get closer. I've seen one in the zoo since, and am certain this was a black panther.'[2]

While the feline shape in Mrs Fryer's photo does not look like a domestic cat or dog, it does not conclusively show a black panther either.

The famous 'fen tiger' was observed by William Rooker in Cambridgeshire in 1994 as he was trying to dub some birdsong on to a film. He saw something emerge from the hedge at the bottom of the field and thinking it was a fox he zoomed his camcorder in on it. The video footage lasts approximately two minutes and shows what is almost certainly a large cat-like animal. It is narrow-waisted like a cheetah, and carries its long tail low like a big cat rather than aloft in the manner of a dog. Mr Rooker described the animal as black and with a flat face. Just on the other side of the hedge, in 2003, two women saw a black ABC chasing a domestic cat.[3]

*Tim Young*

One of the most distinct photos of a black, panther-like animal was taken by Tim Young in November 1988. A keen amateur photographer, he was taking photos of the coastline near Zennor in Cornwall in company with a friend, George Hawkins,

*In December 1999, Cornwall County Councillor Roy Taylor made public some video footage he had taken of an ABC emerging from a disused St Austell clay pit in daylight in August 1994. (Roy Taylor)*

when they spotted a large, cat-like animal sitting on a rock on the skyline. Nigel Brierly subsequently took a photo, from the same place, of Tim standing on the rock in order to gauge the height of the animal. They estimated that at about half Tim's height (he is almost six foot) the cat's head was about three feet from the ground.

*Charles McGuinness filmed this black feline of unusual size, in County Monaghan, Ireland, in the summer of 2004. (Charles McGuinness )*

*Tim Young saw this ABC near Zennor in Cornwall in 1988.*
*(Fortean Picture Library/Tim Young)*

## Alan Davis

In September 2001 Alan Davis was staying on a caravan site at St Leonards near Ferndown, Dorset, when, he wrote:

> '… at about six o'clock in the evening I saw – for the second time that year – a big cat which looked like a puma. The first sighting had been in early May at about the same time in the evening just as the sun was going down. It was lying down and at first I thought it was a deer.'

In September he saw it at the caravan park again, 'sitting near a hedge looking at me,' and this time he managed to take a photograph as he approached it.

> 'I tried not to show it that I was frightened of it, but it didn't seem to be worried about me walking towards it. However when I got to within fifty yards of it moved away, and turning to take a last look at me strolled off into the bushes. It was about four feet in length and stood about two feet to two feet six inches high. Its long tail was curled up at the end as it was walking off. It was a sandy colour with an almost white underside, and its tail had dark rings around it.

> 'I gave it a few minutes and then went over to see where it had gone. There was a large hole under the fence into the site next door where Portacabins were being stored.' [4]

*Alan Davis's photo of a puma-like animal near Wimbourne, Dorset. (Alan Davis)*

*Trevor Beer*

The author Trevor Beer spotted big cats several times in North Devon and Exmoor: he successfully photographed this one below in 1987.

*Raymond Trew*

Raymond Trew, an RAF historian, noticed a jet-black animal prowling across the sugar-beet field behind his house on the outskirts of Watton, Norfolk, at 7 a.m. on the 3rd July 1994. He had never seen anything like it so he grabbed his camera and took five consecutive shots. The animal moved like a big cat, was larger and longer-bodied than a big dog, had a snub nose and a bushy-ended tail which was longer than its body. The line of the stomach was six inches above the sugar beet which was then about nine inches high. As Raymond watched a hare started up in the field and

*A black, panther-like cat on Exmoor photographed by Trevor Beer in 1987. (Fortean Picture Library/ Trevor Beer)*

*Black mystery animal seen in Norfolk in a field of sugar beet, by Raymond Trew. (Raymond Trew/Fortean Picture Library )*

the black animal chased it. It 'loped, bounced, pounded along but with no real speed' and eventually disappeared on the other side of the 100 acre field, still in pursuit of the hare.[5]

*Frank Speake*

Frank Speake was having breakfast one morning in September 2003 when he spotted what he thought at first was a calf by the hedgerow of the adjacent field. He became more curious as he realised it was not moving like a calf and stood up for a better look. He was taken aback to see that it was, in fact, some kind of big cat. He grabbed his camera and rushed outside, managing to capture a few seconds of film before the animal walked out of view behind trees.

Frank described the animal as quite slender but far bigger than a domestic feline – easily the size of an Alsatian dog. Its tail was two-thirds the length of its body and carried in a cat-like way. Its head was set low and its limbs moved very like a domestic cat on the prowl.

As if the size of this cat was not strange enough, it was white – and, though albino forms may have creamy fawn fur, no normal big cat is pure white.

The footage Frank took is only about twenty seconds long but it confirms his identification, showing a pure white cat-like animal. It has a small head and its shoulder movement shows rippling muscles.

News of Frank's film came to the attention of Mark Fraser and another ABC investigator, Chris Mullins, and two weeks later they arrived at Frank's home near Horncastle in Lincolnshire to take a closer look at the scene. They set up Mark's life-size cutout of a black panther (painted white for the occasion) in the place where the

*A frame from footage taken by Frank Speake in Lincolnshire in 2003. (Frank Speake)*

ABC had been, and viewed it from where Frank had seen it. In Frank's words:

> 'When I first saw the model they brought, I thought it seemed very large. However when they placed it in the spot where I saw the cat, it was clearly very close in size to the animal I had filmed. The ground slopes down towards the trees and anything the size of even a very, very large domestic cat would have been impossible to see.'

Mark filmed the white cut-out from the appropriate spot, and the results convinced him, too, of the authenticity of the film, and the size of the cat.

As to what species the ABC was, Mark concurred with Frank's summary: 'Its shape, size and poise, along with the size of its head in comparison to its body and tail size, would suggest it could be a leopard – but no one has heard of a white leopard.'

Yet that was not the only white, leopard-like cat to be seen in the area. Unknown to Frank at the time of his sighting was that eighteen months previously – and but a quarter of a mile from his home – another witness had sat terrified in her kitchen while a large, white cat prowled in her garden. She had locked all the doors and called the police.

*Mark Fraser, left, and Frank Speake, far right with granddaughter, illustrating the size of the experimental 'big cat' cut-out at Minting, Lincolnshire in 2003. (Chris Mullins)*

*A Durham ABC photographed early one morning near a rabbit warren. (John Armstrong)*

A month after Frank's capture of his ABC on video an outlandish, huge, white cat was again seen in Lincolnshire some miles north-east of Horncastle, at Saltfleetby. The size as well as the colour of this ABC also matched Frank's. The witness noted:

> 'The animal was taller than a Great Dane and moved very fast indeed; its movement was smooth and even, with no up and down motion of the haunches such as a lion or tiger would display. There were no visible stripes or other markings. It appeared to be smooth and short haired and although the tail made me think of a lion's tail in terms of length there was no tuft of hair at the tip; it was quite plain…The body gave the impression of muscular strength without the sharp body contours which sometimes go with this.' [6]

An RSPCA Inspector examined the four-inch footprints it had left in the mud and confirmed they were the prints of a very large cat.[7]

A white leopard is a double anomaly since such an animal does not officially exist even in its native countries; but whatever was prowling Lincolnshire in the summer of 2003 has impressive accreditation: separate reports by different witnesses, video film of its physical presence, and its size, at least, verified by experiment.

### John Armstrong

Early in the morning of 10th April 1995 John Armstrong and his mother visited a local rabbit warren to photograph them for a project he was doing for his college. He writes:

'My mam and I stopped at the fence bordering a field at Castle Eden Walkway [8] to watch the rabbits. One of them was stood on its hind legs looking at something which we then saw – a large black cat crouched in the hedgerow. When the cat saw us it did not seem bothered in the slightest but got up and began to walk slowly up the hill. As it did so we saw its full size – the same height but longer than an Alsatian dog – with a downward sweeping tail, about the same length as its body, dragging along the floor. We could see its shoulder blades moving as it walked. At the brow of the hill it sat down again looking at us, and I took a couple of photos of it before it went off again into woodland.' [9]

## Picture evidence

The photos I have reproduced here are a few of the dozens available. Some of them seem to show a creature with the shape, proportions, musculature or movement of a big cat; but nearly all are taken from too great a distance, or by cameras too rudimentary to show any details which might confirm the animal's size, let alone determine its species.[10]

None of these photos is meaningful in itself. Each depends on the testimony of the witnesses that they believed they were, in fact, photographing a big cat of some kind. Indeed it is usually the poor quality of the photos – most of them are barely worth printing – that confirms the honesty of the photographers; few have made money from their snaps.

Some of the video films provide fascinating additional information – demonstrating the way the cats move – which allows better assessment of the creatures they show. In the April of 2002 Rachael Dethridge filmed an animal she took to be a black panther on the Isle of Wight, stalking through grass. Her video – one of the best – shows the typical, undulating musculature of such an animal's back. However, while the Rooker and Taylor videos are of undoubtedly feline animals it is still difficult to say what species they might be.

The 'fen tiger' as it was inappropriately named, seems to have the same shape and movement as a cheetah – but of course it is not cheetah-coloured; it is black and without spots. The Taylor big cat is convincingly feline-looking and its surroundings are reassuringly detailed, but it moves strangely, elongating in an almost leech-like manner!

## Background

The problem of snapping an identifiable big cat does not end with its portrait. Its setting in an identifiable landscape is equally important. It must be seen to be an obvious anomaly in a familiar world.

It is doubtful therefore how much 'proof' a single photo – or even a single piece of film – could constitute. As I have pointed out in an earlier chapter, photographic evidence must be predictably obtainable – just as we do obtain it, albeit with effort, for Scottish wildcats, water voles, otters, pine martens. For though there are no wildlife documentaries to prove their existence, on witness evidence alone ABCs are apparently far more widespread than these native animals.

## Audible evidence: roars, growls and screams

One of the definitions of a big cat is that it can roar. Lions, tigers, jaguars and leopards can all roar, while the puma and lynx are technically classed as small cats because they cannot.

This is because of differences in the hyoid bone which connects the tongue to the roof of the mouth. In big cats this has an elastic segment, while that of small cats is hard all over. It is this which allows big cats to produce a roar, and which also prevents them from purring in the manner of the small cats. As well as roaring, leopards are known for their characteristic rasping 'cough'.

All cats can snarl and growl; pumas are also capable of whistles, purrs and moans. However their unique and distinctive sound is the blood-curdling screaming, yowling or caterwauling by which female pumas signal their readiness to mate.

ABCs are apparently capable of a wide range of sounds, from deafening roars to threatening hisses; but perhaps the sounds most commonly associated with ABCs are screaming or yowling, very like – so earwitnesses say – those of a puma.

*Screams*

Nigel Brierly's first experience of a big cat was of its spine-chilling scream. He writes:

> 'There was an unexpected event in store for my wife and myself. In the early hours of the morning, we were awakened by a weird, almost unearthly scream which seemed to come from just outside our window. I felt convinced this came from no dog. It resembled the cry of a tom cat when defending its territory but magnified at least twenty times… '[11]

At least he assumed it was a big cat. He did not actually see the animal make the noise, but he did find another ABC caught in the act:

> 'One night a farmer was about to turn in at eleven o'clock when he heard the screams very close. It was a moonlit night and on looking out of the winter he saw the form of a large, black animal as it bounded away across the paddock. His description of the scream was the same as we had heard. It was the first and only time I have heard of the scream being directly associated with this large, black animal as it actually made it.'

Charles Pitt also saw an ABC scream, near South Molton, in 1978. He had stopped his car to avoid hitting a stag which had leapt over a hedge and then jumped the hedge on the opposite side of the road, when 'a huge, black cat landed on the road right in the same spot. It turned towards the car, and gave a frightening scream, and then leapt the hedge after the stag.'[12]

In the February of 2005 two workers at a Ministry of Defence site in Scotland happened upon a deer carcass at the side of the road. One of them, George, got out of the van for a closer look.

> 'While standing at the side of the road examining the practically stripped carcass the hairs on the back of his neck stood on end. He then heard several short "coughs" the typical warning sound of a leopard. He estimated the animal making them to be not more than twelve feet away... ' [13]

Michael Davis both saw and heard an ABC. It was exactly five o'clock on the morning of 25th August 2002 when he and his wife were awakened by a spine-chilling noise.' It was like a screech owl, dog, cat all put together.' They decided not to investigate it, but the following morning – curiously enough, said Mr Davis, it was at exactly five o'clock again – they heard it once more. This time they got up and looked outside. Sitting on the low wall directly below their bedroom window they saw a large, black cat of about four feet in length, with a long tail, and teeth which were showing white. 'It sat on the wall next to our garden for about ten minutes but when we opened the window it bounded off.' [14]

In the case of Chris Austin, his wife and friends, Mr and Mrs Hayes, it was an eerie shriek which first drew their attention to what they described as 'a total surprise'. Chris recalled:

> 'We were out rambling at the time, and had stopped to look at the distant view of Corfe Castle from the unusual angle that the walk presented, and saying wasn't it wonderful. Suddenly we heard a high shrieking noise, and looked at each other as if to say what's that?

> 'A bank rises from the side of the path, and we looked up this gradient and saw two cats about thirty yards away in one of the trees on the skyline. One of them moved – at which the branch broke and he fell four or five feet to the ground. The other one was higher up the tree and also climbed down, and they both made off. We ran up to the top of the slope – but they had gone.'

The group studied the rotten branch and Mrs Hayes photographed a pawprint left at the foot of the tree. She was shocked by the incident – 'I was rooted to the spot – I just didn't believe it. We weren't frightened as it was so amazing we didn't get time to think about it.' The group agreed that the strange felines 'were not as big as an Alsatian – about Labrador-sized but with very long tails curled up at the end. One cat was very black and the other was slightly browny-black.' [15]

There is an oddity about all these animals: they were making the noise usually attributed to pumas; yet they were black – and pumas are never black.

*Roars*

Disembodied roars are also associated with areas in which there are sightings of ABCs. Terry Dye was peacefully walking his German shepherd dog one beautiful summer's evening. 'Suddenly', he recalled, 'an almighty roar split the quiet countryside. We both jumped into the air with fright – but as it had come from behind us we saw nothing, and when we turned around it was gone... the nearest sound I have heard was when I was in Whipsnade Zoo and the big cats in the enclosure started fighting.'[16]

A Suffolk farmer was also familiar with the sound of big cats, writing:

> 'Being a regular listener on a calm morning to the big cats at Kessingland Wildlife Park, I was amazed to hear the exact same noise coming from the opposite direction. The wind was WSW at the time and I *know* it was a big cat.' This did not altogether surprise him. 'A black panther is seen on a regular basis here – most recently on a local shoot where there was more than one observer – and a lynx on my farm four or five times in the last two years.'[17]

These roars were made by ABCs only by association. But in at least one case the association was very close. During the summer of 2000, a woman walking her dog near Sizergh in Westmoreland heard a roar coming from nearby woods. Her dog became nervous and she decided to head for home – but on turning to look back at the woods, she saw a very dark, large cat leave cover.[18]

The black panther-like animal had, it seemed, roared rather in the conventional way you might expect a black panther to roar. Yet puzzlingly the person who had the most vivid and terrifying encounter with a roaring ABC described it as being brown and not black. Since pumas cannot roar the description better fits a lioness. Perhaps this was a thought the witness did not want to think, for he assured the press that it was 'almost certainly' a puma.

This witness, a forestry worker, had been felling trees all morning in Quendon Wood, Essex, when he heard a strange noise, and turned off his chainsaw. It was then that he heard the creature roar and saw it ahead of him in the trees. He said: 'I cannot get across how terrified I was. As I heard what can only be described as a roar, a big chill ran up my spine. I literally froze and thought "Oh no, I've turned my saw off now, that's my only defence".' He felt he had no choice but to make a run for it across thirty or so fallen trunks to reach the safety of his harvesting machine cab, turning his saw back on as he did so.

> 'The cat was about fifty feet away and I looked directly at it. It was about three feet tall and moving through the trees. It was huge and I really did fear for my life.'

The forester tried to phone his colleague on another part of the site, but was unable to get through. He then tried the manager of Quendon Park, the estate to which the woods belong, who fetched help and his colleague arrived to pick him up. The foresters subsequently worked in pairs, keeping an eye out for the big cat.[19]

It seems ABCs may sometimes make the sounds expected of their approximate 'panther-like' or 'puma-like' identities; they may yowl, growl, hiss or snarl. Karen

Rees's animal made 'a gutteral noise, difficult to describe.' All these sounds are undoubtedly those of big cats. But, confusingly, it just as often turns out to be a black, panther-like cat screaming, or a brown, puma-like cat which roars.

If I had hoped their calls and cries would help clarify the species of Britain's mysterious big cats I was to be disappointed. They simply wove another anomalous strand into the muddle.

# Chapter 9

# Accounting for anomalies: the Hybrid Theory

I had not been looking at sightings of ABCs for more than a few months before I noticed that oddly-coloured animals cropped up now and again. Nor had they only unconventional pelts – other parts of their anatomy did not always correspond with their normal big cat equivalents.

Frank Speake's cat, for instance, pictured in the previous chapter, is pure white – a colour not available among the big cats. Albino leopards, lions and tigers are pale sandy-coloured with their spots or stripes visible but washed-out looking, while an albino puma has not yet been recorded as far as I know. Yet white ABCs have been spotted in other parts of the country too. A big cat described as 'tall as a good-sized Labrador, but white' was seen wandering around a farm near Hovingham in Yorkshire.[1] A year later another witness observed it again at Hovingham but this time in woodland. 'It was at least four times the size of a domestic cat, with a leopard-shaped head, and a long neck and tail. It was white.'[2] In Scotland Mike Inglis could gauge the size of the cat he saw in a hay meadow – 'the grass was around two feet high but the cat was very visible above the height of the grass. It was very light, almost white.'[3] The animal the Day family studied through binoculars in Cornwall was 'bright white'. 'It was definitely a cat,' said Derek Day, 'bigger than a large dog, but the most striking thing was its colour.'[4] A Somerset man opened the back door and was confronted by 'a large animal standing by the fence'. He estimated it to be 'around the size of a large Alsatian, but cat-like with white fur'. The animal bounded off into the darkness.[5] In the same county two years previously a couple had turned their car around to get a better look at a big cat sauntering along the edge of a field – clearly visible as 'it was bright white, with no other markings on it. We were no more than ten yards from it. It didn't care about us at all, but we were not brave enough to leave the car!'[6]

Other mismatched felines consistently turn up, greatly enlivening ABC research and helping to confound conventional theories. One such was the creature Mr Brands saw. He wrote:

> 'I was able to observe the animal clearly as it walked away from the cattle. It looked very graceful with an oval-shaped head, not unlike a Siamese cat, pricked, tufted ears, and a curved tail with a plume on the end. Its colour was white with grey points. It had

very powerful shoulders and its hind legs seemed to be longer than the front, giving it the appearance of sloping down from the rear. It was the size and height of a large Alsatian dog, not counting the tail, but there was no doubt of its being a cat.

'I phoned the police to find out if an animal had escaped from Paignton Zoo but after reporting my sighting, a rather lengthy silence occurred, and I had a strong impression that they wanted to tell me to take more water with it next time! The animal continued to walk on hurriedly to the end of the field where it sat down on its haunches for a while and then disappeared...I love the countryside and am a keen observer of what wildlife the country offers. I say these things in the hope you will understand I have my feet firmly on the ground. What I saw that evening is something that will live with me for ever.'[7]

A Siamese-coloured big cat would be extraordinary enough, even without the muscular shoulders and plumed tail. Yet it was seen again in the Bideford area by other, unrelated witnesses such as Mr and Mrs Lewis who described a similar animal near Fairy Cross, and Leslie Harris and his wife who watched an ABC which, they stated, was 'far bigger than a dog and creamy in colour, but with a dark head and tail'. They likened it to a huge Siamese cat.[8]

Less striking but equally puzzling colours occur regularly. The cat seen in Hunmanby Gap, in Yorkshire was 'as big as a Labrador', with 'a long tail', but, unusually, a 'dirty grey' colour.[9] The cat Thomas Catleugh observed stalking sheep in Scotland had the large rounded ears of a puma, but was 'dark grey, with a dark sheen along its back.'[10] Near Norwich three sisters-in-law were alarmed by an ABC the size of a large Labrador. 'I was quite frightened,' said one of them. 'There was no way it was a domestic cat, it was much too big.' It had 'a cat-like face and a long thin grey body.'[11]

In December 1999, 'a white Labrador-sized cat, with a beige tail' was seen near Penistore in Yorkshire.[12] In 2001, a local villager and wildlife spotter was amazed to see a two-feet high cat in a car park near Oakham in Rutland, not least because it was 'a white cat with tan patches'.[13]

Mrs Jackie Wyatt's cat was also skewbald. She spotted the extraordinary animal casually walking along an alleyway, stopping to sniff the hedgerows along the way. Subsequent press reports likened it to the 'puma' or 'panther' reported at times in the area, but Mrs Wyatt saw the animal clearly and her description does not tally with either of those big cats. She said: 'I had a good look at it: the animal had a very ugly, large, beige head, a black tail with tan patches, and a beautiful white coat. It was quite astonishing'. Mrs Wyatt was accustomed to the normal wildlife of the area: 'I am always peeping out of the window to see foxes, because it is quite common to see them sniffing around the area but I couldn't believe my eyes when I spotted this white animal strolling along the path rather casually. It definitely wasn't a domestic cat. It was a large white beast about the size of a goat. Now I am dodging from room to room hoping I will catch a glimpse of it again.'[14]

Ed Cose described the ABC he saw as having 'a fawn coloured body', which sounds like that of a conventional puma; he also said it had 'a long black tail', which does not. Could he have been mistaken? Could the animal have had a long but only *black-tipped* tail, as a puma actually has? His description was confirmed when it was seen by another witness a few miles down the road. Maurice Wallis 'saw this cat its ears were pricked and it was in a hurry, and ran past me only about twenty feet away.' He described it as 'about the size of a Great Dane, with a long black tail.' [15]

An ex-Squadron Leader got a clear view of an ABC as it 'lolloped' across the road twenty feet in front of him, and studied it carefully. It was 'as long as a Great Dane dog though only two-thirds as tall, dark brown to black in colour but not shiny. It had no noticeable ears but a cat-like head with yellow, glowing eyes. It had very large padded feet, and its three foot long tail swept down and curled up like an S. The tail was thick, but not tapered as a fox's would be.' This credible witness then adds a strange extra detail: 'The tail also had some white rings on the end of it.'

The ABC an East Yorkshire couple saw was approximately three-and-a-half feet long, with 'a huge powerful tail, as long again as its body, a small, leopard-like head, tawny brown in colour' and 'a brindle-like patterning on its underside.'[16]

This is yet another puzzling detail, because whereas the short-tailed Eurasian lynx might conceivably be called brindled, the adult puma is never patterned. A puma cub is mottled or faintly *spotted*, but on its back and not on its underside; it soon loses that colouration for the smooth *café-au-lait* of the adult.

Oddities are not confined to pelage. A very large, strange-looking cat ran across the road about fifty yards in front of a van driver near Sorn in Ayrshire. 'It was sandy in colour, about two feet in length and eighteen inches high, or thereabouts. It had sharp upright pointed ears, with black tufts. Its tail was as long, or maybe a little shorter than the body, trailed behind in a U shape... ' [17]

The animal was the approximate size and colour of a European lynx, and the pointed ears extended by the typical black tufts would confirm that that was indeed what it was. Yet it could not have been a lynx as it had a tail and lynxes' tails are negligible, about six inches long at most. A West Country witness described a similar ABC, reporting: 'It was the size of a small Alsatian, with tufted ears and a tail.' This cat was even more un-lynx-like, for it was black.[18]

Equally confusing was the animal a Galston, Ayrshire, woman saw when she went out of her back door. A hundred yards down a track leading to fields was a large, black creature, staring back at her. She called her young son and his friend over to have a look. They too saw a sleek, black animal about the size of a large German Shepherd dog. It had a long tail and tufts of fur on its ears. The fur itself was black in colour, with what appeared to be 'white chaffing through the coat and above the hindquarters. It was feline but 'like no cat they had seen before.' Mark Fraser was not altogether surprised at these combinations of anomalous features – 'Now if this was a one off, two, three (maybe a ten off!) we could dismiss it, but it's not. There are literally dozens of sightings of these mismatched cats, especially from up here in Scotland.'

*The Galston witnesses (with Mark Fraser's cut-out panther for size comparison) saw a panther-like cat with tufted ears and white chaffing through its coat. Oddly enough for a few years in the early 1980s Glasgow Zoo exhibited a leopard (subsequently sent abroad) whose uniformly black coat was similarly sprinkled with white hairs which led to her being nicknamed the 'Cobweb Panther'. The condition is known as piebaldism and has been seen in domestic cats and in the black Scottish wildcat/domestic cat hybrids known as the 'Kellas' cats. (Mark Fraser)*

These are but a few of a seemingly endless catalogue of small details which distinguish many ABCs from known species of big cats, and which are such a headache for those ABC investigators trying to pigeonhole them. Karl Shuker put it succinctly: 'The British big cat would need to be nothing short of a shape-shifter to account for the immense variety of felids reported: cats which are black, grey, every shade of brown, striped, spotted, with long legs, with short legs, with long tails, and short tails, with ear-tufts, without ear-tufts, which roar, which scream, which are of small dog-size, which equal the size of the largest dog breeds etc. Certainly no single non-domestic species of felid (indeed no wild mammal of any single species, known or unknown) could possibly exhibit so many markedly different forms for the above-listed variations do not merely cut across pelage coloration, they also involve basic anatomy (e.g. limb skeleture, throat structure etc).' [19]

Yet it is interesting to note that while these anomalous details tend to cast doubt on the species being seen, they also tend to confirm the authenticity of the witnesses' statements – there would be no point in making them up.

*Mr and Mrs Nigel Brierly outside their house in Devon.*

## Accounting for anomalies: the Hybrid Theory

Commonsense, honesty and certainty in the witness, and anomalies of colour and shape in the ABC, are a combination that crops up too often to be ignored. It is, as I have pointed out, one of the factors that undermines the theory that ABCs are released or escaped captives.

Thoughtful ABC investigators have therefore come up with several other theories to account for these anomalies, the most popular of which is that ABCs are hybrids – the progeny of two different species of big cat. Thus a lynx might mate with a puma, so the theory goes, to produce a lynx with a long tail.

More urgently in need of explanation is the number of jet-black ABCs, and the theory often proposes that a puma/black panther cross might be one answer. Nigel Brierly is one of the Hybrid Theory's most eloquent proponents, citing instances of different colours and types of ABCs being seen together which he suggests would make mating possible geographically, and also prove the animals at least temperamentally compatible.

He draws examples from his own county of Devon where ABCs of different colours were seen on the same farm[20] to support this, but the phenomenon is countrywide. The Isle of Wight is only about twenty-four by thirteen miles, hardly the size of what is reputed to be a single puma's hunting territory. Yet during one of the island's recurrent cat-flaps, in 1982, there were sixteen separate reported sightings of big cats in the island, of which ten were black or grey and six were sandy coloured.

ABCs of both colours are seen regularly in Leicestershire. David and Nigel Spencer have been noting occasional associations between black and brown ABCs as part of their research into sightings of ABCs over many years concluding that 'the two species of cat must be aware of each other's presence, or even interacting. The early sightings in Rutland, during 1991 were of a fawn or black cat, which confused the local press... It is interesting to note that the puma, when rarely seen, is always within a few miles of a recent panther report.' [21]

There have been several other instances of ABCs both differently sized as well as differently coloured seen together – an Exmoor farmer who had regularly watched a huge, black, feline animal crossing his fields, was surprised to see it accompanied, on one occasion, by another smaller and brownish cat.' [22] There were many Shropshire witnesses of 'a panther-type, black cat, of larger than dog size' in 1999. One of them also got a clear view of a small, brown animal with the panther, and this was thought to be a cub.[23] During a cat-flap near Tonmawr in Wales three kinds of ABC were seen within days of each other, and within a few hundred yards: puma-sized grey, puma-sized black, and spaniel-sized, grey cats with black stripes.[24]

The idea of leopard/puma hybrids could hardly account for the wide range of other colours, shapes and sizes, but leaving that aside there are other good reasons for such a hybridisation being unlikely.

## Hybrids fact and fantasies

One of the definitions of 'species' is that the offspring produced by crossbreeding different ones will be sterile – the most familiar being the mule. This being the case hybridisation cannot produce new species. Yet belief that it could is an idea of great antiquity: the leopard was originally believed to be a hybrid between the 'pard' (the old name for panther, this being considered a separate creature from the leopard) and the lion ('leo') i.e. a leo-pard.

The belief that different species of big cats readily interbred and produced hybrid offspring was based on the writings of the Roman author Pliny, in his *Naturalis Historia* (*circa* AD 23). Pliny described the 'lustful and competitive' nature of lions, and argued that since many species must flock to a single watering hole, there is opportunity for lust between species, resulting in "many varieties of hybrids". This belief held sway for centuries, leading some authorities to identify Dante's 'Lonza', in the *Inferno* as a leopard/lion hybrid in the style of Pliny.

Outside literature and myth hybrid big cats are artificial creations. No examples of spontaneous crossbreeding have been conclusively established in wild populations, and reports of leopard/lion, leopard/tiger or jaguar/puma hybrids in Africa or America have been based on appearance and on local myth. Where the territories of different felines overlap, for instance those of leopards and lions, or pumas and jaguars, they have different habits and habitats. Accidental encounters are usually marked by mutual suspicion, and for a good reason: there is no natural advantage in crossbreeding.

Hybridisations where the first-generation cubs are of limited fertility are possible between some species of similarly-sized big cats. In captive situations the drive to breed may be so strong that big cats of different species will apparently mate with each other if no mates of their own species are available. This apparently happened in 2000 at a Chinese circus when a lioness accepted a tiger as her mate and

*This dwarfish 'pumapard', like its weakly siblings, died young.*
*(Natural History Museum)*

produced several stillborn offspring. More often such liaisons are engineered by unscrupulous zoos which may sedate the female to ensure her compliance.

## British hybrids

The contention of Hybrid Theorists is that Britain could represent an exceptional circumstance, a larger geographical circus cage, whereby individuals of two different species might be driven to mate with each other due to a lack of more appropriate partners.

However to explain British ABCs there needs to be evidence of successful matings between pumas and leopards – species which, it should be remembered, never meet in the wild as they are native to different continents. The only recorded mating where cubs were born alive was in the late 1890s when three sets of twin cubs with a puma father and leopard mother were born at a zoo in Hamburg, Germany. The 'pumapards' had pale leopard spots on a base colour like that of the puma father, and long tails. One specimen resembled a little grey puma with large brown rosettes. But the 'pumapards' suffered from dwarfism, grew to only half the size of the parents, and died very young.[25]

It seems this combination of species does not work: the cubs were tiny and feeble and even in zoo conditions did not reach maturity. Any cubs born of a black panther and puma would be a genetic dead-end. The idea therefore, that successful matings could occur freely, throughout Britain, between black leopards and fawn-coloured pumas is unlikely; that such unions could produce a thriving population of large, successful, healthy, glossy ABCs is obviously impossible.

While animals bred from enforced matings, between lions and tigers for instance, can be semi-fertile any progeny from such hybrids will be less fertile again. So, far from establishing a new 'species', the 'line' dies out.[26]

Hybrid Theories must therefore be constructed on a system of progressively greater improbabilities yet still without offering a reason for the unconventional appearance of those ABCs which display a range of colours, shapes, and sizes not found in either species.

## Hybrid moggies

Following on from the same imperfect understanding of hybridisation, an idea emerged in the 1980s that somehow the domestic cat gene could have got into the puma and turned it black, or white, or the few other moggy-type colours reported by witnesses.

It follows on from the belief that there exist in Britain 'large feral cats', meaning domestic cats which have become larger and fiercer through having to fend for themselves in the wild over several generations. From this again runs the idea that if 'large feral' domestic cats were to get large *enough*, they could either be up to mating with or even be mistaken for a small puma.

In fact, 'scientific studies carried out with feral domestics at a number of British localities revealed that 'they are on average no larger or heavier than their tame counterparts,' [27] as the proprietor of any stray cat shelter will agree. It makes sense that any moggy that has to work hard for its food rather than being handed it on a plate, will benefit from being smaller. Alan Fleming's personal account confirms this:

> 'We have two cats that were born feral from a large colony of feral cats that lived in the open areas behind our house, all much smaller than domestic cats. Our two, who are now fourteen, were taken from the colony at eight weeks old. They are in the Cat Olympics eating team and yet are still small compared to normal domestic moggies.' [28]

The irreconcilable disparity in their sizes means that to a puma a domestic cat will always represent a cocktail snack rather than a mate.

## Genes and their funny ways

However the idea that ABCs' odd colours are somehow due to some kind of hybridisation with other species is as persistent as it is woolly, and with the advent of the mysterious process of genetic engineering it has now gathered to itself a folk-belief concerning the apparent capacity of genes to mutate spontaneously in such a way as to favour the survival of researchers' theories.

Optimistic claims are made by ABC enthusiasts for the ability of genes 'in a small gene pool' as they describe it, to turn the normal appearance of a species on its head. By this sleight of hand they imply that a smallish number of, say, pumas interbreeding will come up with a kaleidoscopic mix of colours and shapes; or that by this means pumas could simply have turned black on their own. However inbreeding, as zoos which selectively breed for exotic colour variants know, is a double-edged sword. Along with the desired colour enhancement it produces undesirable physical and mental disabilities. By the same token inbreeding speeds the extinction of wild populations. The Florida puma, a close relation of the pumas of the American West but confined to that peninsula, almost died out in the last few decades because inbreeding was producing not different colours but sterile males.[29]

As Nigel Brierly remarks, 'genes are funny things', which is certainly true but do they actually have the power to account for ABCs?[30]

The fact is that the sheer convenience of theoretical hybridisation and/or genetic mutation, as solutions to the mystery of ABCs has, in the minds of Hybrid Theorists, tended to override their biological unlikelihood, if not impossibility. Invoked outside their scientific context 'genes' are best regarded in the same way as Pliny's invocation of hybridisation: as a metaphor for the mystery of transformation.

# Chapter 10

# Accounting for anomalies: the Hide-out Theory

Another ingenious way of accounting for ABC's anomalous shapes and colours is what has been called the Hide-out Theory. It originated with the Belgian zoologist Bernard Heuvelmans, who has become known as 'the father of cryptozoology',[1] and suggests that cryptids of all kinds, including our big cats, might be native species left over from before the Ice Age and which have simply been overlooked by science and the general public. They have been hiding-out, as it were, and are only now coming to public notice because of the huge encroachment of human beings on the last wildernesses of our planet. This theory is favoured by Loren Coleman and Mark A. Hall in the USA where vast, virgin habitats makes it almost plausible. To account for two of the variations among American ABCs they ingeniously postulate a sexually dimorphic hide-out species, of which the females are black, leopard-like animals, and the males are maned, brown, lion-like animals.

While Britain's small size and large population puts a greater strain on the theory, it is true – as its British proponent, Di Francis, points out – that big cats were once native to this country. The bones of at least ten species, some very big, have been found in the United Kingdom, and dated by palaeontologists to the Pleistocene epoch. They include the cave lion *Panthera leo spelaea*, leopard *Panthera pardus*, the common wildcat *Felis silvestris*, and the northern lynx *Felis lynx*. Furthermore, remains of a leopard-like felid provisionally labelled *Panthera Aff. pardus* have recently been discovered at Pontnewydd Cave, North Wales.[2]

Perhaps some of these animals did persist into historical time, for the sixteenth-century historian, Raphael Holinshed (died 1580) wrote: 'Lions we have had very many in the north parts of Scotland, and those with manes of no less force than those of Mauretania; but how and when they were destroyed as yet I do not read.'[3]

Of all these species apparently only one has officially survived into modern times here: the common wildcat, *Felis silvestris*, now supposed to exist only in Scotland. (There have been, as a matter of fact, plenty of reports of wildcats in England, particularly the West Country, over the last century, but that is another story.)

## Objections

There are various objections to the theory. One reasonable complaint is that had they been hiding out in these islands for so long they would surely have been caught or trapped innumerable times by now – just as the smaller, shyer relict species, *Felis sylvestris*, was so successfully shot and trapped to near-extinction in the last millennium, and as leopards and pumas are in their native lands today. Even a tiny population of such animals, it is argued, would have come at least to the notice of the keen and persistent naturalists who have thronged these islands for three centuries, and been thoroughly documented. If they can discover the elusive Bechstein's bat they can discover any mammal, particularly one as large, ostentatious and ground-dwelling as a big cat.

This is a common-sense objection; however it should be noted in passing that it is exactly the same one that can be made to the Escapes/Releases Theory, which is commonly favoured.

Secondly, objectors point out, there would realistically have to be *several* of these prehistoric species surviving to account for the radical differences in colour, shape and size of ABCs – a notion which is several times more unthinkable.

### ABCs in history

A third objection is that if a prehistoric species of cats had lived amongst us since time immemorial they would at least feature prominently in the folklore record.

Such records are thin on the ground, though a curious animal ghost was 'said to haunt the lanes and fields in the Godly Green area of Cheshire. It was yellowish or light tan in colour and although often referred to as a ghost dog some witnesses described it as cat-like. A woman who saw the creature at the end of the nineteenth century thought that it was a lion that had escaped from a zoo. On some occasions the beast was said to have been seen chasing cattle, a feature reminiscent of some mystery cat sightings.' [4]

Big cat reports on the Isle of Wight go back to 1895. In January 1940, livestock and rabbits were reported missing on the island, and a creature with the head of a lion and the body of a dog was seen. It was dubbed the Vectis Monster.[5]

In the spring of 1810 farmers in the Ennerdale water area of Cumberland were finding large numbers of their sheep slaughtered. The animal responsible for the killings ranged far and wide, never attacking the same flock in succession. A shepherd who saw the beast said it was unlike any animal he had seen before – a large, yellow, lion-like creature with dark grey stripes. The 'girt dog' as it became known seemed invincible, ignoring poisoned carcasses and evading Lakeland's finest huntsmen. In the course of one chase it knocked over one Will Rotherby, leaving him shaken and with the firm conviction that 'it was not a dog but a lion.' [6]

### The European cave lion still lurking?

Proponents of the hide-out theory in Great Britain point out that one of the Pleistocene lion species, *Panthera spelaea* the cave lion (the Eurasian version of the American *Panthera atrox* and very similar to the modern African lion *Panthera leo*) seems to have survived into historical Europe. Some of the camels in Xerxes' expedition through Macedonia in 480 BC, for instance, were killed by lions. They are also depicted in European cave art – one drawn on a reindeer's shoulder-blade, discovered in France, clearly shows its tufted tail.[7]

Were these lingering in folk memory as the Scottish lions to which Holinshed referred? Could they even have lingered on in the flesh to the present day? For amazingly enough there are regular 'lion' reports in these islands.

Early on the morning of 29 July 1976, two milkmen saw what they insisted was a lion with a bushy-tipped tail in a field at Tollerton near Nottingham airport. Numerous other reports followed, prompting a huge big game hunt. When it failed to find the animal the police announced that they no longer believed a lion was in the area, and that the sightings could have been misidentifications of large dogs or even of a large brown paper bag. Despite its debunking, the lion was seen three times in succeeding days before vanishing into limbo.

Reports of a lioness in Bramley, in Hampshire in 1994, however were taken seriously by the police, who stated: 'The animal is obviously there'. Two of the witnesses, Peter Giles and his wife Maureen, saw the animal as they cycled through the countryside one Sunday morning.

> 'I'm a hundred percent certain it was a lioness,' Mr Giles said. 'I have no doubts whatsoever. It was three feet high and seven feet long and, you could tell by the sheer size of it. It looked like a fully grown lioness, although it was a bit skinny. It looked quite incongruous, but seemed quite at peace with itself. We watched it for about twenty seconds and it padded off.'[8]

The lion seen near Wrangaton Golf Club, Devon, by Paul Gourley was 'tawny in colour and very big,' shabby-looking, five feet long and weighing as much as twenty stone. It had a mane. Asked if he could have been mistaken, Mr Gourley said: 'I know a lion when I see one.' His certainty was vindicated when a police hunt turned up a six-inch diameter paw-print found in a muddy field nearby 'big enough to be that of a young male lion' according to the keeper at Dartmoor Wildlife Park.[9] The paw-print's maker was never found.

## Three tigers and a cheetah

On the other hand perhaps the lions should be classed with the other, equally distinctive, felines which appear and disappear occasionally in the British countryside. For instance a woman returning home one night in 1999 got out of her car and became aware of a large feline form which emerged from a hedgerow and into the road. When it walked under a street light she saw it was a cheetah, clearly describing the markings and gait of the animal.

She rushed inside, her husband confirmed the distress she had been in and immediately phoned the police who searched the area with no success.[10]

One April evening in the same year Keith Baylis spotted an animal standing in the road as he rode his motorcycle home across Northchurch Common in Hertfordshire. From a distance he thought it was a deer; it was only when he was about ten feet away that he realised it was a full-grown tiger.

> 'It looked at me for what seemed a lifetime and I got a bit panicky. There was no way I was going to stop. I revved the bike up so that

the noise would keep it away and rode around it. It did not appear to threaten me and even seemed used to vehicles. I use the road regularly and often see deer along there. I think the tiger may have been stalking them.'

When Mr Baylis got home he called the police, who alerted the local rangers. The nearest tigers – two at Whipsnade Zoo and four at Woburn Safari Park – were all accounted for.

Only two months later but a hundred miles further north ex-soldier Raymond Cibor was driving a forklift truck down a country lane at Seven Yards Farm, Armthorpe, near Doncaster, South Yorkshire, when a mud-spattered tiger leapt from undergrowth, reared up on its hind legs, snarled and lashed out with its claws at the vehicle. He reversed as the feline roared and attacked the truck again before disappearing into a nearby copse.

'I could see its mouth open wide and its claws looked like razors,' said Mr Cibor. 'It was definitely a tiger; there is no doubt in my mind. It was about six feet in length and three feet high. It was orange and yellow with black stripes.' There were no travelling circuses in the area and no nearby theme parks with any tigers (present or missing), so a police helicopter was scrambled to comb the area and an armed response unit put on alert. Although nothing was found the police remained convinced: 'We do not believe this was a hoax,' said a spokesman, 'because the man was genuinely terrified.'

A week later, James Sutcliffe, 13, was left in tears after apparently coming face to a face with a tiger while cycling home in Auckley, only three miles from Seven Yards Farm.[11] His was the last encounter, for it seems the tiger was never seen again.

## Lynxes

Lynxes are not big cats in the technical sense, but so many are seen up and down the country that they cannot be ignored. The Eurasian (or European) lynx, *Lynx lynx*, was native to Britain into historical times. The recent carbon dating of lynx bones from Kinsey Cave in the Yorkshire Dales showed the animal lived between AD 425 and AD 600.[12] Thus the lynx becomes a plausible candidate for the Northumbrian 'lions' mentioned by the Venerable Bede (*circa* 673–735). Holinshed's 'lions', too, begin to look as if they could almost be folk memories of the lynx. Datings such as these give proponents of the Hide-out Theory grounds for hope that a relict population of at least this distinctive cat might have managed to survive into modern times undetected.

The lynx did last into recent times in western Europe, and is now being reintroduced to its old haunts. In France, for instance, it disappeared as late as 1900, and has now been re-established in the Vosges and Pyrenees.[13]

*Lynx lynx* is a heavily-built cat with long legs. Its coat is thick, soft fur, yellowish-brown in summer, paler in winter and covered in large spots. The average head-and-body length is three to four feet but the unmistakable feature of all lynxes is the short, stubby tail. They also have a distinctive tuft of black hair extending the pointed tip of each ear.

In fact one of the two non-native cats captured alive was a young female European (Eurasian) lynx cornered by police in Barnet, North London, in May 2002. She was thin and in poor condition, while the other lynxes seen – like ABCs generally – appear robust and healthy.

In the Borders area of Scotland locals have been reporting these kinds of large cats with tufted ears and no tails for many decades.

A woman in Glenfarg, Perthshire, was washing dishes on the night of the 10th August 1976, when her terrier started scratching the door, wanting to go out. Once outside it started barking, then the barking changed to a whimper, and she went out to see what was wrong. The dog was standing on the lawn, shivering with fright, staring at the wall thirty feet away, and she peered through the darkness to see what had frightened him. Sitting on its haunches on top of the wall was what looked like a huge cat – as big as a fully-grown Labrador with 'burning orange eyes' staring at her.

The cat-like creature rose to its feet. It had long pointed ears with tufts at the end, and these were touching the overhanging roof of her carport which was three feet above the wall. She realised she had only seen cats bigger than it behind bars at the zoo. It began to spit and snarl at her so she picked up the dog and backed into the kitchen, at which the cat leaped into the fields at the other side of the wall.[14]

Twenty years later Martin Webster, a water bailiff with Don District Salmon Fisheries Board, was counting salmon on the River Urie. Rounding a bend he came face-to-face with a large and unexpected animal. 'The cat was about two-and-a-half to three foot long. It had a cat's head, with large, pointed ears. Its tail was very short almost non-existent, and its coat was dark brown. I knew that what I was looking at was a lynx.'[15]

A lynx bounded across a road near Springfield, Fife, in front of a lorry, jumped on to a wall, and turned and stared at the driver. It was of 'stocky build' with a 'bobtail'. Its face had the lynx-like 'beard' with prominent, tufted ears.[16]

Another witness, in the north of Scotland this time, recalled, 'I had been surveying Whooper swans, and was driving just north of Ballater when a lynx crossed the road in front of me. It was a tawny animal, very deep in girth, short in length with a short tail and ear tufts. It ran steadily across the road in no particular hurry and disappeared into open moorland and surrounding woodland. It gave the impression of a chunky animal and was about the size of a full-grown Labrador dog.'[17]

Reports of lynxes are not confined to Scotland. Their habitat, if that is the word for it, seems to extend from the top to the bottom of Britain. For instance a brown spaniel-sized cat with a short tail and notably tufted, pointed ears was sighted by Marcus Matthews whilst driving through the Mendips in Somerset.[18]

*Steve Archibald was strimming a verge when he came face to face with a lynx*

Further south again, in North Devon, Steve Archibald had an even closer encounter with one:

> 'I was working on the A361, strimming a bank, when a strange animal stood up in the undergrowth about twelve yards ahead of me. I stopped strimming and took off my safety goggles for a better look. We stared at each other for a few moments before it took off and ran down the bank, cleared the five foot fence at the bottom without touching it, and into a spinney. It was a big cat, yellow and black, with a really short tail, tufted ears, and that ruff around the sides of its face that a lynx has. I was perplexed at the time, but when I looked it up I saw that that was what it was – unmistakably a lynx.' [19]

As well as being an obvious candidate for the Hide-out Theory, having once lived in Britain, the lynx is the subject of two slightly more practical theories concerning its provenance. There has been a recent movement to re-establish it in Scotland, along with other formerly native animals such as wolves and beavers. Persistent but unsubstantiated rumours have it that some lynxes may have been illegally imported for that reason.

In 2000 a pro-foxhunting group threatened to release five lynxes into Scotland as a protest, should hunting be banned. There has been speculation that this might already have been done to supplement fox or other types of hunting or shooting.

It is not known whether they carried out their threat, but in any case most lynx sightings in Scotland pre-date it. As with other ABCs, the wide geographical and chronological spread of lynx sightings and differences in the details of their appearance must cast doubt that such an event could account for all lynx sightings.

## Hiding-out in the records

While in many ways the Hide-out Theory is easy to poo-pooh on the purely practical grounds mentioned, it is nevertheless an important idea, and pivotal to the discussion of mystery big cats for two reasons.

Firstly because it *is* an idea – conceived in response to a recalcitrant set of facts; and as such is attractively rare in this baffling field of research. Secondly it questions the omniscience of institutional science, impudently suggesting that it sometimes cannot see its nose for its face.

There is an element of justification for such cheek, for, ironically, one of the commonest hiding places for undiscovered species is in zoological taxonomy itself. New species and subspecies are born and die, according to how biologists re-arrange the pieces of the taxonomic jigsaw. In 1992, it was 'decided that the descriptions of too many apparent subspecies of cats were based on "unconvincing evidence", and that of the 259 previously recognised subspecies of cats as many as 235 should be re-evaluated.'

My trip to the Natural History Museum to get the Lustleigh skull identified as I described in Chapter 7 gave me a glimpse of the great taxonomic enterprise of the nineteenth century. The walls full of antlers, halls of anteaters, tallboys of terrapins, bookcases of bones, sheaves and sheaves of ants made me suspect that identifying my skull was going to involve as much art as science. Obviously it required more than simply opening the drawer marked 'leopards', for it took a nearly half an hour for the zoologist assigned to my case to return with another skull, yellow and dusty with age, almost identical to the Lustleigh skull. The Lustleigh one was a therefore a leopard's skull, she said; very large for a leopard, but obviously within the range since she had found one to match.

I was startled at Di Francis's scorn when I related this diagnosis. She had a better idea, one that made the skull a possible example of a surviving, unclassified species of British big cat. She suggested that the corroborating skull that had been produced might have been that of the mystery big cat shot by the Scottish farmer in 1927 and sent to either London Zoo or the Natural History Museum, neither of which could now, she said, find any trace of it. It could have been put in one of many drawers marked 'leopards' for convenience, she suggested, and now had been triumphantly unearthed to identify wrongly the equally mysterious Lustleigh skull as a leopard.

While her interpretation of the event was admirably audacious, and coincidentally provided evidence for her own theory, it was a salutary reminder of the weaknesses inherent in this circular method of identification whereby variable specimens can be used to identify each other. It also showed me the unthinking readiness with which I had accepted the authority of the institution's 'expert'.

## An alternative Hide-out Theory

The nuts-and-bolts literalism of Di Francis and other proponents of the Hide-out Theory is shadowed by a more radical, more poetic version of the idea. From their studies of other anomalous animals as well as the Surrey Puma and subsequent ABCs

John Michell and Robert Rickard have, they write, 'brewed a theory, which, like all our theories is temporarily and loosely held.'

> 'It is that creatures now extinct which once inhabited a certain district continue after their extinction to haunt that district in phantom form, varied with occasional real, physical appearances, until the time comes to re-establish themselves.'

They point to the reappearance of the Bermuda petrel after three hundred years of apparent extinction, and in Britain the renaissance of the wild boar. 'There were wild boars and large toothed "tigers" in Pleistocene Britain, and probably more recently,' they point out, 'and when Surrey is no more and the commuter train no longer runs to London Bridge, perhaps there will be again.' [20]

## An inheritance

Both the Hybrid and Hide-out Theories are more or less inadequate as explanations of the presence of strange feline animals among us; but they fit together. They are based on the same idea that of a hidden inheritance waiting to be discovered. But while the Hybrid Theory sites the treasure at a microscopic level, beneath the skin of individuals' familiar appearances, the Hide-out Theory sees it on a macroscopic level, concealed in the surrounding landscape. Perhaps they are both best appreciated as modern re-workings of the myth of Demeter, an atavistic sense that half the story is always hidden from us; half the world is in darkness.

# Chapter 11

# Other theories

### Cover up

Among the more suspicious-minded ABC enthusiasts there persists a theory that somehow the government knows all about ABCs and where they come from but fear a variety of disasters – from big insurance claims to mass panic – if they acknowledge these animals' existence. The government agency DEFRA – the Department of the Environment, Farming and Rural Affairs – is usually cast as perpetrator of the cover-ups, although the police are sometimes seen as complicit in the removal of evidence such as sheep kills – ostensibly for examination but actually, so the theory goes, to smother speculation.

There are sporadic claims that this has happened, but they are usually very foaf-loric indeed. Typical is the report from Gloucestershire where the informant was told that his uncle's neighbour allegedly ran over a large black cat near Horsley. The animal was said to have been killed in the incident and the man's car badly damaged. 'Police and the Environment Agency' apparently came and roped off the area and took away the body. The informant noted that: 'There has been nothing in the local press about it although they normally do run Big Cat stories.'[1]

I found one strange report which seemed to take the body abduction scenario one step further. Although the ABC investigator in question reported the incident simply as a puzzling bureaucratic mix-up, or at worst a cover-up, to my ears (infected by the atmosphere of conspiracy perhaps) it seemed strongly reminiscent of the familiar 'officials' of UFO lore, such as the 'Men in Black', who arrive to take the evidence and are never seen again.

A 'panther' had been implicated in the killing of a full-grown Limousin-cross cow. 'The incident' reported the investigator, 'happened at a farm I know well, and the farmer, an extremely sensible and intelligent lady, invited me to inspect and photograph the carcass. I agreed to do this in the early afternoon as I was working in the morning. She told me that the NFU (National Farmers' Union) representative would also be there.

> 'Around noon I had another call from this lady to ask me to come
> as quickly as possible as she had just been called by DEFRA

(whom, she assumed, must have been contacted by NFU as she had not done so) to say they intended to collect the carcass in forty-five minutes time. I was unable to leave my work immediately so when I arrived I found that the DEFRA people had been and gone. The farmer had explained to them that the senior veterinary officer for the county was awaiting the cow for post mortem at the abattoir, and was assured that this was understood and the cow would be taken there. They had then removed the cow but did not leave any paperwork.

'I arrived soon afterwards and stayed for a while discussing the incident. While I was there, a call came from the veterinary officer asking where the cow was as he was ready to proceed.

'The carcass never arrived there, was never seen again, and DEFRA were unable to find out what had happened to it.' [2]

Occasionally ABC investigators do get a DEFRA scalp however. One employee of the Department was working with a colleague in the Vale of Belvoir, Leicestershire, 'trying to gain access to some woodlands we had been sent to inspect'. He wrote:

'I turned to my right and saw a large, black cat about two hundred metres away, walking calmly in a grass forage field. I called my colleague who immediately confirmed my initial impression.   The cat spotted us and just stood still, broadside to us. It stayed there long enough for me to go to my nearby car and get my binoculars. I would say it was the size of an Alsatian or a little smaller.'

The informant described the incident to Nigel Spencer, though not without clearing several official hurdles, reporting: 'I have got clearance "to talk" as you can see. I tried to log the sighting on DEFRA's web site but the email address they give doesn't work and the part on the website dedicated to exotic animal sightings is hard to locate. Makes you wonder why!' He added thoughtfully 'My job will never be the same again.'

Interestingly this DEFRA employee had encountered one of the atypically patterned, black ABCs, and, typically, reported faithfully what he had seen: 'It had looked black, but through the binoculars I could see that its coat was of a brindle/black, stripy configuration.'

## Catting

Occasionally the theory surfaces that some big cats are trained to hunt, and as a result may find their own way to freedom. Nigel Spencer reported that: 'In the 1990s, in a  village in Rutland, there was said to be a certain group of poachers which owned a panther for "catting". The local newspaper was hot on to this, and seemed to be getting somewhere until the proprietor died and the investigation was dropped.' He added the obvious objection to the idea – 'I still find it hard to believe that a panther would release – let alone come home with – its kill'.

A DEFRA official from Devon told me in the 1980s: 'We sometimes get wacky letters about big cats – for example ones that say: "We know what this cat is; it is a pet that its owners let out to kill, and which returns at their whistle".'

More plausible perhaps, and certainly more sinister, is the theory that cat-baiting has replaced badger-baiting in some criminal fraternities, and big cats are imported and/or secretly bred for that reason. Alternatively, the theory goes, they are used as combatants in illegal dog fights, or released simply to be hunted and shot for 'sport'.

A police officer and veteran investigator of big cat sightings, records: 'I heard a story down in Cornwall from a long time acquaintance who is a bit of a "Cornish lad". He told me in all seriousness that he knew of persons down round the mining and clay areas of Cornwall who had been setting up animal fights for quite big money and that big cats pitted against dogs had not been uncommon.' According to this theory ABCs are the unfortunate victims of these practices which have been released when they become injured or difficult to maintain.

He added that his acquaintance had not been to any of these rumoured fights, but claimed to have been invited to go to them, some years previously. 'I am satisfied he was not lying, in as far as his knowledge went, but have not been able to find any other information to corroborate it.' [3]

## Tulpas

Some commentators have suggested that ABCs could be 'thought-forms' or *tulpas* materialised by practitioners of Tibetan Buddhist religious techniques.

Much quoted is the experience of Alexandra David-Neel. As she journeyed through Tibet one of the mystical techniques she studied was that of creating a *tulpa* – an entity materialised by intense concentration and visualisation.

Other occult practices are also credited with the ability to materialize animal-like forms. A ruined hunting lodge on the slopes of Mont Pellier in the Dublin mountains, built by William Connolly as a hunting lodge but later used by Dublin's Hellfire Club (an organisation similar to its more notorious English namesake) is said to be haunted by the form of a huge, black cat once created by their rituals. The creature has been encountered on lonely lanes on the adjoining estate of Lord Massey, in the townland of Killakee, and in other buildings in the district.[4]

## The anti-theory theory

Above are a few of the ideas about the nature and provenance of ABCs, which surface and submerge again at different times. They are sometimes ingenious and occasionally reasonable – but remain unverifiable.

The more such theories I considered the more similar – and less useful – any of them seemed. Finally it was to the visionary Charles Fort that I turned to provide the antidote to theory-fatigue.

Charles Fort was an American journalist who spent much of the first three decades of the twentieth century in the libraries of London and New York working his way through their collections of scientific periodicals and literature. He was also a philosopher who mediated between the world of scientifically-measurable 'facts' and the world as it is experienced.

He took his stand outside the craving for 'proof', concerning himself instead with the phenomenon of classification, classifying the theorists together with the anomalies that disrupted their systems. From his research Fort amassed a compendious collection, mainly from the late nineteenth and early twentieth centuries, of events and facts that could not be squeezed inside the boundaries of conventional science. He looked at the treatment of anomalies in the scientific press, and followed up the explanations for them by correspondence with the authorities concerned. He exposed the determination of official and scientific bodies and their representatives to propose an explanation for every anomaly, even if, as often happened, the 'explanation' was less credible than the original event – a folly for which the writer John Michell later coined the term 'explanationism'.

Fort condemned the practice of trying to force a plethora of recalcitrant data into a single streamlined theory, and ignoring or denying those data that did not fit it – the bad habit into which he believed science was prone to fall.

His method, however, was his greatest stroke of genius; it was through Swiftian parody. He invented a witty, abbreviated literary style. He wryly claimed that no matter how bizarre or ridiculous a theory might be, his archive could supply the facts to fit it.

He was the first commentator to notice the recurrence of ABC sightings. It was he who unearthed the report of the big cat-like animal, killed in Scotland in 1927, whose lost skull Di Francis had invoked as the possible comparison for the Lustleigh skull.[5]

Moreover, according to the newspaper report he discovered, two other similar animals had been shot in the same area during this same period. The press assumption was the usual one – that 'they must have escaped from some travelling menagerie'.[6] Fort mused dryly that they might have been 'teleported' – a word he coined – 'from somewhere in the Carpathians'.

He found a more satisfying way than 'explanationism' of approaching anomalous phenomena, taking the surrounding events – the witnesses' claims, public reactions, official dismissals, official 'explanations', the press reportage and so on – as continuous with the initial event. He simply watched the loop form, reporting the whole with minute accuracy and disinterested relish. 'One measures a circle,' he said, 'beginning anywhere.'[7]

The 'Fortean' approach therefore – the one illustrated by the magazine *Fortean Times* – is a similarly inclusive one. Bob Rickard, who founded the publication, Paul Sieveking and their fellow Forteans, have continued Fort's interest in ABCs, collecting reports over many decades, opting to throw light on the phenomenon not by attempting 'explanations' but by suggesting wider contexts in which to look at it.

Their approach opened a door into the fertile garden of anomalous phenomena in general, and I stepped forward into it, determined to leave no path unexplored in my effort to find my way to the centre of the ABC mystery.

# Chapter 12

# The Earth Tiger

'… Nature's breath contains a twofold element, a male and female, positive and negative, expanding and reverting breath, resembling as we in modern English would put it, two magnetic currents, or, as the Chinese put it, the azure dragon and the white tiger. Where there is a true dragon, there will also be a tiger, and the two will be traceable in the outlines of mountains or hills running in a tortuous and curved course.'

Ernest J. Eitel, *Feng Shui: The science of sacred landscape in old China.* 4th edition 1984

Two writers, Steve Moore and Ivan Bunn, have considered the apparitions of mystery animals, including phantom black dogs and ABCs, in terms of topography.

As a Taoist Steve Moore analysed his part of Essex, Shooters Hill, through the notion of yin and yang, in case it might throw light on both the local black dog traditions and appearances of the ABC known as the 'Shooters Hill Cheetah'.

Yin, 'female' or 'negative energy' is a characteristic of watery, low-lying areas, hollows, caves, cemeteries and other places of chthonic darkness; Yang 'male' or 'positive energy' is found in pointed mountains or buildings, and straight lines. *Feng shui* was the system – part science, part art – which harmonised the yin and yang qualities of the landscape. John Michell points out 'an inspired example of *feng shui* principles in England is the tall spire of Salisbury Cathedral [yang]… rising above the water meadows of the Avon [yin].'[1]

These telluric currents of energy might also be concentrated, either by the natural contours of the land or artificial constructions, at certain locations in such a way as to favour the manifestation of the spirit world in physical forms and effects. Steve concluded that although by reason of its height, television masts and so forth, Shooters Hill is a high yang area, its surroundings were deeply yin. He suggests that black dogs, too, are strongly yin – 'their colour, their associations with death and so on, their appearance mainly at night, all seemed to indicate this' – and by inference might be considered living manifestations of the powerful yin quality of the land.[2]

This Taoist vision of a landscape infused with living currents which may catalyse – or manifest as – creatures such as Black Dogs led me to wonder if the landscapes in which ABCs appear might tell me more about their presence in it.

## The new straight track

ABCs share one obvious piece of terrain with black dog apparitions: as Theo Brown put it – 'Roads. These seem to be the natural home of Black Dogs. I have at least fifty-five examples of these. In addition there are nine which haunt bridges.' [3]

Of course the majority of ABC sightings are on roads too, but as I read and listened to more and more accounts of ABC sightings, I became gradually aware of other patterns emerging. They formed around details to which witnesses attached no importance, often mentioning them only as afterthoughts.

Reports like these kept cropping up:

> 'I was waiting at temporary traffic lights close to the railway bridge on Spitalgate Hill in Grantham. About thirty or forty yards away, I saw through the gate leading to the Network Rail property and the railway embankment, what I would best describe as a lion cub! It was about twenty inches tall, lion-coloured (sort of sandy) and had an unmistakable big cat-like tail… ' [4]

'I drove behind a big black cat. It ran crouching, almost touching the road. The thing that stuck in my mind was the length of its tail. I followed it for a few yards until it jumped a hedge near an old disused, railway track that runs behind our house... ' [5]

A quite disproportionate number of sightings – such as the two quoted above – are made close to, and even on, railway lines. It seems that this pattern is consistent throughout the country because other long-time researchers have noticed the same thing.

Nigel Spencer noted: 'Between 50 percent and 70 percent of sightings are on or near railways, both used and disused. A report was received of a panther actually on the freight railway that runs through Corby, Northants. A worker was crossing the railway bridge[6] when he observed a black cat of about Alsatian size walking on the line below. It had a two-foot long tail and was illuminated by the railway yard lights as it ambled towards the tunnel. He called the police on his mobile. This report was again only half a mile from another sighting the previous year by three workers of a panther-like cat up a tree in the old quarry.' [7] On another occasion on the Nene Valley railway, Peterborough, 'a volunteer was working in a coach in the station when a panther-like big cat walked past at ten feet away!' [8]

Ayr-based researcher Mark Fraser agreed – 'Many sightings that have taken place in Ayrshire… have been slap bang on a railway line.' The orthodox view in ABC investigators' circles is that the railway embankments provide green corridors of food – particularly rabbits – and shelter through built-up areas. This would not be the case in country areas however, where a railway might be the busiest part of an otherwise quiet landscape, and sightings of ABCs by railways are just as frequent in rural areas.

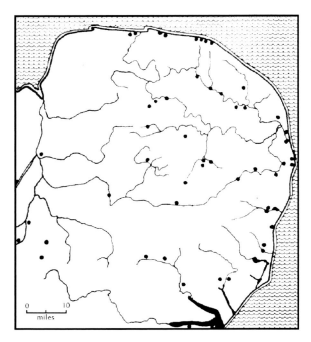

*Ivan Bunn's map of the rivers of East Anglia. The black dots are Black Dog sightings. (Ivan Bunn)*

Spencer Allen, for instance, was driving through Dorset one August morning in 2004:

> 'There are water meadows on the right, divided from a steep hill by a railway track running parallel to the road. I saw a black cat-like animal with a very long tail running diagonally down the hill towards the railway line. I slowed down and watched it for about ten seconds. At that moment a train came along, going the other way. Its size enabled me to gauge the size of the cat, and I thought 'God, that was big!'. I estimated it as just over a metre with a smooth tail of about seventy centimetres, curving down and up again in an S shape. The train obscured my view of the cat, and when it had passed the cat had gone... '

Roy Taylor, a researcher based in Cornwall has also noticed the phenomenon, writing: 'Strange how rail routes, both current and former, keep coming up associated with big cat sightings'. Alan Fleming of West Lancashire agreed with him: 'A lot, if not all, of the sightings near to me in West Lancashire in the last two years or so have been within a mile or less of railways or old trackbeds'.

Does a putative search for food and cover really explain the high proportion of railways incidental to ABC sightings, particularly in rural areas?

## Waterways

Steve Moore's view that energies generated by forms of landscape might be linked to the apparitions of strange creatures received confirmation from other black dog researchers.

*Wildlife expert Jonathan McGowan searches for spoor after seeing a puma in a nearby quarry. (Jonathan McGowan)*

Ethel H. Rudkin did an intensive survey of the black dog legends and stories of Lincolnshire, and found that in the majority of the stories the black dog appears near rivers, streams and ponds.[9] In East Anglia Ivan Bunn plotted all the black dog stories he could unearth, both from local legend and first-hand accounts, on a map and neatly proved Ms Rudkin's point.

Steve Moore concluded his analysis by speculating that the reason black dogs appear in connection with watercourses might be as manifestations of those 'non-straight lines of negative [yin] influence'.

Perhaps the relationships between manifestations of yin and yang in the landscape are more complex. Reverting to the idea, suggested in Chapter 5, that when paired with the indisputable yin of cats, dogs are yang – might not black dogs manifest in opposition to, or complement to, those non-straight lines of yin energy?

Since ABCs' habit of frequenting railways seemed to suggest a connection, perhaps on the same lines as the link between black dogs and waterways, I duly wondered whether the yang black dogs might not balance the non-straight, yin, watercourses; while the yin black cats balance the straight, yang, railway lines.

### Steeps and shallows

Whatever the conjunctions and oppositions of energy within it, topography seems intimately linked with the apparitions of anomalous animals. With this in mind I again reviewed some of the witness statements, and found regular mention of other unusual landscape features. As we have seen, places of yin energy in the landscape include valleys, dips, hollows and pits. Of these declivities quarries – essentially huge holes in the ground – are the most yin, and crop up with far greater than average frequency in ABC reports.

To give a few examples out of many, at Loudoun Hill a black ABC crossed the road into the quarry with such big strides that, the witness said, 'it only hit the road a couple of times... it moved in a sort of leaping movement – not like a dog in the least.' [10] Jonathan McGowan, Chairman of the Bournemouth Natural History Society's zoology section, was out bird watching when he saw a puma walking around the bottom of a quarry in Dorset.[11]

John Earl saw a dark brown, Alsatian-sized, cat cross the road by an old quarry on Whitesheet Hill, also in Dorset. Two weeks later he saw it again in the same place.[12]

Dartmoor National Park guide Roger Hutchings had received reports of a black panther-like animal seen at Mill Hill Quarry. However it was at another one – nearby Yennerdon Quarry – that he spotted a differently coloured big cat circling a dead sheep. 'It was a uniform yellow colour above going to pale white beneath... the details seem to fit that of a young puma.' [13] Another Devon quarry – Barton Wood – was the locality for Maurice Jenkins' sighting of 'a big, black cat-like animal, whose eyes reflected in my headlights'. It sat watching him before bounding off.[14]

### Holes in romantic landscapes

Caves and tunnels are obvious repositories of yin energy. The romantic landscape of the Quantock Hills in Somerset, with its small gorges, would be an obvious place to encounter manifestations of yin energy, and indeed Angela Boyd regularly encountered ABCs in the woods there when walking her dogs. Sometimes she became aware from the behaviour of the dogs that an ABC was following them.... 'When we were quiet and walking along tunnel-like paths parallel with streams – that was when we would definitely get stalked.'

On the Nene Valley railway line a driver encountered an Alsatian-sized, black cat at the tunnel. He threw his pie at it, when it snarled before running back towards the station.[15] It had obviously been around some time, for Nigel Spencer notes: 'Interestingly, there has been a legend here of a mystery black cat seen lurking near the tunnel by the A1, and it has been in the past recorded as a ghost due to its stealth and size.'

While numerous lanes are called after black dogs, cats commonly give their name to caves and cavities in the landscape. There is a 'Cathole' cave in the Gower Peninsula in Wales, a Cathole on Bodmin Moor, a Cathole in Warwickshire, and Catholes – a crook of the river Dee near Sedburgh, Scotland. There is Cathole farm and Cathole copse in Dorset, Cathole Cliff in Devon, and many more. Perhaps these names preserve the memory of our native wildcat, or might they commemorate past appearances of ABCs at noticeably yin places in the landscape?

In a field near Tulsk in Co. Roscommon, Ireland, there is a cave, part-constructed, part-natural. It has a small, insignificant opening, but extends hugely underground. It also looms large in the mythological landscape – named in early Irish literature as the entrance to the Otherworld. It is called Oweynagat – the cave of the cats – because huge, shape-shifting cats were chronicled as having emerged from it.

*Oweynagat or the Cave of the Cats – the entrance to the Otherworld, near Tulsk, Co. Roscommon, Ireland.*

One ABC was seen actually emerging from a cave. The eyewitness, Martin, saw the creature as he was riding his horse through hilly terrain one evening:

> 'As he approached a high ridge his mount baulked and Martin struggled to keep control of the terrified animal. He looked around but could see nothing unusual, though there was a distinct chill in the air. The hair stood up on the back on his neck.
>
> 'Without consciously knowing why, Martin looked upwards to a nearby cliff face and noticed a small cave he had never seen before. Suddenly, an enormous black cat bounded from the opening, landing silently only two metres from where Martin and his horse were now frozen to the spot. The cat looked directly at him for a few seconds that seemed an eternity, then turned, walked off slowly in the opposite direction, and vanished from sight… The horse instantly calmed down; its rider though, could not.' [16]

The cave, it should be noted, was but a part of a larger, geomantically-suggestive landscape which included a 'cliff face' and a high ridge. Was it the combination of these elements that helped to catalyse an ABC encounter? I will return to Martin's encounter and its wider geography in a later chapter.

### Rails, gates, tunnels

A Worcestershire poacher out one night in October 1995, encountered an ABC in a noticeably yin landscape, bisected by the mandatory yang railway line. He wrote:

'I often poached the fields near Stoke Prior at the edge of the main Birmingham and Worcester railway line, and knew the area like the back of my hand.

'This particular night was quite windy, ideal for lampers and lurchers to be out and about, the sky was cloudy and it was past midnight. I had a mate, Donald, with me and what we usually did was stop the car by the gate into the field right next to the railway bridge. Donald would nip out with the dog, Digga, and the lamp, and I would drive under the bridge and park in the car lay-by opposite the row of railway cottages. Donald would get into the field and Digga would do his stuff. By the time I'd got back he had usually got at least one or maybe two rabbits already in the bag, and on we'd go in a two or three mile round trip of the fields.

'Not that night. We got near the bridge and suddenly what we took to be another lurcher ran across the road and leapt into the field, clearing the five-bar gate as if it were a footstool. The first thing I thought was "some bastard's poaching my poaching ground". I was so enraged at the cheek of it that I pulled into the gateway and put my full headlights on, and also shone my one-million-candle powered lamp into the field as well – all thoughts of secrecy had gone out of the window by then. About a hundred yards into the field and running parallel to the railway line, was a big cat, of that I have no doubt whatsoever.

'The field, usually chock full of rabbits, was as bare as Old Mother Hubbard's cupboard. The cat seemed to leap the barbed wire and rush up the railway embankment. I'm no hero, and to be honest we went home then because my dog refused to run into the field at all. He was most perturbed. In five years I'd never seen him shake like he did that night…

'The following day (in broad daylight I must admit) I walked along the track opposite the gateway; this was where we'd seen the animal emerge in the first place. This track runs across fields parallel to the railway lines. About a quarter of a mile from the road a large conduit pipe runs under the railway track and carries overflow water in the bad weather down into the stream that runs alongside the railway line on the field side. The height of the pipe is about four or five feet, and the length of it – I have no idea because my dog wouldn't enter it, but whined and tried to pull off his lead.

'I went back to the car and left him sitting in there along with my wife, whilst I took my lamp from the boot and went back to the tunnel. I shone the lamp up the tunnel but couldn't see the other end, and I must admit there was no way I was going to enter there on my own. I talked it over with my wife and we decided to tell no one, mainly because of the poaching which would have been somewhat curtailed, and also because I thought that people would think that I had finally cracked.' [17]

The geometry of this sighting includes the parallel lines both of the railway and the track beside it. It was beside the cavernous shape of the railway bridge/tunnel that the black creature first appeared, flying over a five-barred gate and disappearing up the steep railway embankment. As well as the bridge carrying the road over the rail tracks there was another tunnel – this time in the form of a huge pipe in the railway embankment, a conduit for water under the rail-tracks. There was something in there – whether conjured by the landscape or not – because whatever it was the poacher's dog did not like it.

In case this apparent recurrence of holes, tunnels and quarries in locations where ABCs were seen was some quirk in my own research, I once again queried this finding with those long-standing researchers who have large archives of witness reports.

They agreed. Apart from roads and railway lines, Mark Fraser put quarries as the most noticeably recurrent locations. Nigel Spencer wrote: 'as well as the usual railways (used and disused), there is also a definite link to quarries, to golf courses, and to high ground (radio masts and hill forts).

Moore was also aware of the high ground in his area around which the appearances of anomalous creatures were constellated. He noted the sharp contrast between the high yang of Shooters Hill which supported 'four radio masts and a Victorian water tower' and its extremely yin surroundings.' [18]

In Chinese geomancy it is steep changes of direction, the places of confluence or divergence of these twin flows of energy, that are most significant. It is tempting to think that it is not only concentrations of one or other of these flows that might produce material manifestations such as mystery animals, but also the turbulence of their meeting or parting.

Some striking examples seemed to show ABCs appearing at points where the terrain underwent a steep change such as railway cuttings, embankments, hillsides, etc. This may simply be a characteristic of the wilder parts of Britain where ABCs are commonly seen: Devon, for instance, is full of small hills and deep combes. But it seemed to me, as I read more reports, that many ABCs appeared at interruptions or changes of direction in an otherwise consistent landscape.

For example a couple were walking with their dog along a moorland path on Exmoor which wound its way halfway up the steep bank sloping down to a swiftly running stream. From the gorse at the top of the opposite bank, they saw a monster black cat emerge which was larger than their own collie dog. It walked slowly along the grass, skirting the gorse, in the same direction as they were walking and about a hundred yards from them. It appeared to take no notice of them. The couple watched it from the other side of the stream and approached to within twenty-five yards of it – but it still took no notice of them. Eventually it returned leisurely to the patch of gorse where it had first been seen and disappeared into it.[19]

Considered through the eyes of a Taoist the report presents a strange tableau. The position of the witnesses halfway up a steep bank with a stream at the bottom sounded geomantically significant, even to a non-initiate like me. It was almost as if they were looking across the ravine to a parallel world, for even though the couple approached to within twenty-five yards of the ABC, it still 'took no notice of them' – as if the stream was more than a physical division.

The terrain around Weybridge in Surrey is about as far from Devon's combes as you could get, but it does boast one geomantically striking feature – the old Brooklands car racing track. It is here that a black ABC has appeared regularly to different witnesses over four years at least. One of them explains: 'The cat sits and walks along the remaining race track which runs vertically around Brooklands. It's difficult to explain but the high side of the track stands as high as a house and is almost vertical then it curves steeply down so that the bottom side runs along the road... '[20]

## The topology of a cavalcade

Steep declivities – like the Brooklands race track – and ravines, nowadays the habitat of ABCs, have always housed anomalous beings: in former times they were places whence fairies traditionally emerged. For instance Hugh Miller recorded what was supposed to be the final departure of the fairies from Scotland, at Burn of Eathie:

> 'A herd-boy, and his sister, were lounging beside one of the
> cottages when, just as the shadow of the garden-dial had fallen on
> the line of noon, they saw a long cavalcade ascending out of the
> ravine through the wooded hollow. It wound among the knolls
> and bushes; and, turning round the northern gable of the
> cottage... began to ascend the eminence toward the south.' [21]

The circuitous route the cavalcade took from the ravine, around the northern gable and up the hill to the south – its yang aspect emphasised by the straight line of the gnomon of the sundial – would have been recognised as a fairy path in Celtic tradition, and perhaps a 'dragon path' in Chinese; at any rate the meandering path and its allusions was a natural braid of yin and yang energies.

It compares to the route of the ABC that Mike and Sarah Sabin saw while they were out feeding cattle in the Malvern Hills in Worcestershire. Mike recalled:

> 'As I approached the gate, I saw this jet-black, cat-like animal the
> size of an Alsatian dog, coming out of the ditch. I would describe
> it as stalking – walking with big, tentative strides... We must have
> watched it for at least five minutes before it moved away, down
> on to the Worcester to Hereford railway line and into a tunnel,
> where we lost sight of it... ' [22]

Gate, ditch, railway line, tunnel...

## Bomb craters

While ravines suggest movement, it was a static anomaly in the landscape – an abrupt hollow resembling an old bomb crater (its powerful yin qualities perhaps enhanced by the cage at the bottom) – which provided the location for an ABC encounter in Devon.

'Shirley' was taking two spaniel dogs and Labrador for a walk one afternoon in April 1988. They passed through a large oak wood to a gate, and through that to a field in which there was a small hollow, deep enough to be hidden from view until one was almost upon it. In this the farmer had placed a cage-trap covered with wire netting for catching crows which were attacking the newly-born lambs on his farm. In the trap, as a bait, he had put a dead ewe.

> 'As the trap came into view Shirley stopped in amazement when she saw a large, light brown animal crouched by it. The three dogs saw it too and stopped, hair on end, so petrified they were unable to bark. As one, they turned and shot back into the wood as fast as they could run. It was a large cat, bigger than any of the dogs. It had its ears flat against its head and was snarling threateningly and the same time slowly moving its long tail from side to side. Shirley's amazement turned to fright and she, too, ran for it. When she reached the far side of the wood, feeling very shaken, she found the three dogs waiting for her.' [23]

'Like bomb craters' was also the phrase Sheila Cumber used to describe the old iron-workings overgrown by Sussex woodland where she, along with several local people, had gone to admire the bluebells. The electric blue of the flowers contrasted dramatically with the black sky for 'although it was mid-morning' she recalls, 'it had got very dark with an impending storm. Suddenly both I and the man behind me saw a black, feline animal, the size of a deer, cross the path fifty yards in front. I couldn't believe it.' Without looking at them the ABC ran quickly down the steep crater's edge and disappeared into the gloom of the undergrowth.[24]

Perhaps sightings of such creatures would not have surprised Ernest Eitel, the author of the first book in English about *feng shui:*

> '… it is best to look for the most secluded retired corner, for in retirement it is that dragon and tiger are most closely intertwined, and there the breath is gathered most abundantly… the rule is then to look near the junction of dragon and tiger for some little hollow or little mound, or in short some sudden transition from male to female or from female to male ground.' [25]

Perhaps the most arresting illustration of Eitel's observation was presented by Mrs Arnold, a witness in the saga of the Surrey Puma which I mentioned in a previous chapter. The reader may recall her closely-observed description of the exotic animal she saw – 'like a king cheetah'. She reported: 'It leapt the width of the lane and went through the hedge, stopping to drink water that had spilled from the cattle trough. I saw it on several occasions in the distance at the dew-pond in the same field, and lying on the air-raid shelter which used to be at Bushylease Farm.'

Consider the picture of the dew-pond, a sudden declivity in a field, again reminiscent of an old bomb crater, and then the inversion of its shape: the domed

*A well-designed golf course in Co. Monaghan where a black ABC has been encountered on several occasions*

air-raid shelter, crowned with the beautiful, enigmatic, cheetah-like animal. Whatever the ins and outs of yin and yang it is a picture that stays in the memory.

**Roughs and smooths**

This brought me to the mystery of golf courses. As Nigel Spencer had mentioned, they, too, feature puzzlingly often as a backdrop to sightings of big cats.

For instance 'Sandy' and friends were on the seventh green of the Nairn Dunbar course beside the Moray Firth when they saw a large cat-like animal. It was only thirty yards away so they had a good view of it, and Sandy knew what it was:

> 'This was definitely a large, male lynx. I've always discounted big
> cat sightings as rubbish, in actual fact probably deer or dogs. But I
> was in the company of my gamekeeper uncle often enough to
> have seen a lot of Scottish wild animals and I know what I saw.
> The beast was about two and a half feet tall with sandy colouring
> and black tipped ears and tail.' [26]

Westhill golf course, to the west of Aberdeen provided the sight of a different kind of ABC, 'the size of an Alsatian dog', for a dog-walker. 'Against the snow, it was jet-black, sleek, with a long tail flowing out behind it... It scared the living daylights out of me.' [27]

Scotland is famous for its golf courses, and as a reason for people to be out and about in that part of the Britain I suppose it should not be surprising that any ABCs nearby will be spotted. Leicestershire and Rutland, the Spencers' patch, however, is not especially rich in golf courses, and yet the same pattern appears there. Nigel wrote: 'I discussed with Mark [Fraser] the fact of golf courses being popular with these big cats. Our hunch is that it's the rabbits being exposed and yet the cats having cover to approach them... We had two more cats seen on or next to golf courses in Leicestershire last week... ' [28]

Nor is the Wiltshire/Somerset area particularly known for its golf courses, but local researcher Clive Moulding found that: 'Going back in my records, golf courses seem one of the most likely places to see a big cat... ' Devon big cats also like a stroll on the fairway: paw prints found in bunkers at the China Fleet golf and country club were identified as those of a big cat.[29] So do those in Surrey – David Radden-Rutt was so alarmed by the sight of 'a big, black cat – in size easily up to waist height' ahead of him that he decided not to tee off on the tenth hole but instead took a four-shot penalty to avoid the area.[30]

## ABC hot spots

It follows that anyone wishing to spot a mysterious feline animal could do worse than look at a map and find a place where two or more of these topographical hotspots coincide, and wait around. This is what an Aberdeen couple unwittingly did in the July of 2003:

> 'My wife and I were cycling along the old Deeside railway line just outside Aberdeen at around 2.30 pm. We had stopped behind the Deeside golf course to admire the view and to look at the tee shot of three golfers just below. After they had played their shots we turned to get our cycles. My wife first exclaimed "Jeepers – what's that?" About seventy yards away was a big cat emerging from the undergrowth at the side of the track.

> 'It was not very tall, around the height of a collie dog or so, but it was long. It had a long tail curved upwards at the end and was a dark sort of dirty fawn colour. It moved away from us on the track for about ten yards pacing quite slowly and went back into the undergrowth. It did not seem particularly interested in anything, just having a look around. Its movements seemed just like you see with any big cat – with a sort of muscular definition. It looked like a puma to me.' [31]

The magic combination also produced an ABC for Insch golf course worker Dave Wilson, who saw a large, jet-black animal with a cat-like face and a long curling tail. 'I had just completed the raking of the ninth green,' he said. 'There's a small field between the Kennethmont Road and the railway, and I saw a huge beast walking along quite casually. It was in the open for about a minute, and then it disappeared. It appeared again on the railway line sniffing around a pole... ' [32]

Whereas it is possible to argue, as do the adherents of the Releases/Escapes Theory, that railways and quarries could simply provide food and hidey-holes for ABCs, the same cannot be said of golf courses. Mark's and Nigel's hunch that they could provide easy-to-see rabbits seems rather speculative: these ABCs are seen in daytime when few rabbits are about, but a lot of humans are; and although the 'rough' will provide good cover for a golf-ball, it is not suitable camouflage for a big cat.

Golf courses are not traditional haunts of black dogs; nor are they sacred sites in the accepted sense of the word, though golfing enthusiasts might disagree. They are, however, geomantically interesting, being wholly constructed landscapes designed with the harmonious balance of yin and yang in mind – or, as golfers call it, rough and smooth, bunker and green.

Have the architects of these shrines to leisure unknowingly manipulated a confluence of earth energies such as yin and yang to create the conditions for the emergence of monsters? It was an agreeable idea – as aesthetically pleasing as it was ridiculously far-fetched. But was it any more far-fetched than that of extraordinary big cats appearing on golf-courses, or at all? You simply take your choice.

# Chapter 13

# Daimons and their slippery nature

At this point I stood back from my researches and tried to see where I had got to. The ABC experience was still as clear and incorruptible as a diamond, but as I had held it up to the light it had generated a kaleidoscope of moving colours around itself – patterns I have explored in earlier chapters.

For a start it had become clear that these anomalous big cats could not be caught or killed in the normal way – too many people had tried to do this for too long. I suspected it was no longer realistic to expect conventional methods to succeed.

I had looked at every available still photo and concluded that while some undoubtedly showed large felines, their species remained indeterminate. The videos in existence, though exciting and tantalising, likewise compounded rather than clarified the mystery, showing up insufficient or anomalous detail.

I had considered disembowelled sheep; I had been taken up and down hills on shepherds' quad bikes in pouring rain; I had looked at big cat paw-prints – but paw prints that led nowhere. It had all been wonderfully enjoyable, but as evidence it remained inconclusive.

I had collected and categorised innumerable sightings of ABCs: they were of various colours, shapes and sizes, and showed a range of probable and improbable behaviours – but only a minority of these exactly matched known species of big cats.

I had examined every probable source for them, and considered the various hypotheses about their nature and provenance. Some theories were based initially on common sense, but the more data became available the more it stacked up against them; others tried bravely to account for this data, but the effort of including it all attenuated them to the point of collapse.

I had searched up and down the wilder shores of probability, considering ABCs in terms of traditional black dog folklore, Taoism, paranormal animals or types of experience, or the products of occult practices of various kinds. Yet ABCs were not wholly compliant with any of these categories either – conforming in some ways, but remaining glaringly incompatible in others.

In short while I had dispelled many of the erroneous facts and fallacies about ABCs, I was not much nearer to resolving the problem to my own satisfaction. I now knew what ABCs were not, but still had no idea what they were.

I considered hanging up my binoculars at this point, wondering whether to abandon the quest after all. But just when all my research seemed to have come to dust, I became aware of something else. I noticed that everyone who looks closely at ABCs begins, after a while, to smell a rat.

## The rat

The veteran ABC investigator, Mark Fraser, alerted me to this first. He noticed the subtle aroma that hangs around the endlessly proliferating ambiguities associated with the ABC hunt. 'I sometimes smell a rat; I get the impression that they are playing with us,' he mused. 'I occasionally feel I'm being teased... '

It was this insight that pointed me at last towards a new trail. I too had smelt that rat, but had ignored it as an annoyance. For the first time I wondered if this very ambiguity, this trickiness, had a significance to it – whether it could be the key rather than the obstruction to understanding the ABC phenomenon.

The idea that their chronic elusiveness and the frustrating inconclusiveness of the evidence surrounding them might be the whole point of their existence, led me in a circle right back to my own doorstep.

It was my brother Patrick's work which showed me where else I might look for the antecedents of British ABCs. He pointed out that other people had addressed the matter of creatures like ABCs long before I or the cryptozoologists of the past two centuries had taken up the chase. They were, for instance, an essential part of the philosophy of the Ancient Greeks.[1]

## Daimons

According to those philosophers the world seethed with invisible – or occasionally glimpsed – beings. Every stream, wood, hill, cave, tree and valley had its inhabitants, so they tell us: the naiads, undines, satyrs, dryads and hamadryads. 'All things,' Proclus remarked, 'are full of gods.'

They lived amongst humans even in the heart of domestic life, at the hearth and in the kitchen: household gods, the *lares* and *penates*, to which small offerings were made in recognition of their place in the house, and the intangible aspects of domestic life which was their jurisdiction. The Greeks called them, collectively, *daimones*, or, in English 'daimons' (*not* to be confused with demons). Daimons were an essential link between mortals and the grander deities of Greek cosmology.

The greatest authorities on the place of these intermediate beings were the Neoplatonists who flourished from about the middle of the third century AD to the middle of the sixth. Following Plato's mystical dialogue, the *Timaeus*, they recognised the daimons as the inhabitants and expression of the *anima mundi* – the soul of the world. The *anima mundi* was a middle realm between the One – the transcendent source of all things – and the materiality of Earth and human life.

Recognition of daimons was thus mandatory at all levels of society because they were part of a continuous strand of being which linked the human world to the divine one. The role of daimons from a human point of view, the view from the bottom of the heap as it were, was to make explicit, visible – even tangible – that unbroken thread.

## Personal daimons

The smallest, most idiosyncratic and localised of daimons, according to the Neoplatonists, were related to, and flowed into, the larger, impersonal gods. Moreover this relationship is not static but dynamic; it forms archetypal patterns, narrative actions which we call myths. *En route* they might appear as personal guides. Napoleon had a familiar spirit 'which guided him, as a daemon, and which at particular moments took on the shape of a shining sphere... or which visited him in the figure of a dwarf clothed in red that warned him.'[2]

At the philosophical level a strange Gnostic figure, Philemon, was the personal daimon of the psychologist Carl Jung; while the poet W.B. Yeats experienced his daimon as a kind of muse: 'I think of life as a struggle with the Daimon who would ever set us to the hardest work', and whose nature was essentially paradoxical: 'I am persuaded that the Daimon delivers and deceives us.'[3]

## Classifying the daimons

I have said that the daimons traditionally bridged two worlds – the sensory material world of humans and the spiritual transcendent one of the gods. In mediating between them they not only partake of both, but embody the contradiction between the two.

Therefore daimons' characteristics are as contradictory as their role dictates. They are as easily material as immaterial; sometimes benign and at other times malevolent; sometimes inspiring and sometimes indifferent to individuals. As Yeats put it, they both 'deliver and deceive' us. It follows then that their most irritating attribute – to a modern mind at least – is that by their very nature they resist formal classification.

The Syrian Neoplatonist, Iamblichus, (died AD 326) undertook the worthy task of trying to do just that. He laboured to describe all the orders of beings from gods major and minor, to angels, archons, heroes, and so on, and their defining characteristics. This he successfully managed – but when he came to daimons he was defeated by their plurality.

Plurality has also distinguished the daimons of later times – in her *Dictionary of Fairies* Katharine Briggs names hundreds of British and European daimons: fairies, kobbolds, brownies and so forth, and dozens of local variations on their names and guises.

Many of the daimons Katharine Briggs recorded are still seen to this day; others have faded from view or from fashion, while still others have emerged in a modern guise within modern Western preoccupations – the small black-eyed aliens, or tall shining-eyed beings supposedly from 'outer space', their UFOs, men in black, vanishing hitchhikers, foo fighters, the Owlman, mothmen, Bigfoot and so on. Even the shining, winged beings (originally derived from Neoplatonism) which became part of Christian dogma at the Council of Nicaea (AD 325) are currently popular again as 'guardian angels'.

Like Iamblichus I had believed that I would be able to find out what ABCs were by sorting the many hundred of sightings I had painstakingly gathered into categories, in which meaningful patterns would, I hoped, emerge. The categories I chose initially were the obvious ones, such as colour, size, and behaviour. These quickly ramified into categories within categories – behaviour, for instance, subdivided into behaviour with other animals, fear/acknowledgement/indifference/curiosity *vis-à-vis* humans, road-crossing techniques, attitudes to cars, supposed attacks, etc., etc. These distinctions proliferated further until finally each ABC seemed almost to need a category of its own.

In the face of the daimons' incorrigible heterogeneity Iamblichus was obliged to fall back on a few constants that he thought could be ascribed to the whole jumbled, teeming race. Following his example I, too, tried abandoning my own pigeonholes and approaching the phenomenon from the opposite direction – to see whether there were any features which ABCs had in common. I found that there were indeed a few, and that, moreover, they shared them with the daimons about which Iamblichus had been forced to generalise.

He had found at least three characteristics that he could safely ascribe to all daimons, namely: 'They appear at different times... in a different form, and appear at one time great, but at another small... Their operations appear to be more rapid than they are in reality.' [4]

**More rapid**

Mindful of Iamblichus's remarks I began re-reading the reports in my collection of endlessly proliferating categories, and wondered why it had never struck me before how often witnesses remarked on the preternatural speed and movement of the ABC – 'more rapid than they are in reality.'

The ABC seen at Galston in Scotland, for instance, was typical in that it stood and stared at the three witnesses until one moved closer, when it turned and raced off at what they considered 'an incredible speed.' [5]

Many witnesses elaborated further on the swiftness of ABCs: Stan Silver's ABC 'turned on its heels and ran... so fast... right across that field. I have never seen anything move like it in my life – a greyhound would not have caught up with it.' [6] The Cumbrian woman travelling along the M6 who saw an ABC said: '... suddenly it started pounding up a hill faster than I have ever seen any animal running. It had a huge, huge stride... '

Galloway man Billy Morrow saw 'a big beast, definitely not a dog... big and jet black' with 'a long tail and was travelling at a tremendous speed.' In fact Mr Morrow said that he had never seen an animal run as fast, while an amazed witness near

Longney in Gloucestershire saw an ABC 'going so fast that it crossed a five-acre field in about ten seconds.' [7]

Raymond Dougherty was hill walking near Braemar when 'I stopped to get something out of my rucksack. I looked up and saw a black object moving through the heather. It kept moving out of sight – one minute I could see it, then I couldn't see it, then I could. I thought it was a big Labrador and I looked round for the owners. But then I realised it wasn't a dog... It was amazing. It went like a bat out of hell... with the fluid, flowing motion of a cat.'

The ABC that David Walters saw 'streaked' across the road in front of him. He said: 'I haven't seen anything like it in my life. It came across like the wind.' [8]

Michael Iggleton used the same simile as Mr Dougherty to describe the speed of the ABC he saw in the Isle of Wight – 'It was like a bat out of hell.' This creature performed another feat characteristic of ABCs – a gigantic leap: 'It came out from the left about twenty feet in front of me, hit the middle of the main road with one leap and at the opposite pavement with the next.' [9]

The ability of ABCs to make gravity-defying bounds, particularly over roads and lanes which serve as measurements of the length of stride, is frequently remarked upon. A woman driving near Waltham on the Wolds, Leicestrshire, came round a bend to see, directly in front, of her, a cat-like animal of about three foot high and six or seven foot long, and sandy brown in colour. Travelling at fifty miles per hour, she thought she was going to hit it, when – in a split second – it sprang from the centre of the road and cleared both the seven foot wide verge and six foot high hedge in one leap. She was used to local deer species and was sure it was none of these.[10] A leap like this from a standing start sounds more akin to flying. Mr Atherton, a road transport engineer, described the ABC he and his wife saw as they drove home through Hall Green in West Lancashire as doing just that. He explained: 'There is a bend near the school and in my headlights I picked up this black cat which looked like a young tiger, except of course it was black... it was in flight, jumping... '

Maurice Gibb of the Bee Gees rock group saw a cat-like animal 'at least twice as big as a black Labrador and very muscular' in the garden of his Surrey mansion. He said: 'Our guard dogs suddenly tensed. They were let out and had got half way across the lawn when they stopped dead and this huge shape sprang clean across the drive and disappeared.' [11]

Pearl Thorburn narrowly missed an ABC which took only two strides to cross the road: 'It came out of nowhere, landed on the white lines and sprang right up over the hedge, it was amazing.' The shape of the animal she described sounds convincingly like the fastest and most sinuous of mammals, the cheetah – 'It was huge, it had really long legs and a long tail but the body was quite small in comparison. It had a very athletic sort of build... ' But it could not have been a literal cheetah because it also had 'jet-black fur'.[12]

An ABC appeared in front of Damian Bell while he was driving: 'It seemed to bounce once in front of the car and then on again into a field.' [13]

Irene Watson and her husband gave a detailed description of the ABC they saw at close quarters as it crossed the road in front of them: 'The movement too was unusual. It literally sprang forward and was gone in a flash.'[14]

The composite picture of these flying animals was interestingly unlike the indolent big cats we are used to seeing in wildlife documentaries or parks. While cheetahs are capable of running at very high speeds, the black panther is a leopard and leopards are not habitual runners, relying on ambush at close quarters or short sprints to catch their prey.

Now that I was approaching the evidence by a different route, so to speak, I was even able to add to Iamblichus's observations. If, like daimons, some ABCs 'appear to be more rapid than they are in reality', sometimes, paradoxically, they move in a manner suggestive of unreal slowness:

**Slow motion**

In August 1983 a couple camping in North Wales by Tal-y-Bont emerged from their tent to see an ABC 'about fifteen feet away from us. The colour of it was black, and it was moving slow, like slow-motion... It noticed us and stopped.' When they called their dog the cat 'took off at a terrific speed. Our dog is fast, but the cat left him standing.'[15]

Another couple, driving just outside of Insch, Aberdeenshire, had to brake sharply to avoid hitting an ABC running across the road in front of them. They, too, described the cat's speed as 'amazing': fast and yet 'almost like slow motion'.[16] Larry Parkes used the same phrase of the two 'jet black panthers' he encountered while walking his dog. 'One was the size of my Great Dane and the other about the size of my collie. They stood in the field for about thirty seconds,' he said; 'I could see their yellowish eyes... When they took off they loped, like in slow motion... '[17]

As with the purposeful smoothness of actions in slow-motion film, witnesses often comment on the fluidity of the movements of ABCs. 'Gliding' is a word that often crops up. Mrs Friday reported a sighting near Guildford in Surrey, writing: 'We had a very clear view of the large cat-like animal which was gracefully leaping, no gliding is a better word, across the field... '[18]

Gloucestershire taxi driver George Hearn was driving to Minchinhampton when an ABC 'glided across the road in front of me.' Mr Hearn was in no doubt about what he had seen. 'It moved far too fast to be a dog and it certainly wasn't a deer. It didn't stop to glare at me; it just glided across the road and disappeared into the hedge... '

Driving towards the A30, in Cornwall a woman and her passengers noticed a strange animal crossing a field. 'At first I thought it resembled a gangly young horse; but then when it glided over the wall, we all gasped – it was obviously a very large black cat with a long, curved tail... '[19]

In Rutland in 2001 a woman saw an ABC which 'simply floated across the field at such great speed... ', while the cat two workers saw in their south central Leicester industrial estate 'moved with a "liquid" type flow movement.' An ABC encountered in Norfolk also 'ran extremely quickly and fluidly' and then just 'slithered' away.[20]

When security lights were triggered at the rear of another Leicestershire house, the householder was amazed to see an ABC which 'almost floated across the lawn.'[21] Mr Allen Trump, an Oxford University librarian, was walking in bluebell woods in Devon when his eye was caught by a flash of movement, and he saw 'a most peculiar creature.' He said: 'It was cat-like, and seemed to have a crouching, gliding movement.'[22]

## Appearances and vanishings

Sometimes ABCs appear and disappear almost magically by means of extraordinary speed. At other times this effect is caused by their seeming to materialise out of and into shadows. In August 1983 a naturalist was out walking in a country park near Hamilton, in Lanarkshire. He wrote:

> 'In a remote area of the park I saw a "shadow" move from beside the path, about fifty feet away. It stopped and turned, and that's when I realised it was *real* – a big, dark grey cat, as big as an Alsatian dog. It had a long tail and small ears. It stood still for a second or two – I was rooted to the spot – then it moved, leaped from one side of the path to the other into woodland, jumped down a ten foot drop, and bounded off downhill into dense woodland, where I lost sight of it.'

He added: 'I know the area well and am used to seeing the usual wildlife; what I saw did not match anything I have seen in the wild before.'

A classic black leopard sighting dissolved into ambiguity when a witness near Stoke Gabriel in Devon saw an ABC, no more than thirty yards away, crossing into a field the other side of the lane; in the driver's words: 'One moment I saw it as it entered the field and the next it just seemed to disappear into the background. No wonder people have problems looking for them.'[23]

Often they seem not to be bounded by space at all: certainly they disappear into small amounts of undergrowth, such as hedges, and are never seen again despite intensive searches. Trevor Beer ruminated on this phenomenon, writing:

> 'Many is the time I and others have watched such a cat crossing an open hillside when it has "vanished" as if into thin air, presumably into a cave or some hidden goyal as we locals call the smaller coombes or unfarmed bits of countryside hereabouts. Yet, as often as not, on going to what seems the exact spot, we find that the animal has disappeared, with the terrain showing no obvious hiding places.

> 'At such moments the air feels charged with electricity as one's own "hackles" rise at the back of the neck and one feels as if one is in the presence of unseen, watching eyes, which is probably the case. Once two of us watched a black leopard coming towards us

along a disused green lane, from a vantage point looking down
along its length. The lane was bordered with trees and bushes
with steep-ish fields on either side and leading to a waterway
below. The cat came to a gorse patch but instead of appearing out
of the other side it vanished. I say "vanished" because though it
might simply have lain down to rest up amongst the gorse, when
we went down to look, it had gone. Yet I feel sure that at no time
as we walked down to the lane did I lose sight of the spot...' [24]

The animal Mr Jack Marr and his colleagues saw seemed to disappear suddenly.
They had been strimming hedges near Anstruther, Fife, when all of a sudden only
fifty yards ahead of them beside a humped back bridge, they saw what they first
thought was a black Labrador, then realised was a big, jet-black cat three feet high.
Mr Marr, a keen naturalist, was startled by its 'large size, feline posture, small face
and a very long tail.' But in the seconds it took Mr Marr and his colleagues to run to
the spot where it had been, the animal had disappeared as if into thin air. 'We
looked and listened but couldn't see or hear any trace of it.' [25]

Adrian Carson came face to face with an ABC which also vanished. He was fishing
on the River Lugar, when, he said:

'... as I stalked along the river in pursuit of salmon I came round a
bend and there in front of me, as plain as day, was a large, black,
panther-like cat. It stood there looking at me with a glare that
unnerved me. I was rooted to the spot with fear and could not
move. Then I slowly started to walk backwards, back the way I
came. I stumbled on a log and took my eyes off the animal for a
spilt-second, when I looked up it had gone... ' [26]

Jonathan McGowan, head of the Mammals Section of Bournemouth's Natural
Sciences Society, and one of Dorset's leading wildlife experts, surprised a puma
drinking from the river. He and three companions had walked over a footbridge to
small island in the River Stour when they spotted the animal. He warned his friends
to stand aside so as not block the animal's escape route. Sure enough the puma
made a dash for it back along the footbridge, but half way across it seemed simply to
vanish before their amazed eyes. Mr McGowan ran to the spot in disbelief and found
one, wet, puma-like footprint on the wooden boards.

They also appear as if from nowhere. Sarah Carpenter, a deputy matron at a nursing
home in Ellesmere, got into her car to leave work and suddenly saw a mysterious big
cat as she turned to shut her car window. She said: 'It was outside the car, just
looking at me very strangely. It had just appeared. It wasn't there when I got in the
car. It was just like a big cat and had got something in its mouth, a rabbit or
something. It was the size of a big dog.' She added, 'I panicked and started the car
up.' This ABC, however, disappeared more conventionally: 'It just jumped over the
wall. I don't know where it went.' [27]

A Dorset cyclist did not know whether he was seeing things or not when he glimpsed
an ABC near Burton Bradstock. He wrote:

'It would have been late afternoon with the sun very low in the sky. I was cycling west along Bennetts Hill Lane when I noticed a disturbance in a group of cows further down the hill. For a moment I thought I saw a black animal moving fast about twenty feet from the cows but I had sweat in my eyes which I wiped away. When I looked again the animal was not visible… '

Perhaps the cows were aware of an invisible presence, for he noted, 'they were clearly still excited… they seemed panicky and unsure of where to run.' [28]

## Doubling back

In appearing and disappearing with such confusing rapidity, ABCs can be said to share an important quality of daimons – their trickiness. I have quoted Mark Fraser's remark that the more you know about ABCs, the more you get 'the feeling that they are teasing you.' Cornish farmer Daniel Wilson would agree. He and a friend spotted the big cat which became known as the Beast of Bodmin Moor, lying on a wall on his property. They chased it, and a tantalising hunt through woodland ensued. Whenever the two men flagged or gave up the giant cat would suddenly reappear at the end of long lines of trees. This happened so often that Daniel and his friend began to get the uneasy feeling that they were being played with.

The cat that Stephen Clarke saw also performed the teasingly daimonic trick of appearing in the spot he had just passed. Mr. Clarke was in his works van at the entrance to Bennachie Park, Aberdeenshire when he saw a very large feline creature, jet-black, with a three foot long tail. He stopped his van only twenty yards from the cat, and they stared at each other. He described it as being 'as large as a fully-grown Alsatian, but longer in body, sleek and very graceful in its movements. It had bright green shining eyes, with a small head.' When he got out of the van the cat ran into the undergrowth. Mr Clarke followed it but after a couple of minutes he became terrified when he realised that the cat must have doubled back because he suddenly saw it staring at him from the undergrowth a matter of feet away.

## ABCs as daimons

In their quicksilver movements ABCs resemble traditional daimonic beings. But daimons in their traditional mediatory job – forming a bridge between two worlds – also embody a Janus-faced view of both. When they suddenly appear and vanish – or vanish and re-appear – they double-back behind terrestrial logic, offering humanity an additional perspective beyond it.

This dual perspective, the Neoplatonists believed, is humanity's means of access to the Otherworld, through which we mortals might ultimately approach the gods.

## The vocabulary of ABCs

Perhaps I had already begun the process of acquiring a daimonic perspective when, following Iamblichus's example, I returned to look again at my huge file of eyewitness evidence. It was evidence that I had believed to be long since exhausted in the search for facts and conclusions: but by cutting it a different way – and listening to the language of the narratives – I saw a different picture of ABCs beginning to form.

Certainly a significant number of them did fulfill Iamblichus's first criterion – 'Their operations appear to be more rapid than they are in reality.' [29] Moreover it was plain that ABCs' operations often defied a normal time-scale in other ways, were too brief or too slow, and sometimes jumped clean out of it.

Could ABCs be modern daimons? If so, they are perhaps the most plausible, most material, most insistent ever to animate our landscape. My research reinvigorated I fell once again to excavating my orderly field-system of categorised evidence to see what else lay beneath the surface that Iamblichus would recognise.

# Chapter 14

# A dragon as big as a kitten

The most striking difficulty for people who see ABCs is trying to describe the size of the animal seen, for, just like the daimons of Iamblichus ABCs apparently 'appear at one time great, but at another small.' [1]

I was impressed by the effort most put into the task. Syd Tucker had encountered numerous feral moggies while out with his gun over the years, but one black feline which sat watching him for a moment before running off into undergrowth, confounded him. Nevertheless he did his best:

> 'I could only say that it was the same size, and shape as a panther or puma, but not so fat or big around the body. Higher than a puma with a longer tail, the end of which rounded and not tapered as in house cats. When sitting, before it turned into the bushes behind it, I had the impression that the eyes were red. For a comparison with a dog, I would put its size near to a Wiemaraner pointer, or full grown Doberman – but with the head of a cat, the size of a medium teapot.' [2]

It is difficult to gauge size, except by comparison with the size of another, more familiar, animal. The majority of witnesses describe ABCs as being the size of large dogs, usually citing Labradors or German shepherd dogs as examples; others are at pains to modify their own dogs – 'the size of my own border collie but chunkier, with a tail like a pump handle.'

However, to paraphrase Charles Fort, it seems one can measure a cat beginning anywhere.[3] ABCs vary from the so-called Beast Of Ongar, called 'as big as a fox' [4] to the ABC two witnesses saw when out shooting rabbits in a field in Rutland and described as 'approximately the size of a small cow.' [5]

In Gloucestershire in June 1994 an ABC was seen near Monmouth – 'jet black and about the size of a large dog', and another seen alongside the M5 was 'three times the size of a fox.' A couple were driving from Newent when they saw a cat-like animal walking along the side of the road, which '... could not have been a domestic cat because its legs were too long. It was at least two feet high. It wasn't a fox and it was too high for a badger. It was about the size of a large dog. I wouldn't like to say what it was.'

Was this the same creature Margaret Jones spotted not far away, near Dymock? The black animal she saw walking down the road towards her was 'about as high as a sheep, but it had the swaggering roll of a cat.' In October the same year Police Inspector David Morgan was driving near Staunton early one morning when a 'panther' leapt in front of his car. He described it as '... black, larger than a fox but smaller than a small horse'!

In April 2002 in Leicestershire a man camping out in Grace Dieu Woods with his dog, saw a large, black panther-like creature, which he described as about the size of a Great Dane. Civil servant Gerry McGarry's cat was a similar size 'about the length of a cow, but only about half the height.' [6]

Russell Barnes wrote: 'I am an ex-police officer and am well aware of the difficulties of judging size at a distance, but I used to own a border collie and I am sure the cat we saw was as big as that.'

John Devlin's ABC was much bigger again – 'I had to have a reality check because it was almost the same size as cows in the nearer of the two fields. I was shocked to say the least and would have stopped but for being in a traffic queue. I am a hundred percent sure of what I saw.'

Charles Crosthwaite, from Minions in Cornwall, saw a creature he described as 'most definitely a cat.' He spotted it wandering past calves and sheep early in the morning and was able to estimate its size from the nearby animals: 'It was bigger, lengthwise, than a calf.' [7]

Jan Edwards was able to estimate very accurately the size of the ABC she saw from only a hundred yards away, because it was walking through a flock of sheep. 'It was as long as the sheep, with a tail as long again. Height-wise – not quite as tall as the sheep.' This was considerably bigger than the cat Ian and June, a couple from Aberfeldy, saw as they let their dog out one night. 'The security light went on and Ian saw a very large cat which turned to look at him before running out of the garden. It had yellow slits for eyes, short hair on its face, but the rest of body had long hair. The whole cat was extremely sleek and very glossy – in really good nick.' He was able compare its size to their Labrador as the latter vainly chased it. 'Our dog measures twenty inches to the shoulder, and I reckon the cat was about two inches taller; the dog's tail is fifteen inches, and the cat's tail was about half as long again.'

The opportunity to compare the sizes of ABCs against measurable surroundings occasionally presents itself: in Leicester two workers saw a big black cat on their industrial estate, and used a pallet behind it to gauge the size accurately of the animal. 'It had a three foot six to four foot long body and a two foot long tail curved in an 'S' shape.' [8]

The people travelling by car from Falkirk, whom I quoted in Chapter 1, gauged the size of the cat they saw by the height of the fence it was travelling beside. 'It must have been three feet high and four to five feet long.' [9]

It was Nick Pounder's extraordinary experience which definitively established the size of at least one Dorset big cat – he could compare it with three other species of animal. He was driving along a lane near Askerswell with his brother-in-law, Jerry, and 'we were pottering slowly along, chatting, as it was a beautiful evening – when a domestic cat crossed the road in front of us.' To their surprise, this was followed a few seconds later, in the same place, by a fox, and then – amazingly – a badger.

'Jerry was just saying what a lot of wildlife there was about when his expression changed and he said "Look at that!" A coal-black cat at least as big as an Alsatian came out of the hedge in the same place and followed the route that the procession had taken across the road – we were just flabbergasted. It had a long, thin tail which curved to the ground and up again. We saw it go across the field towards Eggardon, but neither of us felt like getting out of the car!' [10]

## 'At one time great, but at another small…'

Whatever means of comparison is used, one thing is sure – compared to, say, a domestic cat an ABC is an impressive, sometimes frightening, size.

In this ABCs compare with monsters of folklore and legend. Perhaps the latter are a race-memory, for on a purely literal level the pre-Ice Age animals that our ancestors hunted, such as mammoths and sabre-toothed tigers, were a third again bigger, or more, than their modern animal equivalents.

Leaving literal prehistoric species aside, the folklorist Ruth Tongue has noted that tradition is always ready to enlarge, sometimes monstrously, the size of anything or anyone whom it feels important. 'Early gods and heroes often become giants.' [11] Finn McCool in Ireland, Arthur and Guinevere in England, become bigger in the mythic landscape. 'Even Macbeth's grave, near Dunsinane is many yards long, and Macbeth was a contemporary of William the Conqueror. In fact, in legend the characters are like those in the Bayeux Tapestry – the important ones are large and the unimportant ones are little.' [12]

In folk and fairytales, too, the themes of bigness and smallness, size-changes and relative proportions are endlessly reworked – as in *Alice in Wonderland.* But in these traditional narratives the reverse is more often true: the important ones are little.

Cinderella, the small, despised one, achieves the grandeur of a princess. The lowly positions of the traditional characters – the poor wood-cutter, the daft younger son, the penniless traveller, the simple youngest sister are inverted: they become the highest in the land, the winner of the princess, the finder of the treasure. Similarly in Irish folklore the smallest bird, the wren, is 'the king of all birds.'

In *Jack and the Beanstalk*, for instance, the bean is as small and insignificant as Jack is poor, young and unimportant. The giant is huge and powerful, yet Jack defeats him. The point of the story is the comparison between the actual and metaphorical sizes of the two. Their two worlds are linked by a daimonic item – the bean – which, though small and worthless, has the capacity for monumental size-change as its essential nature, as anyone who grows runner beans can attest.

## The Lambton Worm

The story of the Lambton Worm[13] from Fatfield Parish, Washington, in Northumberland describes very powerfully the daimonic realm of changing and significant sizes. I quote it in its entirety because it has a direct application to the ABC phenomenon, and I shall refer to it again later:

Around the time of the Crusades (in some accounts) John Lambton, the young heir to Lambton Hall, was fishing on the River Wear one Sunday morning, while all the other villagers and residents were at mass in Brugeford Chapel. He caught a small, black worm-like creature with the head of a salamander and needle sharp teeth, and nine holes along each side of its mouth. As he wondered what to do with the creature, an old man appeared from behind him, and warned him not to throw the creature back into the river. 'It bodes no good for you but you must not cast it back into the river, you must keep it and do with it what you will.' At this the old man walked away, disappearing as quickly as he had appeared.

Walking home Lambton threw the catch into an ancient well, forever after known as Worm's Well. Years passed and John Lambton went off to the crusades, and with every passing year the worm grew in strength in its deep, dark hole. One night the worm, in full maturity, slipped out of the well and wrapped itself three times around a rocky island in the middle of the river. It had no legs or wings, but a thick muscled body that rippled as it moved. Its head was large and its gaping maw bristled with razor sharp teeth, venomous vapours trailed from its nostrils and mouth as it breathed.

During the day the worm stayed in mid stream and at night it came back to land and coiled itself three times around a knoll known as Worm Hill, leaving spiral patterns in the soft earth.

However the beast eventually became hungry and started to rampage around the countryside, always returning to Worm Hill or Worm's Rock in the River Wear. It took small lambs and sheep and ate them whole, and it tore open cows' udders with its razor teeth to get at the milk, which it could smell from miles away. Some brave villagers tried to kill the beast but were torn to pieces with its razor fangs.

After seven years had passed, John Lambton returned from the crusades, and when he heard of the plight of his village he went to the wise woman who lived in Brugeford to gain her advice. She told him to have a suit of armour wrought with razor sharp spearheads studded throughout its surface. However she told him that if he slew the beast he must also put to death the first thing he met as he crossed the threshold of Lambton Hall; otherwise 'three times three generations of Lambtons would not die in their beds.'

Next day John Lambton, clad in the specially-made armour, engaged in battle with the dragon in midstream. The more tightly the worm clasped him the more it cut itself to pieces, pieces which the torrent swept away so they could not re-grow together, and finally John despatched it.

Unfortunately the servants forgot to release a dog from the house to meet him as he had arranged, and as John passed over the threshold of the hall his father rushed to greet him. He could not kill his father, so the vow was broken and for nine generations after none of the Lambtons died in their beds. It is said that the last one died while crossing over Brugeford Bridge a hundred and forty years ago.

The story affords a variety of interpretations: its structure is mythic, yet its specific locality and time have the flavour of memorate; the nightly depredations on sheep and cows mirror the attacks attributed to modern ABCs; and in its razor action on cows' udders we even hear an echo of the animal mutilations of recent decades in the American mid-west and elsewhere.

## The size of daimons

The worm bears all the characteristics of a daimon. It is a tiny thing, a negligible detail: yet suddenly everyone becomes aware that it is in fact a huge and menacing monster.

It is contained at first within the small, round shrine of the well: but the picture is then inverted, for when neglected and ignored it grows large and wraps itself around the huge, circular shrine of the knoll.

In common with many creatures in folklore it demonstrates that the intermediate, daimonic world is not one of fixed largeness or smallness: it is one of unstable and fluid dimensions – big becomes small and small may seem big. I was reminded of the words of one of the *Sidhe* to a Sligo man: 'I am bigger than I appear to you now. We can make the old young, the big small, the small big.' [14]

Big things may be tiny because far away or small things may be big because near by, and each may change from one to the other as the onlooker changes position. The confusion, we are to understand, is just a matter of perspective. The emphasis on extreme and significant size changes in folktales gives a clue to the nature of the daimons' world. The Otherworld – the *anima mundi* as the Greeks knew it – it seems, is continuous with this world but is a different perspective on it.

The same condition of wildly fluctuating sizes apparently characterises ABCs. But what I had perceived at first as a major problem now became a motif drawing attention to the daimonic aspects of perspective: how it changes, and where it places us in the landscape.

The more I – and the ranks of earnest witnesses – failed to bring them into a single focus, the more their varying, and therefore indeterminate, sizes seemed to point to a daimonic aspect to the mystery big cats.

# Chapter 15

# Traditional daimons and ABCs

'I mean Negative Capability, that is when man is capable of being in uncertainties, Mysteries, doubts, without any irritable reaching after fact and reason.'

John Keats (1795–1821)[1]

The daimonic perspective, considered so necessary by the Neoplatonists, began to seem a liberating way of approaching the mystery of Britain's ABCs.

Rather than try to define, categorize, classify or explain them, I decided to adopt another method of rendering ABCs intelligible: the one which, I was beginning to perceive, was exemplified by the daimonic world itself.

I would explore rather than solve, include rather than exclude; I would present the remaining data assembled about ABCs in a more 'daimonic' way, adopting a loosely associative approach, allowing natural similarities to emerge between ABCs and the daimonic world, and between different ABCs themselves.

In short I would attempt an imaginative – even poetic – standpoint which might make better sense of their irregularities and paradoxes than any 'irritable reaching after fact and reason', as Keats put it. In this way they would not so much be 'explained' as made intelligible.

## Home-grown daimons

If ABCs are a variety of native British daimon, they have emerged into a landscape already brimful of these intermediate beings: pixies, gnomes, boggarts, Herne the Hunter, elves, lake monsters, 'white ladies', wyrms, and so on; in Scotland there were seal-folk, brownies and glaistigs; in Wales the Twylyth Teg. Less localised daimons such as Will-O'-the-Wisp, Robin Goodfellow and the most adaptable of all – Puck – weave their way in and out of myth, folklore and literature.

## An Irish ABC

Ireland was, and is, home to its own traditional daimonic beings – such as the *puca*, analogous to our Puck, and the *Sidhe* (Shee), reputed to be the pre-Celtic inhabitants of the land. An encounter with one of the inhabitants of what the writer Dermot Mac

Manus calls 'the Middle Kingdom' – and the Neoplatonists called the *anima mundi* – was an everyday occurrence in his native country and he gives numerous examples.[2]

For instance there was the cool fairy a friend of his in County Carlow saw as she was herding cows through a gate. This daimon 'looked fresh and young.' He passed in front of a cow which tossed its head at him, and as it did so 'he looked round at it, in what seemed to her a friendly and possessive way, and gave it a light tap on the nose with a switch of osier' – freshly plucked, for it had a couple of green leaves at the tip – which he carried in his right hand. 'He then glanced quickly but intently at the girl,' before stepping over a ditch and into a grassy bank. 'He seemed to walk into the earth with the same ease that an ordinary human being would walk through a bead curtain.'

His tangible specificity, quick, intent glance and the way he melts into the field boundary are reminiscent of a modern ABC. But another strange Irish 'monster', seen in 1921, was virtually identical to one of our big cats. 'A respectable, intelligent elderly man,' Thady Byrne, had been alarmed to see what he called a 'monster', and reported the incident to the writer Edith Somerville, who took down the details:

'He had been going home through the woods where he spotted it sitting on a rock looking at him. He described it as "Black, and as big as a greyhound, but it was like a cat. It had long bristles cocking out from each side of its jaws, but not a braid of hair upon its tail. It had a great jowl on it, like a bulldog, and a great wide chest and shoulders, and he tapered away to his tail. You'd hear him barking at night in the woods, and the bark was like the squeal of a seagull."

> 'I asked, "Did you go fast past him?"
>
> '"You may say I did!" said Thady indignantly. "I thought it was hardly I'd bring my life with me! It's the way I am thinking, it come in off the torpedo boat."
>
> 'By Sunday afternoon Thady had summoned up all the lads of the country to bring their dogs to hunt the monster. The hunt had no results, save that the dogs put out a fallow deer and found two foxes. The creature, whatever it was, was seen at different times for about a week, by reliable men, even though their accounts of it were difficult to reconcile.
>
> 'Then, after a few days, we heard it had killed all the priest's fowl, and that Paddy Neill's dogs had hunted it for a long way, and never came up with it. Finally, it was said to have been "screeching through the country, and running in the fields, quicker than a bird, ten miles away".' [3]

The regular components of modern cat-flaps are all there: the alarming encounter during an otherwise unexceptional day; the animal's unafraid posture and calm appraisal of the witness; its blackness, dog-like size and feline appearance; the screeching by night; the depredations on farm stock; the irreconcilable sightings by unimpeachable witnesses; the fruitless hunt; and even an 'explanation' similar to the urban legends surrounding American GIs' alleged mascots, that it had escaped from one of the wartime 'torpedo boats'. Familiar too is its preternatural speed – 'quicker than a bird' – and final disappearance.

As Miss Somerville concluded: 'The end of the monster, like its beginning, was Mystery.'

## ABCs and threshold: gateways, portals, liminal zones

The gateway where the Carlow fairy appeared is the kind of literal threshold or liminal zone where, as I mentioned in Chapter 6, the daimons of the past were apt to make themselves known, and where ABCs, too, have occasionally been encountered.

One ABC appeared momentarily between the opening and slamming of a literal door, but long enough to give a 'human-like stare' to a woman who recalled in detail how the alarming event occurred out of the blue on a normal, workaday morning:

'It was the winter of 1968–9 and I was ready to leave for school, so it must have been around 8.30 in the morning. I opened the back door and saw, on the back step, a huge cat which was just about ready to rummage through the dustbin which sat to the right of the door.

> 'I got such a shock that I slammed the door shut immediately. I didn't tell anyone as I knew that they wouldn't believe me. When my brother and I left for school about five minutes later there was no sign of the cat.' [4]

The ABC that two boys met on Exmoor in the summer of 1983 was also glimpsed through a gate. They said it was jet-black apart from a dirty white front. It turned in a flash at the moment it saw them and bounded back down into the ravine and vanished. [5]

Laura Jones was bringing in her pet goats one evening and everything was normal except that she noticed that the goats were acting 'a bit strangely… Then, out of the corner of my eye,' she said:

> 'I saw a large cat just by the gateway. It was about the same size as an Alsatian and black, but there was no mistaking that it was a cat. I think it was a panther. It walked forward a bit and then crouched as if to pounce. I just froze. We all froze – the goats too. It was like that for about a minute. Then it just got up and melted back into the shadows and went back up the lane. I could see its outline against the hedge. It didn't run or anything – it just slunk off the same way cats walk. It was really creepy.'

## The Wild Hunt

There is an interesting link between gateways, the haunt of daimons, and the Wild Hunt of Northern European myth, where the god Woden sweeps through the country

*A black ABC passed across this gateway near Burton Bradstock in Dorset in February 2005*

on a spectral hunt. In Denmark, traditionally, gates were opened for him on St John's Day, which were heard slamming as he passed by.[6]

The sound of thundering feet or hooves is a feature that also crops up now and again in ABC reports. For instance David Spencer was taking the family dog out for an early morning walk and had just opened the gate to cross the lane adjacent to his house, when he heard the sound of pounding feet coming down the hill side opposite. Thinking it was a horse and noticing the field gate was open, he was just about to cross the road to close it when he saw it was not a horse but a black feline creature of about the size of a Labrador dog, but lower to the ground. As it bounded down the frozen field and through the gateway, he realised it was heading straight for him. He shouted and the creature swerved some six feet away and ran down the lane.[7] Stan Windsor, too, was able to track the progress of two strange felines he found feeding on a carcass, by the sound as of a stampede the other side of a hill.[8]

## Streams and rivers

Rivers and streams often provide the daimonic threshold – and divide the witness from the ABC they are looking at. A fisherman on the River Mole near its junction with the Taw, in Devon, saw an ABC loping along the river bank opposite from where he was fishing. 'It stopped and stared at me, and I thought I hope it can't swim. After a minute or so, during which I sat very still, it just went off on its way.'

A Leicestershire woman was similarly at the confluence of several boundaries – on a narrow footpath by a stream, at the kissing gates – when she saw a big cat of a 'golden honey colour with grey in its fur, long legs with very large paws, and long tail which curled up at the bottom.' In the manner of a conventional puma it also had a three-inch black tip at the end of its tail.[9]

## Opening a portal

Liminal places imply that rules exist – that appearances of Otherworld beings are not simply random but have particular places of access, and limits which are defined by boundaries. These conventions may be used not just to escape from such beings, but to invoke them.

Harry was sitting on a gate very early one summer's morning, in the garden of his country cottage in Wales, when, to his astonishment, he saw what he had no hesitation in calling a fairy.

He had woken early because the family pet cat had gone missing and he was worried about it. He went outside, and wandered about searching fruitlessly, and then despondently climbed the gate that led into an orchard, which extended downhill to a river.

> 'I was just sitting on the top bar and rather hopelessly calling the
> cat when a being ran past me, skipping lightly and fleetingly down
> the hill through the orchard to the river. It was about the size of
> an eight-year-old child.'

The word Harry had been calling as he sat on the gate was the cat's name – 'Grimalkin.'[10]

It seems that physical factors were included in whatever mechanism that caused the fairy to appear. Not only was Harry near a gate, he was actually on it; not only was he physically in a liminal zone, but it was a liminal time – the break of day. If any conditions were likely to trigger a liminal creature it was these. But in addition he uttered a magical word – Grimalkin, the traditional name of the witch's cat, her shape-changing familiar.

A being appeared momentarily in response to his unwitting invocation, and, like the cat the two Exmoor boys saw, moved with preternatural speed and fluency downhill to a river.

## 'Oh whistle, and I'll come to you, my lad.'[11]

Summoning a liminal creature – such as a witch's familiar – was traditionally done in the way Harry unwittingly had: simply by calling it.

One such being reportedly appeared before a group of witches in Somerset in 1664: 'On Thursday night before Whitsunday last, about the same place met Catharine Green... and Henry Walter, and being met they called out "Robin". Upon which instantly appeared a little man in black clothes…'[12]

Among ABC reports too, a sudden or unusual noise or call sometimes seems to precipitate their appearance.

People who see ABCs are very often walking their dogs – and very often, like Harry, calling them or whistling. Was it only curiosity that brought this ABC to the woman walking dog on the hills on the edge of Oakham, in Rutland, in the early evening in June 2001? She called her dog, and as she did so a 'large, panther-like creature' stood up in long grass close to her. She was shocked and ran out of the field.' [13]

Donald Mackenzie was out hunting foxes in the Scottish Highlands with his son James, when their spotlight picked out an ABC emerging from River Naver. 'It ran across the fields and we chased it in the Land Rover, but it was moving at an incredible speed. I stopped and it stopped. I whistled and it started coming back towards us... ' [14]

A Cambridge writer, Jeremy Holford-Miettinen, had also noticed a connection between whistling and ABCs. One of his informants, 'Dr A.', described an event which had occurred in May 1983 when he had taken an American friend to Thetford Forest, hoping to see red squirrels:

> 'We parked, walked up a Forestry Commission track and sat on a fallen tree enjoying the sun. My friend was whistling. I happened to look across the track to the right, looking towards the forest, and saw this animal under the conifers about thirty five or forty feet away. I thought it was a dog then I realized it wasn't – it was a cat with its head raised. It was listening to the whistling.
>
> 'It came about three or four feet closer. My friend saw it and stopped. The cat watched us. She whistled again and it came towards us again. By then it was clear of some undergrowth and we saw how big it was. My friend said "You have mountain lions in Britain?" I think I said, "No, it's a feral cat". She said, "That's stupid. I know a mountain lion when I see one." By now it was a lot nearer, about twenty-five feet from us. She whistled and it stopped moving and listened.
>
> 'It was mid-brown and about four foot long in the body. I didn't notice the length of the tail. It had large ears, dark eyes and white fur under the chin and round the mouth.
>
> 'My friend was getting very worried and I suggested we should slowly back away but she believed that might encourage the cat to attack us. We stared at the cat; the cat stared at us. Then it turned round and went back into the conifers.'

Dr A. gives an accurate description of a puma observed at very close range; and his friend who, unusually, was familiar with native American pumas confirmed that that was exactly what it was. Yet its behaviour in being drawn to the whistled tune was not exactly typical of any big cat, certainly not the ultra-secretive puma.

One of the most interesting events concerned not human whistling but a 'silent' dog whistle. It occurred on the edge of a village a few miles north of Cambridge, and Mr Holford-Miettinen took it down verbatim from his informant, 'Mr S.':

'At about six p.m. I took Micky [his Alsatian dog] down to the common for a run like most evenings. We got to the bottom of the common, right by where the bushes are. Micky went tearing off; he likes to go mad, and I let him…It was getting a bit bloody cold, I had just a jacket, so I called Mick and the bugger never paid any notice. So I blew. I have this whistle you can't hear – we can't – but it makes Micky bloody sit up. I was whistling and there was this noise, and I shouted 'Mick, Mick' and whistled – and this head came out of the bushes….And it wasn't a dog. This was a cat face; round, you know. It was a big bugger, too. We looked at each other, then I thought Christ that's a lion or something…Brown, darkish sort of brown but not very dark. Not black. Like a cat not a dog. I reckon the ears were flat back. Then I bloody cleared off – it was too bloody near, fifteen or twenty foot – and so did the bloody cat.

'I got leery of the common then, and I took Micky down the other way for a week. Only there was nobody else ever saw any lion or whatever it was, so I went back to the previous route.

'It was about the same time of evening again, only we was on the far side by the old hedge. Micky was going mad, same as he did most nights – then I couldn't see him and I reckoned he'd gone through the hedge and I'd be half the night getting him back. I had a think – you know, thought twice – about blowing the whistle; but I'd got a sheath knife and a stick with me, so I blew.

'And then – not right away, maybe after another blow – this bugger comes out of the hedge-side. That's not more than twenty yards off. Bit less, could be. It came out, walked out, and looked at me. I reckon my knee could be level with the shoulders, and it was long, a bit longer than Micky…I was watching it for a minute and a half at least and it didn't come any nearer. It didn't look angry or fierce… it was looking interested.

'Then Micky come down the common barking and it went into the hedge – wham! I mean one jump and it was in the hedge. I went back a day or more later and paced the jump. I reckon about eight foot. Just jumped, no trouble.'

The witnesses in these incidents felt sure the cats in question were attracted to, or interested by, the whistling. The appearance of Mr S.'s cat on two separate occasions seems to diminish the possibility of coincidence. The immediacy with which it appeared the second time – after only the second blow – suggests it was already there, just waiting for the signal. The way it remained looking at Mr S. for a minute-and-a-half, was curious, as though it was perhaps waiting for another signal.

## Traditional whistlings-up

It is possible to speculate endlessly about the psychology of ABCs. Better known to history and folklore, however, are other results of unguarded whistling – for, traditionally, whistling may dissolve a barrier which keeps two worlds apart. This old belief lingers in the superstitions of sailors, who, in Northumberland and elsewhere, will not go to sea if on the way to their boat they hear someone whistling, believing that it portends death.

The belief that whistling can produce otherworldly beings is very widespread. In the Marquesas Islands of the South Pacific Paul Attallah, a transplanted American, once innocently made the mistake of whistling at night. This completely terrified his native-born companion, who told him that the act could literally 'whistle up a ghost.'[15] In Ireland a priest restored his drowned brother to life that way: 'Father Dominick took out his breviary and began to read. After a time he whistled, and began to read again. He whistled a second time, and returned to reading. Upon his whistling a third time [his brother's] spirit appeared in the doorway.'[16]

Not just human whistling, but the whistling of wind has traditionally heralded the arrival of anomalous and otherworldly beings. The American Bigfoot or Sasquatch is often accompanied by a sound like this, as were the fairies of former times. Irish country people took off their hats in acknowledgement of the fairies that both they – and the Scots – believed travelled in sudden gusts of wind, the *gaoth sidhe,* and particularly in the small whirlwinds that seized and whirled the hay on hot days of hay-making. In Co. Roscommon up until the 1940s at least parents instructed their children to lie on the ground and avert their eyes when one of these winds whirled across the meadow.[17] Whirlwinds carry an added symbolic freight for they are the invisible (wind) made visible (a column of hay) – and as such may also be vehicles of revelation, just as God spoke to Job from out of a whirlwind.

In Devon Nigel Brierly noted that 'a peculiar "whistling" sound' had been heard and reported to him by several farmers when they had known that 'the animal has been killing sheep on their farm.' Mr Brierly also observed: 'This noise has been heard when the animals have been moving at high speed over open fields.'

A sound as of wind heralded this animal, seen by Jeff Crook at a liminal point, the corner of the house – again momentarily, but unforgettably:

> 'One autumn afternoon three years ago, I was relaxing on the patio and enjoying a beer while grilling some steaks, when I was overcome by the strangest feeling or compulsion to walk to the corner of the house and look into the front yard. At the same time, I heard a rather strange rushing sound, like a strong wind – only there was no wind.
>
> 'Just as I reached the corner of the house and the wind noise reached its loudest level, a large grey cat, about three-feet tall at the shoulder and with very long legs, bounded across the drive and raced over the top of the hill bordering our property. With its disappearance, the rushing sound of wind also faded into silence.

'I gave chase and reached the hilltop within seconds, but the cat (or whatever it was) was nowhere to be seen.'[18]

## Clothes and guises

The daimonic world is shape-shifting but not formless; many conventions are observed in matters of appearance. The colours of fairies' clothes are traditionally green, red or brown – the colours of nature. Black and white also feature in their garments. The Co. Carlow fairy I mentioned above was elaborately dressed in 'a black cap turned up in front, rather like a sou'wester but neater, of much finer material and more closely fitting, and a bright red coat which was buttoned up in front.'

A superficial glance at the many shades and patterns ABCs see fit to wear gives the impression that – outside the normal pure black and smooth fawn – there are no rules which govern the arrangement of anomalous combinations of colours. Indeed I have already quoted Dr Shuker's protest – 'The British big cat would need to be nothing short of a shape-shifter to account for the immense variety of felids reported.'[19] Quite so, but a closer look reveals that there are a few strange features described again and again by witnesses which imply at least some minor conventions of dress even among apparent shape-shifters.

Many black ABCs sport white bibs. Witnesses never report the white paws, or white-blazed face most common among black domestic cats – or indeed among border collies – but they often observe a white patch, spot or slash of white under the ABC's chin or on its chest. For instance in Norfolk a mother and her two children watched just such a cat strolling nonchalantly across the field – a feline five feet long, 'dark brown or black, with a white patch under its chin.'[20]

Similar animals live in the Lake District. 'The witness was only ten feet from it and got a really good look. It was a slender cat, twenty inches to the shoulder, and jet black with white on its chest. He subsequently spent a long time searching through pictures of big cats but could not find one that looked like the cat he saw.'[21] Chris Johnston who investigates ABC reports in Lancashire was not wholly surprised: 'I have had three other sightings of cats with white on their chests.'

Devon has its share of these strangely-marked felines too. Teenagers Wayne Adams and Marcus White saw a huge, feline animal. 'I looked over a gate and saw the animal about ten yards away,' said Wayne. It stared straight at the boys before it 'sort of pranced away.' It was 'jet-black, apart from white markings on its chest.'[22] A Plymouth man hunting rabbits on Bodmin Moor with five friends sent his dog into a patch of scrub to flush them out and was amazed when a cat bigger than his springer spaniel emerged instead. 'It just came out,' he said, 'a puma-like animal [sic] – black with white flashing on its front… '[23]

The creature Gill Douglas-Mann and her husband saw was 'definitely not a dog or a fox. It ran in the distinctive way cats do and we were only about thirty feet away.' She was digging rhubarb with her husband when their terrier Jack, began barking and ran off towards a hedgerow where 'he started yelping horribly.' She followed him, whereupon a feline the size of a collie dog came loping out of the hedge and ran off. 'It was jet-black with a white bib and it kept looking round and back towards us as it ran. We were both gobsmacked. It was very surreal.' [24] Trevor Beer, the well-known Devon writer and ABC researcher was not so surprised, commenting: 'A lot of black cats have been seen with this distinctive white bib marking.'

Sightings of such animals are most common in Scotland. The ABC that Donald Mackenzie and his son saw while out hunting foxes, and which responded to their whistle, had the traditional red eyes of a black dog, but was 'a big cat the size of an Alsatian, dark coloured with a white chest... '

Perhaps this is not surprising for similarly marked felines have been well-known there for at least two centuries, but have never before been identified with the zoo animals we customarily compare them to nowadays.

The Highlanders of the past called such an animal the *cait sith* – the 'fairy cat'. The witnesses that the nineteenth century folklorist, J.G. Campbell, interviewed described it as being 'as large as a dog, black with a white spot on its breast.' [25]

One such white-bibbed, black animal seen in Scotland in 1995 seemed to confirm such an incommensurable identity for a modern ABC. Mark Fraser visited a couple who had seen a black ABC with a white throat patch. The animal had simply 'disappeared' when it reached a certain point in their meadow. Mark, too, remained mystified: 'I've been to see this point and there is nowhere, really, that it could have gone.' [26]

## Pointed ears

Pointed ears used to be fashionable among daimons – elves, pixies, Pan and even Lucifer are depicted as sporting them, whereas – apart from that strange being Mr Spock[27] – modern daimons such as 'greys' tend to be boringly deficient in facial detail generally, and frequently have no ears at all.

It has fallen to some ABCs to keep up the tradition of having noticeably pointed ears, in defiance of the rounded ears of their zoological leopard and puma counterparts.

The ABC that Ayrshire gamekeeper Stanley Windsor took a shot at was 'jet-black, larger than an Alsatian and with small pointed ears.' [28] An Inverness-shire man opened his back door on to an animal he had never seen before: a three-foot long cat, it had a smooth, black coat and 'small pointed ears.' [29]

Mark Fraser's huge and constantly growing database of sightings contains many more such descriptions. 'We do get a lot of pointed-ear reports', he notes. 'Again it is a factor that makes these cats different from the expected, known species.' Typical of his highly observant informants was the man who rang him to say he had farmed near Tealby in Lincolnshire all his life, 'but had had only one encounter with a mystery feline,' Mark recorded, 'and that was out shooting five years ago.'

> 'He was approaching a group of rabbits about thirty-five yards
> away on his hands and knees. In between him and the rabbits was
> a large clump of nettles which he had in mind to crawl up to and
> hide behind. But as he got to ten yards of the clump, this ruddy

great jet-black cat jumped up and just stared at him. Obviously both after the same rabbits. The farmer in his shock and panic fired his twelve-bore shotgun over the cat's head, which in turn ran.

'He says it was not a leopard as it was too small, and there were definitely no markings on its sleek coat. In fact his impression of the animal was of a cheetah, but black. It did have pointed ears, and was as big as a Labrador. He mentioned the possibility of a hybrid to me.

'He then got a magnificent view of it running along the top of a ridge outlined against the sky, and likened its running to a race horse, where the two front legs meet the two back ones when running.' [30]

Sarah Miles's Sussex ABC had 'pointed, erect ears,' [31] while in Somerset Jason Moy, aged fifteen, and his sister watched another black ABC cross their path. 'It was about the size of a German Shepherd dog – not that tall but longer, with really sleek fur and little pointy ears on the top of its head.' [32]

At the other end of the country, in Yorkshire, witnesses had time to study a panther-like creature 'slightly larger than an Alsatian dog' wandering through the woods when it stopped to look at them before running off through the trees. It was 'huge, very black and shiny, with a big tail curled up' and 'pointy ears.' [33] And to the North West, in Cheshire, the ears of another black ABC were described as 'small, triangular, pointed.' [34] In Derbyshire Kevin Tryner was walking his dog at the old Ripley Pit site when he spotted a black cat the same size as an Alsatian, which 'just looked at me and walked away, vanishing into the trees.' It had 'a curled tail, yellow eyes and pointed ears.' [35]

Moreover it is not only the black ABCs which display this unusual feature. Mrs Jewitt's ABC was golden fawn in colour but with 'pointed upright ears!' [36] Angela Partridge was struck by the size as well as the shape of the ears on the ABC she encountered – it was 'creamy beige with tiny, pointed ears.' [37] Two dog walkers reached a liminal place in their route – the point where the road terminated in a footbridge across a canal – and saw a cat, bigger than their own Labradors, but 'chocolate brown in colour with pointed ears' walking along the other bank.[38]

I could go on, but suffice it to say that every county in Britain has a range of ABCs adorned with what was the unmistakable badge of the daimon in times past – unusually pointed ears.

### 'Quis est iste qui venit?' [39]

The occasional clear-cut picture of what could pass for an escaped zoo animal is nearly always jumbled-up by its anomalous details, odd shape or colours, or unconventional behaviour. The only definite thing to be said about ABCs' appearance is that they seem to be sufficiently like their zoo equivalents to be recognisable, but not sufficiently like them to be identifiable as such. The panther and puma forms are like the clothes more traditional daimons wear – familiar but timeless and differing in detail and from individual to individual.

Could it be said, therefore, that ABCs are related to the daimons of the past? Are they perhaps a modern re-working of the white-bibbed *cait sith*, the fairy cats of the Highland Scots? Could they be descendants of the early twentieth century fairy that walked calmly into the earthen bank? It is amusing – and perhaps instructive – to glimpse aspects of the old-fashioned daimons in many descriptions of modern ABCs.

Moreover, while ABC witnesses have scant time to analyse their own reactions to the bizarre creature they are looking at, those reactions are sometimes more in keeping with a brush with a traditional denizen of MacManus's Middle Kingdom than a literal big cat. 'I had to rub my eyes,' explained June Edwards about her sighting in Somerset.[40] Jeanette Forester found the huge panther-like animal, 'black with a gingery tinge,' that crossed the path twenty feet in front of her 'mesmerising';[41] while John Bilboe, who encountered an ABC near Ormskirk in Lancashire, noted 'there was an air of mystery about it that was hard to understand.'[42]

# Chapter 16

# Blackness and shine: ABCs and modern daimons

## Men in black

While some ABCs bear the insignia of daimons of the past, when it comes to their eccentric behaviour they have more in common with some of the modern daimons I mentioned in Chapter 13.

For instance I sometimes fancied I saw, in some lights, a resemblance between ABCs and 'men in black'. It was a resemblance in only superficial details, but in the daimonic world, as with Jack's bean, it is the unimportant details which often turn out to be most significant.

'Men in black', or MIBs, are one of the most peculiar and intriguing aspects of the UFO phenomenon. As well as being frighteningly sinister they are unintentionally funny. They sometimes visit those who see mysterious, craft-type objects in the sky (and sometimes even before the witness has told anyone else of the experience) claiming to be from a source of military or government authority and telling them in menacing style to forget all about it. They usually come in pairs and wear new-looking, but oddly old-fashioned black suits; their black hair is often worn in the smooth, slick hairstyle of the 1950s; in the USA they often drive shiny, black Cadillacs of an out-of-date model and in the UK too they are transported in black cars which despite their outdated design look brand new and extremely highly polished.

Their movements, speech and manner seem mechanical and stiff, and they sometimes 'run down' becoming increasingly slow and unsteady. Most curiously, their knowledge of everyday social mores is absent. MIB lore is full of amusing examples: for instance they are not sure what to do with food or drink – on being offered a plate of jelly by a Minnesota UFO witness one tried to drink it. Eventually, she said 'I had to show him how to eat it with a spoon.' [1]

Unusually for modern daimons, and in common with ABCs, MIBs interact on a personal even social level. But the quality that MIBs' clothes and cars most obviously share with ABCs is their studied blackness.

## Pure blackness

When ABCs are black they can be almost unnaturally black. Witnesses almost never remark on one of the most noticeable details of a black panther's pelage, which is that despite its dark coat you can still see the spots underneath, revealing its true identity as a black-coated leopard.

The man, for instance, who encountered a black, panther-like ABC one bright morning near Braunston in Rutland was close enough to the creature and observant enough to notice the entrancing detail that its fur 'was covered in water droplets from the dew on the long grass and hedge' – and yet he did not notice any leopard rosettes in its black coat.[2]

ABCs are usually described in the uncompromising way Mike Attwood did. He spotted the beast in broad daylight walking across a piece of open land close to his home in Gloucestershire. He was in no doubt 'it was a panther by the way it moved, and in the length and curve of its tail. And then there was the size and the blackness of it. It was as black as night.'[3] Diane Davies also noted the intensification of darkness: 'The road was grey-black but against it it was like a black hole. As though it was sucking up all the light. But yet there was a sheen to it.'[4]

James Richardson's ABC, he said, 'stopped and hissed at me. It was a panther with a jet-black, shiny coat ... '[5]

Ray and Evelyn Robson 'stood for ages' watching an animal dubbed by the press 'The Beast of Tynedale' strolling along a dry-stone wall. Evelyn said 'it was absolutely huge and pure black.' Ray added: 'It is the gospel truth. My wife and I were so shocked. It had a beautiful, shining fur coat. It was gorgeous.'[6]

Equally gorgeous was the 'panther-type' creature Jan Edwards saw in a remote area of the Pennines:  'This cat walked lazily through a field in broad daylight... It was jet-black, and with the sun shining down on it, it looked like liquid velvet... absolutely beautiful.'[7]

Many ABCs are seen in bright light, or at very close quarters, or both, and yet the most common description of their colouration is the unambiguous term 'jet-black.'

## Shine

'Liquid velvet' was Jan Edwards' evocative expression. Many witnesses are similarly entranced by the lustre of the big cat they are looking at – as Ray Robson put it – the 'shining fur coat'; or in the words of the Dorset witness Karen Rees, 'its glossy, glossy fur.'

As well as blackness, ABCs share with MIBs and their cars the quality of shininess. Shine, you could say, is the favourite daimonic texture. It extends to UFOs which glint in the sun, and the metallic fabric their inhabitants often wear. It is easy to see why: it is reflective. It confuses – it de-literalises – the surface of things. At its extreme point you see no object at all, but only your own face. In the tangible world it is both a literal change of perspective and a metaphor for it.

## Running in a crouching position

The robotic stiffness of MIBs contrasts, of course, with the extreme sinuosity of ABCs, which I have discussed in an earlier chapter. But, inevitably there were exceptions that refused to be caged by my generalisations. A farmer from Chittlehampton, Devon, was amazed to see a creamy-brown, puma-like cat, bigger than his own sheepdog, climb a large tree and disappear into the foliage. 'It seemed to walk up the side of the tree in a curious manner, without bending its legs!' [8] Mark Fraser has come across similarly odd descriptions of ABC deportment: 'One witness told me that "its legs seemed to be stuck on the four corners of its body and moved stiffly".'

But if they do not generally have the co-ordination problems of MIBs they do share some of their behavioural ones. One of the ABCs' most curious habits is that of running in a crouching position.

Leopards, pumas and domestic cats will run close to the ground for a short distance if taking evasive action, such as running for cover, or trying to remain concealed while stalking prey, but it is not a normal way of crossing country. And yet a woman out walking her dog near Lucklaw, Scotland, was one of many witnesses who report this unusual behaviour. She observed a huge black cat, at least twice the size of her Labrador dog, for about five minutes crossing a field about fifty yards in front of her. The cat had 'a very long body and a long tail, and kept its body close to the ground as it travelled over the field.'

Another witness, from Little Brickhill, south of Milton Keynes, wrote: ' I drove behind a big black cat... the thing that stuck in my mind was the length of its tail. It ran crouching, almost touching the road.' An Ayrshire ABC performed this difficult manoeuvre with ease even when being chased by a dog – 'it ran low down to the ground, very agile, much faster than the dog.' [9] So did the ABC which crossed the road by a disused quarry at midnight on Midsummer's Eve 1999: it was 'about Alsatian size, but low to the ground.' [10]

Some ABC investigators have speculated that witnesses may have mistaken mere short-leggedness for the crouching movement, and that the animals in question might be otters! This, however, does not seem plausibly to explain any of the animals seen, least of all the one observed in broad daylight, by three men beating during a weekend pheasant shoot on Taymount Estate in Perthshire. Sandy McKay described the beast he saw as:

> 'a huge, black cat which was running, crouched low, under the trees. It was no more than ten yards from me so I had a clear view of it for just a few seconds. I was shocked at its size. It had a cat's head and it was quite thin. It had a long tail. It was a big cat, like a panther.'

The cat's unusual movement was confirmed by another beater, Ryan Hurley, who reported 'It got up and ran away, hunkered down. It moved with amazing speed through the trees.'

The same curious gait was observed by a man walking to work in the early morning twilight. 'I was passing the wooded, dry moat of Farnham Castle when an enormous, fawn-coloured cat leapt over the picket fence in one bound, run down the embankment, across the road and disappeared into the gardens opposite. It ran crouched with its belly against the ground, but still came up over my knee in height. Its shoulder muscles were very powerful.'[11]

The big cat Alistair McLeod of Livingston saw was crossing the road with a dog or domestic cat in its mouth. He stopped his car thirty feet away and looked on in amazement that 'a creature of that size was so close to a housing scheme... it looked at me for about two minutes before it slowly crept away, keeping very low down on the road, turning its head towards me as it went.'[12]

## Weird behaviour

Perhaps, like MIBs, ABCs are out of kilter with their surroundings, adopting inappropriate attitudes. Bus driver David Crest saw an ABC with a body around three feet long and a tail almost as long again, 'It appeared to be cowering from something as it crossed the road.'

Very often ABCs seem to be reacting to invisible stimuli in this way: Ian Clark of Carnoustie saw a cat-like animal 'too big for a dog and jet black....Whatever it was, it was running gracefully through the undergrowth, arching its back while it ran. All of a sudden it changed direction and disappeared into the trees.' An ABC near Potters Bar was watched as it ran along a line of trees only to double back along the same route and out of view.[13]

Joanna Baker was Education Officer at Twycross Zoo and very familiar with its big cats. The one she saw when walking her dog near Snarestone, Leicestershire, however was not part of the zoo's collection. She wrote: 'It was approximately twenty feet away, black and sleek. It was about two-and-a-half foot tall, and three foot long, measurable by comparison with my dog.' The animal was engaged in a game of its own, and as Ms Baker approached to within twenty feet of it 'it pounced on something on the path I was on,' before it looked up and ran off.[14]

One witness described the movements of the ABC he saw as 'slow deliberate steps as it was following an unseen something.' The 'black panther' that Worcestershire Farmer Mike Sabin and his daughter-in-law saw was also creeping up on something invisible, 'stalking, walking with big tentative strides.'

Whatever the intention such deliberate movement implies, it seems always to remain unfulfilled. As often as not the ABC just goes away without actually grabbing the unseen prey. The impression they give is of mimicking the purposeful actions of zoological big cats, but without a purpose in mind.

To this extent too they are again faintly reminiscent of MIBs. I have described how imitation – often ludicrously incompetent – is how MIBs relate to human life; but that has been a favourite method with daimons for centuries. Walter Johnson witnessed a fairy funeral at a ruined house at Tom na Toul, in Perthshire, observing 'two wee men... carrying a coffin between them. Curiously enough they were wearing bowler hats.' [15] (It is amusing to note that when they affect human apparel traditional daimons are always – like modern MIBs – out of date. The fairy that an Englishwoman and child encountered in Ireland in 1919 wore 'a close-fitting, green, cutaway tail coat… the traditional clothes of the country a century or more before.' [16])

While some of ABCs' misplaced behaviours do imitate that of zoological big cats, there have been more bizarre encounters difficult to match to any known animal. A man was walking on the golf course near Coalville, Leicestershire, one morning in July 1999, when he was confronted by a black, panther-like cat. 'The cat ran up to within a few yards of him and stopped. They both stood facing each other, and although not scared, the man was obviously concerned and began to talk to the panther as one would with a dog. The cat sat down and was visibly foaming at the mouth. After a short while, it twitched the end of its tail, turned, and shot off as fast as any animal could run. He described the animal as Labrador-sized but longer, with a 'butch' cat-like head and a very long, curved tail.[17]

Another ABC was seen at 4.45 one morning 'lying on his car bonnet' by a witness who called the police. Their scepticism was quashed when another, independent sighting was immediately reported, and within fifteen minutes of that an electrical contractor saw the same animal 'no further than ten feet away from me… I had never seen anything like it.' [18] But if that one was ostentatious, an Ayrshire ABC's bid for attention amounted almost to a death-wish. John Jackson was driving a taxi full of passengers to Beith when he came across it 'sitting on its haunches in the middle of the road and I was forced to stop. I was within a few feet of it and my headlights were full on – but it would not move. I waited for about five minutes, and then drove round it. In doing so my car brushed against it and it growled.' [19]

### In a world of their own

There is something dysfunctional about such reckless behaviour – courting attention, only to make themselves scarce again. For animals that have eluded so many police hunts it seems rash to ignore the presence of humans at close range. As a Dundee lorry driver put it, remarking of the black, 'full-grown puma' [sic] he saw twenty yards from the road, 'it didn't seem scared at all by the passing traffic. In fact, it looked to be very much in a world of its own, like it was out for a morning stroll in the sunshine.' [20]

They are dreamy animals, absorbed in a world of their own. 'Unconcerned', 'not bothered', 'totally at ease' are phrases constantly used of their padding along with barely a passing glance at the furore they leave in their wake. Just such a big cat was seen strolling past tennis netting at the Cuffley and Northaw Tennis Club, Hertfordshire, by an excited crowd of people: Franco Melidoro was with a group of twenty people who were sure it was a black panther 'because of the sheer size of it. It was bigger then a Labrador dog', he said. It wandered into trees behind the tennis club. 'It did not seem bothered. It seemed to be minding its own business.'

In contrast the Cuffley community was extremely bothered: a full-scale police hunt was immediately launched, which included the use of a helicopter; but it seemed the cat had wandered dreamily off the face of the earth, for it was never located.

*This is the animal that looked at the witness through his sports car window. (Somerset witness)*

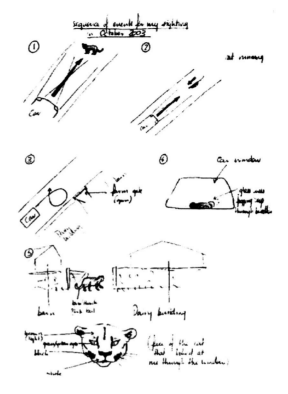

Geoff Drew was nearly as close: he drove to within fifteen feet of big black cat larger than a Labrador and 'so supple and sleek. It stared back at me as if it was completely unconcerned by my presence.'[21] The ABC a security guard spotted in Norwich 'was large and black and sitting passively on the side of the road. I was about ten feet away from it and nearly jumped out of my vehicle with fright.' The ABC on the other hand was markedly blasé about his proximity: 'It looked at me and yawned. I could see these two big teeth … '[22]

Perhaps the last word in insouciance was displayed by the ABC three people near Somerby, Leicestershire, saw while they were making the village Guy Fawkes Day bonfire. 'The panther was walking along the hedge line next to the brook, with the Cottesmore Hunt hounds in full cry on the other side! They said it was not in the least bothered… '[23]

It is as if Charles Fort's tease were true – that they have just been teleported here, and are still not fully aware of where they are, and what the conventions and dangers of their new landscape are. Or perhaps they have not been teleported thoroughly enough, and their heads are still in another world, engaged in other purposes.

Curiously enough the number of times their heads are reported as being invisible is notable; but mainly, according to the witnesses, because they are engaged in walking head first into hedges. Walking into a hedge is not an easy task if the hedge is at all dense, but ABCs are never seen struggling to negotiate brambles – they disappear into them as smoothly as treacle.

## Windows

Steve Gardiner's ABC, despite being only four paces away, stopped to stare at him through his patio doors before ambling off – 'It didn't seem the least bit concerned by me.' [24] In modern folklore windows and glass doors are liminal zones every bit as potent as their traditional equivalents and provide a useful metaphor for the transparent yet impenetrable barrier between two worlds. 'Space aliens' have the habit of looking in through windows, and so do ABCs.

It may be recalled from Chapter 2 that Trevor Bartle's ABC 'stretched up' to look in his car window. Similarly anglers Roy Henderson and Eric Walker stopped their car when a panther-like animal five foot long with bright yellow eyes, appeared in the road ahead of them – it walked round their car looking in before vanishing into a field.[25] Another motorist skidded so hard to avoid a puma which had strolled into the road ahead of him that his car came to rest facing the way he had come; when he looked round to see where the animal was he found it staring at him levelly through the window of his low sports car.

## The Oz factor, waking dreams or metachoric experience

People who encounter modern daimons such as UFOs sometimes experience what has been called in that literature the 'Oz factor.' [26] This is when the percipient reacts with abnormal passivity to the event, or feels dazed and subject to a dreamlike sense of altered reality or powerlessness. People who invite MIBs into their home, for instance, wonder afterwards why they did not simply kick them out sooner instead of remaining mesmerised by the odd creatures' implausible menaces. When I began to consider ABCs as a species of modern daimon I wondered whether any could have had the same effect on percipients.

I did discover two attentively recorded but isolated occasions when witnesses had described their encounters with an ABC as having something of the 'waking dream' about them.

Paul Screeton's sighting of a black panther in Northumberland had, in retrospect, a dreamlike atmosphere. He logged his classic ABC encounter – he was in a friend's car when one crossed the road – with the caution and insight that might be expected of an editor of the journal *Folklore Frontiers*:

> 'An all-black cat of panther form crossed road a hundred or so yards ahead of us, from right to left, and disappeared into the undergrowth… It appeared as high as an adult Doberman dog, twice the length and lower slung, moving with a powerful, quick, feline gait.
>
> 'I blurted out "Was that a deer?", but why I did so is something I have often wondered, as it in no way resembled such an animal. When we discussed it afterwards my friend felt it moved more slowly, and was greyish in colour.
>
> 'Despite the high strangeness of the incident, he neither stopped nor braked, and afterwards wondered why he hadn't. I had a

loaded camera in my pocket and it never crossed my mind to attempt to take a photograph. In fact, our whole lack of real co-ordination and inability to have a common perception of the event is odd.'

These odd, dreamlike reactions, Paul felt, might point to a psychic dimension to the event. As if in confirmation of this thought he started to dream about big cats. 'Previous to this encounter, during what might be called anxiety dreams, I had a dread of being attacked by dogs. Immediately after the "panther" sighting the dog dreams ceased and occasional big cat ones started. These peaked with one in which a leopard was gently biting me. When I ordered it to stop, it talked to me… ' [27]

Janet Worsley lives in a rural village in Cumbria, surrounded by fields and woodland. During the night of 5th March 2003 she was woken by a noise outside; or at least, as she described the event a few days later – 'Something woke me up – and then I heard the sound. I have a wooden front gate and it sounded as if the wind had blown it shut.

> 'I got up and looked out the window, only to see under my (upstairs) bedroom window, just feet below, what appeared to be a black panther looking straight up at me! I have a pet black cat,  so I could see immediately that I wasn't looking at a normal domestic cat as it was around eighteen inches to the shoulder
>
> 'I knew I was looking at a black panther because I'd seen them in zoos and on the television; and that was the shape of it – it had a very long tail; a black panther tail. It was about three feet six inches long – a long, lean body – and its head and shoulders were higher than the garden pot that it was standing beside which is sixteen inches high.
>
> 'I thought I was dreaming. It is so vivid even now. My heart was racing. The street light was shining on that particular bit because there were no leaves on the trees. I could see the lights shining on its eyes, a yellow-orangey gleam.
>
> 'I wanted open the window for a better look, but I have to open two latches to open the casement, and when I then looked out it had gone. I thought to myself "Stupid woman… !" and went back to bed.
>
> 'Next day I thought it might have been a bizarre dream – but it was still so vivid I started to feel uncomfortable because dreams normally go, don't they? So I told friends at work about it, and they then showed me that day's local newspaper – it reported other people's sightings of a panther-like cat.' [28]

The noise of a slamming gate, reminiscent of the passing of Woden in Danish folklore as I have mentioned before, had heralded the arrival of this animal. It was unmistakably a 'black panther' – Ms Worsley could measure its size and shape very accurately. And yet the fact that it was staring up at her, and then seemed to vanish in the moment when her attention was directed elsewhere, adds to the quality of a 'bizarre dream' that she considered for a while as an explanation of what had happened.

The 'Oz factor' is perhaps a superficial, lightly-drawn version of what has been called 'metachoric' experience – described by the academic psychologist Celia Green as a kind of waking dream, in which 'the whole of the environment is replaced by a hallucinatory one, although this may provide a precise replica of the physical world and appear to be completely continuous with normal experience.' [29]

This would obviously be consistent with most ABC witnesses' claims that they were not hallucinating but watching something just as real as the road itself – though it would scarcely be the most economical interpretation of those claims. The idea that metachoric experience may go some way to 'explaining' ABC sightings as hallucinatory is also disqualified by multiple observers of the same animal, the heterogeneous and often physical nature of the evidence and so on. Besides which it still fails to account for the particular form of the ABC as an anomalous hallucinatory element in a hallucinatory environment which is in all other respects identical to the normal one!

A metachoric experience implies a 'normal experience' to which the percipient returns and can compare it. In contrast, before, during and after their ABC encounters the overwhelming majority of percipients feel perfectly normal – and that the ABC has intruded into the almost boringly commonplace. Another thoughtful witness, Allan Brown, was at pains to make this point:

> 'My mystery big cat sighting was all the stranger because it was completely mundane, there was no accompanying sense of a rising weirdness or a premonition that something strange was in the air. I was on a train from Brighton to London and just past Hayward Heath there is a really lovely stretch of countryside and the train looks down on to it from a height. Just as it started to level off I saw a black, big cat in a field. It was about the size of large Labrador, but with feline movement, a cat-shaped head and a long tail. I would say that it was most like a black panther, and it really looked as real and solid as everything else I was watching. It wasn't floating a little off the ground or anything; it just gave the impression of being a real black panther or puma, sort of slinking alongside the hedge… ' [30]

## Modern ghosts

The experiences of Paul Screeton and Janet Worsley may have included the same mixture of subjective and objective elements which parapsychologists describe as characterising apparitions such as ghosts. This interpretation was in Allan Brown's mind too – but on examination of his own reactions and the cat's appearance he refuted it: 'It wasn't floating a little off the ground or anything… '

However perhaps the witness who most firmly contradicted the idea of ABCs as ghosts was Mark Fraser. The ABC he saw was 'as large as a fully grown Alsatian, with a black almost fluffy or long coat, and a long tail.' He wasted no time in jumping out of the car and, armed with a torch and a walkie-talkie, ran into the field where the torch beam caught the cat's green/yellowy eyes, and he cautiously approached it. 'It was sat on its haunches about fifteen to twenty feet away looking at me, and was about two and a half feet high. It seemed to have lost its rough look and appeared sleek, calm and knowing.' Mark had time to call his friend on the walkie-talkie and describe the scene. 'But then,' he continues, 'the cat must have ducked down and slunk away under the fence, because one moment it was there and then in the next instant it wasn't... '[31]

This cat was paradoxical. It had an 'almost amused' expression on its face, and the small, pointed ears that distinguishes many ABCs from leopards. Indeed, Mark was sure that 'this was no leopard.'

Its sudden disappearance when Mark looked away might suggest the cat had been some kind of phantom, but Mark refuted this idea. He is psychic and has encountered ghosts and even animal apparitions before – including once a wolf on a forest track which did actually vanish before his eyes – but he felt his encounter with this particular cat was of a quite different order. Uniquely qualified to distinguish between dimensions, as it were, he stresses: 'It was solidly and unmistakably of this dimension, the one we term "normal".' He allowed me to quote his encounter only 'on condition that you make it clear that this cat was flesh and blood.'

## Flesh and blood

It was actually a congenial thought. The longer one explores the tricky, daimonic aspects of ABCs the more one yearns to return to their predictable side – the 'flesh and blood' animals that constitute the other half of the equation.

Perhaps one of the reasons for the present neglect of traditional daimons is that within modern terms of reference they are tiring to think about. Their qualities of ambiguity and evanescence begin by entrancing the unwary researcher, and end by exhausting her or him, like the traveller caught up in the legendary fairy dance. Their heterogeneity can become oppressive, so that after many months of pondering them I began to feel like Reginald Scot who, in 1584, complained in exasperation that 'our mothers' maids have so terrified us with... spirits, witches, urchins, elves, hags, fairies, satyrs, pans, faunes... dwarfs, giants, nymphs, Incubus, Robin Good Fellow... and other such bugs.' [32]

But of course my faith in the restful simplicity of flesh-and-blood creatures was quickly dispelled by the recollection that there are examples in modern times of 'normal' flesh-and-blood animals taking on powerfully daimonic guises.

The Viscounts Gormanston, for instance, have always been visited by foxes when one of them is dying. One instance was when the fourteenth Viscount was on his deathbed in 1927: foxes were observed in great numbers sitting on the lawns outside the house, and scratching at the doors of the chapel where his body was lying. Despite all efforts by Lord Gormanston's brother, Colonel Richard Preston DSO, to remove them they would not budge until daylight.[33] Local people had seen them travelling towards Gormanston Castle in daylight for several days beforehand.[34]

Such totemic creatures are clearly not wraiths in the accepted sense: they are recognisable as solidly tangible by many witnesses and are present over several days; but they are obviously not exclusively biological specimens either.

Anyone seeing a Gormanston fox would swear – as ABC witnesses do – that it is a 'normal', flesh-and-blood animal. The ghost of a domestic cat demonstrated the same quality – a woman visiting the convent it was reputed to haunt, picked it up. She wrote: 'I was just entering the corridor when I saw the figure of a grey cat comfortably seated in the middle of the path before me. I approached it, for fear went at the sight of the beautiful animal. That it was alive I was certain. I stopped and lifted the creature into my arms.' She put the cat out of a window on the ground floor, locked it and turned to descend the stairs. Below her on the last step 'and looking up with large staring eyes' was the same cat. At this, she recorded, 'I had the uncanny feeling that this really was a ghost. I fled.' A resident nun subsequently explained: it was the night Sister Aileen died. It was a favoured cat of hers and never comes back any other time.' [35]

Like a Gormanston fox this moggy was apparently material, but obviously transcended the literalism that the phrase implies. Perhaps ABCs partake of the same compromised flesh-and-blood – crossing the boundary that our materialist culture draws around those substances; or perhaps revealing such boundaries as more permeable than is generally believed.

# Chapter 17

# Physical encounters and half-hearted attacks

In the previous chapter I touched on the belief that ABCs cannot be daimons, ancient or modern, because they are unequivocally flesh-and-blood. I suggested that whatever the status of ABCs, daimons may indeed be flesh and blood -- though equivocally so.

But insofar as the phrase 'flesh-and-blood' is synonymous with 'tangible.' there is no doubt of the impact – even dents – ABCs can make on cars, bicycles, other animals and sometimes humans.

Two young mothers, Susan Stritch and her neighbour Lynn Wardell, were driving along a Somerset country lane with their five children in the back seat, when a 'panther like' creature pounced on their car. Susan said: 'It looked like a huge, black cat with massive teeth. It hurled itself against the side of the car and the kids started screaming.' Lynn confirmed: 'It was a big animal like a panther or a puma. And it bared its fangs when it charged at the car.' The animal sprang into a clump of bushes when Susan stopped to see if she had killed it. 'There was no blood but it left a huge dent in the car,' she said.[1]

A similarly ill-conceived lunge by the so-called 'Cadmore Cat' hit the bicycle of the aptly named Ty Gurr, bending his spokes, as he cycled between Chedworth and Barnsley, Gloucestershire, in December 2000. A year later another cyclist, Paul Taylor, was free-wheeling downhill at speed as dusk was beginning to fall. He said: 'I heard a noise like a low growl and the animal ran from the hedge at the side of the road in front of my wheel causing me to come to a sudden stop. I had a good view of it for a split second before I was thrown to the ground. It was large, shiny and had the flattish face of a cat. I'm used to animals and it certainly wasn't a dog or a badger.'[2]

Were these attacks? Or should I instead have quoted these in the previous chapter as examples of ABCs' curious behaviour, and that with the clumsiness reminiscent of MIBs the animals had simply mistimed their dash? It is anybody's guess. At any rate it was the machines in these cases that bore the impact of the ABC, and not the people.

## Mick Cole's lynx

Mick Cole from Gravesend in Kent, however, was scratched on the arm by a strange cat. He had just garaged his car when, he said:

> 'I saw what I thought to be a large fox, with its head down, walking down my back alleyway. There was a black and white rabbit in its mouth, which was still kicking and obviously very much alive. Assuming this to be probably a domestic pet, I went to rescue it. When I was less than an arm's length away, the "fox" looked up and I immediately realised that this was not a fox at all, but in fact a lynx, about the size of a Labrador dog, and instantly identifiable by the tufts of black fur on the tips of its ears. Obviously thinking it was being attacked the lynx swiped out with its right paw and caught the back of my already outstretched right hand with its claws, leaving three long and very deep wounds. I leapt backwards, my wounds already bleeding quite badly, and retreated back towards my garage. The lynx ran off down the alleyway, with the rabbit still in its mouth, towards the fields at the end.' [3]

Mick Cole is an optician, had a very close look at the animal, and is interested in wildlife. There seems little doubt that this was a lynx if he says so, and this is probably the least controversial attack on record.

## Doris Moore's 'sleek, black beastie.'

Rather more ambiguous was the unpleasant experience suffered by Doris Moore:

> 'It was a dark, freezing night in January, 2002, and Doris had just finished feeding her horses and begun walking the few yards to her car. At the same time Wilfred, her friend, was locking the stable door. He was having difficulty closing the padlock and began to bang down hard on it making a rather loud noise. Doris was also having difficulty keeping upright on the solid, hard ice which was all around. The night was black, with no street lights and no stars to illuminate the surroundings. Suddenly Doris heard a low whistling sound, rather like the blowing of air. She then felt something tugging at the bottom of her trousers, and thinking she had snagged on something she tried to pull free. The same thing happened again. Then she felt a searing pain tearing through her thigh. Shocked she turned to see a large black animal with its jaws clamped firmly on her leg. Doris began screaming and in her panic started hitting the animal with her large bunch of keys. The animal would not let go of its grip.
>
> 'Wilfred on hearing the screaming turned and rushed towards Doris, wondering what on earth was happening. He saw what he describes as a "sleek, black beastie" about the size of a Labrador, run away from her and into the inky darkness.' [4]

Doris could not describe the animal to Mark Fraser, who investigated the incident, in much detail; he noted that she was 'obviously still in a state of alarm' several weeks later. However he makes meticulous distinctions between the initial impressions and later recollections of the pair. He continues:

> 'Doris recalls turning to see this large animal on her leg, the hairs on its neck she describes as "like bristles", believing in hindsight that the hackles were raised; she remembers seeing whiskers.

> 'Doris actually made it to the car with the animal still clamped around her leg, and it was at this point that Wilfred saw the incident. Later he described the animal as a black panther.

> 'Doris said: "I didn't hear a growl or anything – it was all very quick, like the sound of the wind, as it lunged towards me. It was jet-black and was scrabbling with its paw at my trouser leg. It then sunk its teeth into the top of my thigh and I screamed. I was trying to get into the car but it was tugging at my leg. I tried to break free by banging my keys down on its neck two or three times. I hate hitting animals but it was hanging on and trying to drag me down. Its coat was rough fur but it was too muscular for a dog. It finally fled but I lost my keys."'

Wilfred took Doris to the hospital where her wounds were treated.

There is no doubting the accuracy of Mrs Moore's statement, and the nasty wounds she received wholly corroborate it. She was able to feel this animal – not just its grip on her thigh, but its solid body and dense fur as she belted it with her keys. Thus it seems almost perverse to notice, as I could not help doing, the daimonic signifiers embedded in the incident: the emblematic keys in both their hands; the sudden, loud rap Wilfred made on the gate with the lock; most of all the whistling noise, as of wind, that traditionally heralds a daimon also preceded Mrs Moore's experience.

**Four clawings**

The following four attacks also left wounds on their victims, with photographs to prove them, but the reports do not provide nearly as clear a picture of the creatures responsible.

Mrs Kathleen Topliss arrived home to find a black cat 'about the size of an Alsatian dog and with yellow-amber eyes and a pungent smell' crouched on a bedroom wardrobe. She managed to entice it downstairs, but when she tried to open her kitchen door to release it the animal bit her. The police, who assumed the animal had entered through her dog-sized cat-flap, said that she had been traumatised by the incident although she required only two stitches to her wounds. They subsequently attempted to trap the animal but without success. The animal had looked like a black leopard and was declared by the police to be such. Its ineffectual bite, however, did not resemble one.[5]

One Saturday in August 2000 Josh Hopkins was playing with his brother near his home at Trellech, Wales, where he thought he saw his pet cat in the long grass: 'I

*Sally Dyke shows the scratches she received in Inkberrow churchyard. The claws had apparently penetrated her wax jacket and several layers of clothing.*

saw a big, black tail and thought it was Sylvester – but then it jumped up and slashed me in the face and tried to pull my head into his mouth, ' Josh explained. 'It was large, black and slinky-looking – much bigger than a domestic cat. At the start I thought it was playing, but when it struck its paw at me and I saw the blood fly past, I thought I was going to die.' Josh was left with five long claw marks on his face.

Tony Holder was also looking for the family cat one night in the garden of his home in Sydenham, London. He said:

> 'I heard her crying so I went to the bottom of the garden, which is quite overgrown, to try and find her. She sounded in a bit of distress. Then I saw what I at first thought was a fox on top of her but it wasn't – it was a big, black cat about three feet tall and five feet long, nose to tail.'

The animal lunged at him, knocking him to the ground where, he said, 'I could see these huge teeth and the whites of its eyes just inches from my face. It was snarling and growling and I tried to get it off but I couldn't move it, it was heavier than me. I was scared. I really thought my life was in danger. It was an absolute nightmare.' Managing to free himself Mr Holder ran inside, shut the door and called the RSPCA and the police, who arrived with an armed response unit which, despite other sightings reported throughout the day, searched without success.[6]

Sally and Nick Dyke had read about a three-foot long, black cat said to have been spotted over thirty times in four years in parts of rural Worcestershire. They determined to lure the animal with dead chickens. On a gloomy December evening in 1993 they went with torches to check the bait they had laid in the graveyard at St Peter's church, Inkberrow.

Sally said: 'My husband was rooting around in the shrubbery when all hell broke loose. All of a sudden a huge, black animal, the size of a Great Dane, erupted out of the undergrowth and careered into Nick. He actually stepped on the creature and there was a terrible commotion. It didn't cry out but it knocked Nick over as it struggled to get away.

> 'The only escape route was up the narrow path where I was standing, about ten yards away. It started running towards me and it couldn't get past. It suddenly reared up and took a couple of swipes at me. One missed and the other struck me to one side and I was knocked over... I didn't notice the pain at first but I started bleeding quite badly. It's still tender now, four months on, and I'm sure I will be scarred for life.'

Nick witnessed the attack, saying: 'It catapulted away from me and ran toward Sally. Suddenly it performed some really peculiar acrobatics – its shoulders went one way, its hips the other and it swatted at her with its right paw. If it had clubbed her round the head it could have killed her.' [7]

### Daimonic impacts

Three months before Sally Dyke's attack an ABC had apparently knocked out Jane Fuller as she was walking her dogs on Bodmin Moor. According to newspaper reports 'she came round to find the terrifying beast stalking her about thirty feet away at as her dogs growled and barked. Under a full moon she could see the animal's front legs were shorter than its hind legs – and it had a three to four foot long tail. The creature was finally chased away by the woman's Labrador. A police officer said: "it could be the so-called Beast of Bodmin. The animal made grunting noises but did not attack. It was a terrifying experience and the woman was scared witless. She managed to stumble away. We are treating the incident seriously."' [8] Next day the remains of two sheep, one disembowelled and one decapitated, were found in the adjacent field.

### Two nineteenth century attacks

Though they are proof that ABCs seem to be tangible animals, none of the attacks I have quoted so far is in the style of a normal, man-eating leopard. It is useful to compare them to two other curious 'attacks' from the nineteenth century. The first is often cited as an example of an early ABC encounter: 'Midway between Mr Hunt's farm and the village is what is familiarly known as the halfway place, which is designated by nothing more than a fence dividing cleared land from the woods.' A man had encountered here 'some monstrous animal that had pursued him down the road.'

A few evenings later a girl named Mary Crane and a companion set out on the same road when they were startled by a peculiar scream or shriek issuing from the woods.

They then heard a rustling in the bushes and a strange animal 'as big as a good-sized calf, with a tail as long as the door' mounted the fence and pursued them along it for a short distance as they ran. It then leapt to the ground began to gain on them at which the young man fled to the village to raise the alarm, while the beast caught hold of the girl's dress and she fell fainting to the ground. 'She says she knew nothing more until a few minutes before she was rescued, when she awoke and felt something holding her around the body, when there appeared to her the sensation of something licking her face.' The arrival of the villagers frightened it 'and with a shriek, it leapt the fence and bounded off through the woods, the cracking of the brash and the splashing of the water being distinctly heard for a short distance. Next morning a large party of men and dogs started out to hunt for the animal… The hunt was kept up for two days, but without success.'[9]

Another attack, this one suffered by Peggy Barratt began like Mary Crane's with the creature's pacing its victim along a roadside fence before leaping. She had been in a field weeding potatoes, and going home, she recalled:

> 'The moon was up, and on the other side, where the sun had set,
> the sky was red and fiery through the trees. I walked to the end of
> the demesne wall, and all of a sudden I heard a rustling among
> the branches, on the right side of the road, and saw something
> like a small, black goat standing upon its hind legs upon the top of
> the wall, and looking down on me.

> 'My breath was stopped, and I couldn't move for near a minute.
> But at last I made a rush, and went on; but I didn't go ten steps
> before I saw the very same sight, on the wall to the left of me,
> standing in exactly the same manner, but three or four times as
> high, and almost as tall as the tallest man.

> 'Just as I passed the spot where this frightful thing was standing, I
> heard a noise as if something sprang from the wall, and felt like as
> if a heavy animal plumped down upon me, and held with the fore
> feet clinging to my shoulder and the hind ones fixed in my gown
> that was folded and pinned up behind me.'

Only by blessing herself twice did Mrs Barratt manage to make the creature release her.[10]

The thing rustled the undergrowth like Mary's cat-like animal, but resembled at first 'a small, black goat.' In classic daimon style it then changed size, standing on its hind legs and becoming 'taller than the tallest man.' again returning to a size able to cling to her back, her calves hitting its dangling back legs as she walked.

Both animals emphasized their liminal natures by running parallel with their victims on dividing lines – the tops of the fences – and yet both spanned the divide with their gaze. Both women were in liminal places – Mary at 'the halfway place', Peggy 'at the end of the demesne wall' at dusk on May Eve, with the moon to her left and the sun to her right.

Peggy was well aware of an Otherworldly dimension to the creature and that the way to rid herself of it was to bless herself – make the Christian sign of the cross on herself – yet she was equally aware of its complete solidity, 'like as if a heavy animal plumped down upon me.' Mary's animal was just as weighty – pinning her down and 'holding her around the body.'

These dramatically physical encounters with daimons took place in Indiana, USA, and Ireland respectively. But perhaps the most mysterious and suggestive 'attack' happened in Wiltshire, England, and by comparison only the other day – in the March of 1996.

## The Sloggett twins' cat

The thirteen-year old twin sons of the vicar, the Rev D.G. Sloggett, were playing on a track behind the vicarage in their village of Upavon in Wiltshire. Rev Sloggett related the story:

> 'The track starts at the pottery and leads to the golf course. It is on a steep slope upwards, with high, steep embankments at the lower part. They were in a den or base as they call it, situated on the top of the north embankment of the pottery track, when they observed what looked like a large, black animal crouching on the south bank looking at them. When it saw that they had seen it, it ran at high speed (they said that they had never seen an animal move so fast before) up the south bank in an easterly direction and out of sight. As they started to talk about what they had just seen, the animal reappeared close to them on their side of the track.

> 'They described the cat as being black, broad at the front with a sleek rear, with a long thick tail with a rounded, not tapered, end, and about the size of a German shepherd dog. It moved quickly and quietly and had a strong smell which they described as metallic. They also said it had large teeth and very bad breath and it had tufty hair coming out of the ears. I showed them a picture of a lynx with its tufts of hair on the ear, but they said the hair came from inside the ear.

> 'When they had first sighted the creature they had been playing with a long piece of bailer twine and two yoghurt pots as a phone, and Matthew was winding the twine up on his arm. When the cat reappeared it made a high noise, which they described as a hissing growl, and snatched at the twine around Matthew's arm and started to pull at it. Jonathan kicked at its head with a drop kick to which it made a noise and lashed out with its paw, but did not let go of the twine. He then kicked it for a second time. They were both, of course, screaming. Matthew managed to get his scissors out that they had been using on the twine, and cut the twine, making the cat fall a little backwards. It then caught hold of Jonathan's coat, which slipped through its mouth, catching the zipper clasp.

'Jonathan hit it hard with the open palm of his hand twice on the nose. At the second blow the end of the zip broke away and the cat slipped off and fell backwards down the embankment. As it struggled to climb back up the slope the boys ran for home which was only about fifty yards away.

'As they ran, Matthew still had the twine round his wrist and the cat carried on chasing the twine catching it several times before they reached the proximity of home. After the boys had burst into the house it took a while to calm them down and to get the story… ' [11]

This thorough and thoughtful report from the boys' father is a treasure trove of fascinating details about the ABC that they encountered. Particularly notable is the one concerning the animal's ears: Rev Sloggett established by means of a photo of a lynx, that the tufts came from within the ears rather than from the point as do those of a lynx. The smallness of this detail and the boys' refusal to make their animal conform to a known species implies that the other details the boys gave of the cat's appearance were very accurately rendered.

It was a solidly concrete cat – Jonathan's kicks and blows, and his broken zip, established that beyond question. But in addition to its physical quality there are as many daimonic features to the event as blackberries in brambles. Readers will have picked them one by one as they read Rev Sloggett's account. There is the amazing speed of the animal (in the familiar phrase – 'like no animal they had ever seen before'), its anomalous appearance, strange, 'high' noise, and of course its odd pursuit of the twine even after being kicked and hit and falling backwards down the embankment, to begin with just a few.

The twins were, perhaps not coincidentally, engaged in a type of daimonic activity of their own: they were linked by a line stretched between them as a telephone, with yoghurt pots to receive and amplify the sound – a system of communication popular with children since the invention of tin cans, but probably now defunct thanks to mobile phones. Daimons respond to symbolic paraphernalia – symbolic in particular of a division between two worlds, and the means of passing through or conjoining them. Keys, gates, screen doors, roads, windows, railways, dog whistles, and now a telephone line. Perhaps fancifully, I found it an appealingly daimonic image – the straight line linking one boy to a world the other side of the looking-glass, to his mirror-image, his twin. Matthew was winding up the twine when the cat appeared close to them, almost as though he had reeled it in.

Comparing the peculiarities of the Sloggett boys' cat with other daimons shows more similarities. It performed the typical daimonic feat of speeding away on the far embankment, to reappear suddenly next to them on their own side of the track – Peggy Barratt's *puca* swapped sides instantaneously in the same way. Its 'strange, high noise' perhaps echoed the 'shriek' that Mary Crane's cat emitted.

A 'metallic' smell, such as the Sloggett twins reported is often reported of encounters with UFO-type apparitions and is often attributed to some kind of electrical discharge. The 'bad breath' is also characteristic of encounters with other alien animals: the North American Sasquatch or Bigfoot, for instance, is famous for its accompanying sulphurous pong, or that of rotting vegetation.

To add to the agglomeration of daimonic detail, the two high embankments bordering a straight track sounds just like the kind of topography conducive to an ABC appearance, as I discuss in Chapter 12, the Sloggetts' track even culminated neatly in a golf course!

The unusual features of this 'attack' and the others in this chapter – and I have quoted all the examples I know of in Britain – seem to confirm ABCs status not as escaped biological leopards but as daimons: creatures which are real and corporeal, but whose presence at the same time extends beyond the literal and temporal constraints of corporeality.

## Leopard attacks

One other thing which disqualifies ABCs from being normal, standard, biological leopards or pumas, it is the inefficacy of the very attacks I have mentioned. Let us remind ourselves of the way leopards in Africa, India and Asia, and pumas in the Americas, really do attack people.

Pumas in California have found a new food source – joggers. Several have been killed and eaten in the past two decades. The big cat most dangerous to man is, however, the leopard. Leopards remain invisible until the moment of ambush – which is so decisive that victims simply never know what hit them. They break necks and tear flesh off bone in a matter of seconds.

In 1998, for example, an armed Kruger National Park ranger, driving a party of tourists, was taking a break by the side of the road when, without warning, a leopard sprang from the darkness behind him, and sank its teeth deep into his neck, knocking him down to the pavement. He never even cried out as the cat gripped him in the throat and proceeded to drag him across the road to the bushes in the far side, only a few dozen yards from the thunderstruck tourists, and immediately ate his left shoulder. A post-mortem showed that the ranger died instantly from the initial blow, from a broken neck or fang wounds into the spinal cord.

They are as silent as they are decisive and ruthless: when the mother of one informant of mine, Robert Cowan, awoke one morning in her house in India, she found her pet monkey had been taken by a leopard which had come in through her bedroom window. The attack had been too swift for the monkey to scream, and too quiet to wake her, and had left nothing but a bloody collar.[12]

There is only one British ABC recorded as having actually killed someone. In 1477 an important South Yorkshire landowner, Sir Percival Cresacre was returning to Doncaster after a meeting with the Knights Templar, when a 'wild cat' came out of the woods and attacked his horse. Cresacre was thrown from the animal, and a vicious fight began between man and cat. The battle continued through the woods, right up to the steps of St Peter's church at Barnburgh. Cresacre eventually succumbed to his many wounds and fell to the ground, fortuitously crushing the beast to death beneath him.

With his dying breath Cresacre gasped his story to a servant who attempted to tend to his wounds and according to the local legend his blood stained the porch of the church and can be seen 'to this very day.' [13]

Leaving aside Sir Percival's demise, it is clear that compared to the lethally effective tactics by leopards that mean business the assaults by ABCs hardly qualify as attacks at all.

Her ABC somehow managed to 'knock out ' Jane Fuller without leaving any wounds, and then seemingly failed to press home the advantage over its inert prey. In Mary Crane's case she awoke to find the ABC rather sweetly just licking her face.

In the case of the Sloggett boys the ABC seemed only to want to play, grabbing at the string as it trailed behind them. Josh Hopkins, too, assumed at first that the animal was playing. Doris Moore's cat likewise was tugging at the hem of her trousers, more like a kitten than a big cat, before delivering what for a normal leopard would be a very tiny bite, and making off.

The widely-spaced but light scratches inflicted on Josh, and Tony Holder, could have come from the right-sized claws, but not the same kind of claws that can eviscerate a deer even while the leopard is throttling it. But in that case what did scratch them?

## Daimonic human flesh

Attacks like these, and in particular the witnesses' wounds, are generally cited as further proof that ABCs are exclusively 'flesh and blood' animals, but in fact all it proves is that the victims are flesh and blood.

Human flesh can, however, respond to contact with the Otherworld without the approval – or even knowledge – of our conscious minds. The world has as many reluctant stigmatics, for instance, today as it had in medieval times.

In fact a whole extra category of flesh wounds has grown up to meet modern demand: abduction scars. Many people who claim 'abduction' experiences or simple UFO sightings suffer the spontaneous appearance of inexplicable but medically-verified scars, wounds, bruises, incisions, burns and rashes.

Modern these may be, but not new: a journey into the Otherworld is traditionally marked by scarification. It is the outward sign of initiation in many tribal societies – even the duelling scars of young Germans in the nineteenth century proclaimed their membership of an aristocratic brotherhood. The rituals of initiation always simulate the individual's death – to which the initiation scars bear witness – and signify the passing away of the old life, or role, or persona, which has become transformed into the new. While it might be pushing the comparison too far to note that both Josh Hopkins and Tony Holder said they thought they were going to die, close contact with a daimon, be it spaceman or ABC can leave a long impression – 'scarred for life' as Sally Dyke put it.

Even in our non-tribal society it was common knowledge, up until the seventeenth century, that contact with the Otherworld left its mark on flesh. The lightest touch of a fairy – its 'stroke' – could leave the recipient paralysed or lame. In that era of religious polarisation, when the established Church set about demonising daimons, one of the signs that an alleged witch had been in contact with Satan was three scratch-marks on the left side of her ribs.[14] In our more enlightened times that can happen to someone in a churchyard at night innocently putting chicken out for a mysterious animal.

If flesh turns out to be itself a daimonic substance, blood is even more equivocal. It represents life force, a universal metaphor for energy. In occult practices it is used literally to transfer energy to phantasms, helping them to become corporeal; in religious practices spilt sacrificial blood is an invitation to a god to warm itself at the fiery, mediating substance.

Flesh-and-blood is perhaps more of a catalyst between two worlds, and not, after all, a workable definition of what we call 'real.' Indeed its ambivalence lies at the heart of Western theology too, in the form of the transubstantiation of the 'body and blood' of Christ in the host.

**Shadow attack**

The daimonic nature of flesh is curiously illustrated by some strange scars which appeared on the body of Anthony Lupus. He writes:

> 'My cat, Shadow, died from leukaemia and after her death I would hear weird noises here and there, like a door opening, or the lock on my door being opened while still remaining locked; nevertheless I would rarely have thoughts about my house being haunted. But this last thing that happened to me convinced me that it is.

> 'One night, last year, I was lying down, about to fall asleep, and I heard my door creak open the slightest bit and it started to get cold. I didn't do anything because the window was open, and I assumed it was the wind.

> 'So I'm about to fall asleep, and something told me to open my eyes, so I do, and there's a black figure of a cat on my bed, on the other side. I sit up, and the figure runs out of my room, and doesn't come back.

> 'Well, the following morning, I feel a sharp pain on my right thigh, and I look, and there are cuts all over my leg. There were about fifteen cuts in rows of three, going in different directions (kinda like a cat's paw); but the thing that got me scared and confused was that I looked at my jeans (I wear jeans when I sleep) and there was not a single cut, or drop of blood, on them.

> 'Nothing else has happened since then, but I know my cat's still in the house.' [15]

The 'ghost cat' had not attacked him, and the wounds, if the jeans are to be believed, were not inflicted from outside. Like 'abduction scars' where the marks of incisions appear without cause overnight, and like the unprovoked wounds of stigmatics, the ghostly encounter apparently produced a spontaneous outbreak of scratch marks on his own flesh.

Although Anthony's scratches invites comparison with some ABC-inflicted wounds, the notable feature of his experience was that it did not feature a big, black, panther-like animal: it was a small, black cat resembling his own pet, Shadow.

It was not the first time that small, black cats had insinuated themselves into the picture. It was Tony Holder's pet's cries that introduced him to his attacker; Josh at first thought the tail trailing out of the grass was that of his moggy Sylvester; Janet Worsley, too, had a black cat that she could compare with the panther-like animal that stared up at her.

I had noticed these small cats lurking at the edge of many witness reports like the ghost cat that I used to see out of the corner of my eye in an old farmhouse I once lived in Herefordshire. They seemed to solicit attention too; and I had to concede that they have stalked through our cultural history for far longer than ABCs.

I began to wonder therefore whether they could cast light on our present cultural relationship with their big cousins. I decided that this was the moment to take a brief look at the folklore of Shadow and her ilk – the witches' familiars of fairy tale and legend, and the gods of the Egyptians.

# Chapter 18

## 'I never sleep if one is near... '

'But cats to me are strange, so strange
I never sleep if one is near;
And though I'm sure I see those eyes,
I'm not so sure a body's there.'

*The Cat.* W.H. Davies (died 1940)

Sir Algernon Blackwood (1869–1951) a writer, novelist and luminary of the Ghost Club relates how, as an experiment in animal behaviour, he brought a dog and his cat, Smoke, to stay in a haunted house one night:

'The dog, an unusually courageous collie, was terrified beyond belief by the presence of the spirits and lay whimpering in a corner. But... Smoke jumped down from my arm-chair and occupied the middle of the carpet, where, with tail erect and legs stiff as ramrods, it was steadily pacing backwards and forwards in a narrow space... Its stiffened legs and arched back made it appear larger than usual, and the black visage wore a smile of beatific joy. At the end of every few paces it turned sharply and stalked back again along the same line, padding softly, and purring like a roll of little muffled drums. It behaved precisely as though it were rubbing against the ankles of someone who remained invisible.

'A thrill ran down my spine as I stood and stared... There rose in me quite a new realisation of the mystery connected with the whole feline tribe, but especially with that common member of it, the domestic cat – their hidden lives, their strange aloofness, their incalculable subtlety. How utterly remote from anything that human beings understood lay the sources of their elusive activities. As I watched the indescribable bearing of the little creature mincing along the strip of carpet welcoming, maybe, some fearsome visitor, there stirred in my heart a feeling strangely akin to awe... So remote, so inaccessible seemed the secret purposes of its real life, so alien to the blundering honesty of other animals... ' [1]

Blackwood's observation seems to sum up the tremendous attraction of cats for some people, and why others find them repellently eerie. The implication is that cats can see the world of ghosts. The ease with which they move across the divide – in Smoke's case actually rubbing himself against the legs of someone unseen – shows they half belong in that invisible world themselves.

This seems to be a universally recognised faculty since folk tales in all cultures attest to the supernatural qualities of cats. Sir Walter Scott agreed, observing 'Cats are a mysterious kind of folk. There is more passing in their minds than we are aware of.' It is perhaps because of what Blackwood called their 'incalculable subtlety' that there are also more superstitions attaching to domestic cats than any other animal.

## Crossings

Probably the most familiar of these is that to have a black cat cross the path in front of you brings good or – depending on which part of the country you live in – bad luck. The cat is seen as an intermediary for a supernatural power, for good or ill, but particularly when they are black or white and when they are encountered at liminal places – divisions and boundaries – such as roads, gates, streams, bridges, or doorways. In France there is a superstition that it is bad luck to cross a stream carrying a cat. It was also thought that a black cat could lead to buried treasure if let loose at a crossroads where five roads connected.

Moreover the manner of the encounter plays a large part in its meaning. In Yorkshire, for instance, while it is lucky to own a black cat, it is unlucky to come across one accidentally. If a cat runs ahead of a sailor to the pier it brings good luck; if the cat crosses his path, it brings bad luck. Seeing a white cat on the way to school was sure to bring trouble; to prevent the bad luck, children had to spit or turn around completely and make the sign of the cross.

Curiously enough Britain's big black cats seem to have adopted the same habit as their small cousins – the majority of them do no more than cross the road. But some of them also appear to make a particular point by the act of crossing your path, or by inviting you to consider the manner in which they do it.

A Perth couple were driving south on the A92 when, they said 'something caught our eye… It was a big cat standing on the west verge as if it was waiting to cross. We were driving quite slowly. The animal waited until the very last moment before bounding across the road.' It sounds almost as if the creature wanted to be sure of being noticed before making the crossing.

The same thing happened to Geoff Brown who was driving home when he saw a large, black panther-like cat, and 'as my car drew nearer the animal crossed the road.'[2] Andrew Gilpin was riding home on his motorcycle when a similar animal 'jumped out about a foot away from me… It was so close I had to lift my leg to avoid hitting it.'[3]

A Cornish witness confessed 'I haven't told anyone this… I was driving very slowly on the Mylor Bridge to Flushing road when this huge, panther-like animal jumped off the top of the stone hedge, landed on the bonnet of my car and ran across the road.'[4]

## Collisions

The moggies' subtle reference to liminality – their passing from one side of the road to other, in the same way that they pass between worlds – is writ larger in the irrational behaviour of their larger counterparts. It seems they can even be over-emphatic. At Kilmarnock a witness reported: 'A large cat-like animal jumped from the bushes on to the front of my car. It dented the number plate.' The ABC, typically, was not hurt – 'after a couple of seconds the cat seemed to regain its composure and ran off to the right.'[5]

In another ineptly-timed crossing an ABC 'roughly the size of a golden retriever, light tan in colour with a long tail' lunged at the driver's window, smashing the wing mirror. Before Mark Fraser had had time to publish this report another had come in of a separate ABC collision, bizarrely 'on the same stretch of road as above and practically in the same spot. The only difference being that this time the driver was a woman and that the cat was jet black!'[6]

I realised this inclination to put at least one of their nine lives at risk might afflict small cats too when I came across a comical report of a domestic cat doing the same thing: 'One of my former neighbours had a moggy which would sit patiently by the side of the road and wait for a car to come along. When the car was about ten feet away the cat would run across the road in front of it and then wait at the opposite side for another car to appear... '[7]

## 'The secret purposes of its real life'

In folklore the cat acts traditionally as an intermediary – or daimon – between this world and the otherworld. They also connect the terrestrial human and animal worlds, forming a bridge between the indoor, human world of the warm fireside and the nocturnal wilderness, coming and going between the two with equal purposefulness. As a Galway man said: 'Some ways they would put a dread on you. What company do they keep? When the moon is riding high and the wind tearing the trees, and the shadows black with cold, who is it calls them from the hearth? Tell me that.'[8]

## Witches' familiars

The role of domestic cats as witches' familiars is well known. The Essex witch Elizabeth Francis claimed in 1566 that she had been given a familiar 'called Satan... in the likeness of a white spotted cat; and in 1582 another Essex witch Elizabeth Bennett claimed to possess two spirits 'one called Suckin, being black like a dog, the other called Lierd, being red like a lion.'[9]

But more than mere companions, witches' cats were believed to be half-human – interchangeable with their owners. A wound inflicted on a witch's black cat showed up as a wound on the witch herself. One such witch, Jinny Gould, lived by the tollgate on the old road to the Isle of Purbeck, in Dorset. She used to sit out on the gate at nights in the form of a cat, getting fun out of terrifying travellers, until one drunken carter picked up enough daring to land her a blow across the back with his whip. Suddenly the cat vanished, and back in the cottage Jinny was found dead.[10]

Variants of this event are repeated in numerous British and European folk-tales dating from the Middle Ages. Yet the association goes back further, even, than medieval times: Norse legend tells of Freya, goddess of love and fertility, whose chariot was pulled by two black cats. After serving Freya for seven years, the cats were rewarded by being turned into witches.

The cat's powers of transformation extend even beyond witches. The Persians believed djinns or afreets often assumed feline forms and therefore hesitated to slay a cat. In Egypt too it was believed that a djinn takes the form of a cat when it wishes to haunt a house.

British hauntings also sometimes take the form of cats. One night in the summer of 1939 the author James Wentworth Day was exploring with a friend the ruins of Borley Rectory in Suffolk, often described as the most haunted house in England. As the two men stood in the bright moonlight looking up at the empty windows of the house something shot between Wentworth Day's legs and into the house. It was a gigantic, black cat. Local inquiries revealed that many other people had seen a huge, phantom feline dashing into the house.[11]

On the evening of the day of the death of Sir Robert Grant, Governor of Bombay, in India in 1838, a cat was seen to leave the house by the front door and walk up and down a particular path, as it had been the Governor's habit to do. The Hindu sentries interpreted the circumstance to mean that the spirit of the deceased Governor had entered into one of the house pets. Thereafter for twenty-five years a tradition stipulated that any cat passing out of the front door after dark was to be regarded as His Excellency, the Governor, and saluted accordingly.[12]

**The King of the Cats**

Such traditions attest to a universal folk belief that the domestic cat mediates between worlds – is itself a daimonic creature. But paradoxically this daimonic creature is the one among all domestic animals which is physically closest to us, sitting solidly and contentedly on our laps.

It is this unique capacity for combining a daimonic self and a cosy, settled appearance that forms the basis of a powerfully resonant folk-tale, the King of the Cats. One version goes as follows:

> 'Two young men were once staying in a remote hunting lodge in the Highlands, and one of them had been overtired the day before and chose to stay at home while the other went out shooting. He returned late at night, and all through supper was very quiet and absent, but afterwards, when they were sitting by the fire with the old, black household cat between them, the young man said: a strange thing happened to me this evening, I lost my way home, that's why I'm so late, and it fell dark whilst I was still wandering about. At last I saw a light in the distance, and made towards it, thinking it might be some cottage where I could ask my way; but when I got to it I saw that it came streaming out of a hollow oak.

Look at that cat! He said, breaking off. I'll swear he understands every word I'm saying. And indeed, the old cat was looking steadily at him with a very knowing air.

'Never mind the cat, said his friend. What happened?

'I climbed up the tree and looked down inside. It was much bigger than it looked, and furnished like a kind of Church. I was looking down and heard a kind of wailing sound, like singing and howling, and a procession came up into the place – a funeral, a coffin and mourners all in black with torches, but the queer thing was that the mourners were all cats, and they were all wailing and howling together; and on the coffin there was a crown and Sceptre, and – but he got no further, for the old cat had started up, and suddenly shouted – by Jove, Old Peter's dead and I'm the King of the Cats! At that he was up the chimney in a flash, and was never seen again.' [13]

Versions of this story occur throughout Europe, but while the details differ the same contrasts are always made between the hearth and the wilderness, the man returning home and the cat leaving. The way the cat talks – always shocked into an exclamation – suggests that it has always had the ability to speak but has always pretended otherwise. Its ubiquity and consistent pattern gives the story the character of myth, alluding to the existence a complex, secret, invisible world of which we see only one aspect.

Cats which suddenly exclaim also occur in oriental tales. In 1795, it seems, a Japanese cat declared, 'What a pity!' when his master, the abbot of a monastery, frightened away some doves for which he had been lying in wait. However this cat added a further cryptic sentence. It told him: 'A cat who is a cross between a fox and a cat can speak before the age of ten.' Then it took its departure with three ceremonious bows and was never seen again.[14]

Oddly enough the secret ability of cats to talk and understand speech is a theme that also crops up in some amusing modern anecdotes. The following one has very much the same feel as the King of the Cats – in the moment of mutual revelation. Particularly interesting is the cat's reaction to the momentary overlap of two worlds, as though it had been traduced in some way:

'A few years ago I had a gorgeous, white-footed, ginger cat called Bart. I had walked into my bedroom and shut the door behind me. He was being quite a nuisance at the time so really I had shut the door to get some peace from him! But he sat outside the door meowing until I let him in.

'I opened the door slightly and stomped away and said angrily, "Well if you're coming in, shut the bloody door behind you!"

'At which point I turned and saw him facing the door, paw up pushing it! (He had never done this before. He could open a door from the inside if it was ajar. He would hook his paw around and pull, but he'd never pushed a door shut before.)

I then said, in amazement, "You understood me!"

'It was a weird kind of moment, like I just 'knew' something – 'knew' he understood me beyond doubt, and by that I mean the words I spoke not the sentiment or tone of voice. He then seemed to click out of it too and ran up and scratched me! It was almost as if he were trying to distract my thought, and almost as if to say, "You're not allowed to know that you weren't supposed to see that" and promptly shot off out of the room!'

This story produced a rush of similar experiences to the *Fortean Times* notice board.[15] Another contributor described her parents' cat, Sammie:

'The front of the house they lived in at the time was fieldstone, and the cat would climb the stones to the doorbell, and ring when he wanted to come into the house. Dad used to tell him, well, if you're going to come in, bring the paper, why don't you? Shortly thereafter Sammie began dragging the daily paper to the doorstep before ringing the bell…'

'One afternoon, years ago, I was sitting in an armchair reading. I was vaguely aware that the family cat was curled up dozing on the sofa. The silence was broken when I heard a small voice from the sofa clearly say my first name. I quickly looked round at the cat, which was now sitting looking at me! It completely freaked me out.'

Jason Hanrahan described how his cat took things a stage further:

'I spent an evening over Christmas at a party hosted by one of my neighbours, where, as we all huddled around a coffee table in her front room joking and telling anecdotes, I related how my pet cat has seemed to be able to pass through walls. On occasion I have seen the cat, Peekay, a large black tom, inside the house, but having gone out and locked the front door behind me I have then been met by him at the end of the street. I had put this down to possibly being mistaken – but it had happened on enough occasions to make me wonder.

'A number of jokes were made about Peekay, particularly since my neighbours have nicknamed him 'Devil Cat' because he can be a bit boisterous, and dislikes being touched by strangers, or pretty much anyone other than myself. We laughed at the thought that he was at home playing West Life CDs backwards on my hi-fi to hear satanic messages. Suddenly, one of the other guests looked up and swore, because sitting directly behind me, on the inside of the closed window, was Devil Cat. Somehow Peekay had got into the room, through the front door was closed, and the door to the room in which we were sitting was also shut.[16]

Having steeped myself in moggy-lore of this kind it became increasingly difficult to resist the growing suspicion that small cats – like ABCs – might be daimons all along, but prefer to distract our attention from what Blackwood called 'the secret purposes of their real life.'

## The lion sneezed and brought forth a cat

Returning from small to big cats, I wondered in what way the perceived ability of moggies to change from one world or persona to another might throw light on our anomalous big cats – on the mystery of their nature and provenance.

An Arabian creation myth credits the lion with the cat's genesis. The pair of mice originally installed on board the Ark increased and multiplied to such an extent that life was unbearable for the other occupants; whereupon Noah passed his hand three times over the head of the lioness and she obligingly sneezed forth the cat.

Another fable, related by Pierre Palliot in *La vraye et parfaicte science des armoires* (Paris 1664), asserts that 'at the moment of the creation of the world the Sun, great, fiery, and luminous, formed the lion, beautiful, sanguinary, and generous. The Moon mirrored this act of creation and caused the cat to come forth from the darkened earth.'

This generative relationship between big and small cats takes another, darker twist in the context of Scottish Highland folklore. Carl Van Vechten recounted, in 1922, a story concerning what was called in Gaelic the *Taigheirm*.[17] This was an infernal magical sacrifice of cats in rites dedicated to the subterranean gods of pagan times, from whom particular gifts and benefits were solicited. They were called in the Highlands and the Western Isles of Scotland, the Black-Cat Spirits. Van Vechten writes:

> 'Black cats were indispensable to the incantation ceremony of the Taigheirm... The midnight hour between Friday and Saturday was the authentic time for these invocations to begin.'

They involved roasting cats to death on a spit, continuously for four days and nights, during which period the operator was forbidden to sleep or to take nourishment, and after a time infernal spirits would appear in the shape of large, black cats.

> 'One of the last Taigheirm... was held in the middle of the seventeenth century in the Island of Mull. The spot is still marked where Allan Maclean, at that time the sacrificial priest, stood with his assistant, Lachlain Maclean. He continued his sacrifices to the fourth day when he was exhausted in mind and body and sank into a swoon. The infernal spirits appeared, some in the early progress of the sacrifices, in the shape of black cats. The first, glared at the sacrificers and cried, '*Lachlain Oer*' (Injurer of Cats)... At the end of the fourth day a huge, black cat with fire

flaming from his eyes perched on the end of a beam in the roof of the barn and his howl could be heard quite across the straits of Mull into Morven.

'Allan was wholly exhausted by the apparitions and could utter only the word "Prosperity" before he became unconscious. But Lachlain was still self-possessed and able to continue. He demanded prosperity and wealth. Both got what they asked for. On his deathbed Allan informed his friends that if he and Lachlain (who had died before him) had lived a little longer they would have driven Satan from his throne. When Allan's funeral cortege reached the churchyard those persons endowed with second sight saw at some distance Lachlain Oer, standing fully armed at the head of a band of black cats, from which streamed the odour of brimstone.' [18]

I have already mentioned the Isle of Mull in an earlier chapter as an example of a location too remote for released pets to be a credible explanation for the black big cats that are seen there to this day. Could the 'Black Cat Spirits' which the Taigheirm produced be linked to the presence of huge black cats seen on Mull in the present day?

Perhaps the Taigheirm is still producing them, for, writing in the 1920s, Van Vechten turns the gruesome tale from fabulate to memorate in a footnote. He adds: 'The night of the day I first learned of the Taigheirm I dined with some friends who were also entertaining Seumas, Chief of Clann Fhearghuis of Stra-chur. He informed me that to the best of his knowledge the Taigheirm is still celebrated in the Highlands of Scotland.' [19]

## Complicity

The infernal ceremony of the Taigheirm finally produced the huge cat-like apparition from the sacrifice of a number of small cats. But this procedure was not the only way in which small, domestic cats seem to catalyse the appearance of big cats.

It had crossed my mind that our small moggies with their mysterious powers might be somehow complicit in the appearance of ABCs. Now and again I had read about black panther-like animals seen with 'cubs', usually 'about the size of domestic cats.' One Devon woman, for example, saw in the headlights of her car a puma-like animal cross the road in front of her. The following week it appeared again, at the same time of night and at exactly the same spot, but this time running along close in front of it was 'a kitten' as she deemed it to be – about the size of 'an ordinary domestic cat.' [20]

I could not resist the speculation that the smaller animals might not be kittens at all – that they might in fact *be* domestic cats, off to some party of their own, or perhaps a funeral – with the King of the Cats.

This fantasy was encouraged by the mysterious disappearance of numbers of house cats during ABC flaps. This has been widely documented, and is generally attributed to ABCs' alleged habit of eating them. The veteran ABC investigator, Nigel Brierly, writes: 'It is something I have noticed from time to time in North Devon when these large cats are about – that at the same time a number of domestic cats disappear from houses in the village.'

If, however, one were applying the rules of folklore these numerous small cats would actually have gone to pay their respects to the huge, representative form, the archetype, of their race – and disappeared up the chimney 'never to be seen again.'

As I have described in an earlier chapter one of the anomalies of ABCs is their varying sizes, and the phenomenon becomes odder when cats of different sizes appear together. For instance, what were this odd group of differently-sized cats up to? 'Mr C.' was driving to work when he looked in his rear-view mirror and, he says, 'saw a large cat followed by three smaller cats crossing the main road at speed. The larger cat although 'far smaller than what I would call a panther' was about the size of a fox, with the smaller ones the size of domestic cats.[21]

This was obviously no panther chasing its dinner as the three smaller cats were following behind the larger. And what was the larger cat? A panther the size of a fox is no more than a cub itself and not capable of producing young.

On other occasions it almost seemed that small cats were morphing into big cats and back again, such as when PC Mark Jones and PC Jodie Warren went to the hamlet of Goldcliff, Newport, Gwent, after a farmer reported a big cat. At first they believed it to be domestic, but 'then the animal broke cover and through binoculars we could clearly see that it was far too large. It was about two feet six inches tall with a quite strikingly long tail, slightly bigger than an Alsatian dog but more powerfully and sleekly built.' [22] About fifteen minutes later the officers spotted another cat about half the size of the first. They said they were certain it was not domestic either. After a few minutes they saw the larger animal again. PC Jones said: 'It came across the farmyard and passed between a trailer and a tractor, and as it did so it blacked out one of the tractor tyres completely.'

A Scarborough man described how he and his wife looked out of their dining room window to see the animal in a tree on allotments. 'At first I thought it was just an ordinary cat, but then I realised its size in comparison with the tree.' Anne Barnes, was hanging out washed nappies in the large garden behind her house in Odiham, Hampshire, when she saw what at first 'I thought was just a well-fed cat, but when I looked closer I could see the animal had huge shoulders like a bear.' The creature confirmed her second impression by leaping in one bound on to a ten foot wall – not something even the most athletic moggy could achieve.[23] Dorothy Johnstone spotted a large black cat near their smallholding on the outskirts of Insch. 'For a second I thought it was a normal cat, but it stretched from the edge of the road across the centre, and the road is six feet wide… ' [24]

But if small cats can become big the reverse it seems can also happen. Big cats sometimes leave the footprints of small cats behind them. The cat that Stephen Clarke saw was a very large feline creature, 'as large as a fully grown Alsatian, but longer in body, sleek and very graceful in its movements, jet-black, with a three foot long tail. It had bright green, shining eyes, with a small head.'

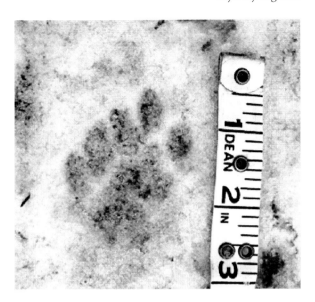

*Stephen Clarke's ABC's footprints turned out to be moggy-sized. (Aberdeen Press and Journal)*

He was in no doubt about this description because he had stopped his van only twenty yards from the cat, and they stared at each other for a few seconds before he got out. He saw it leave its footprints in the snow as it made off, and the *Aberdeen Press and Journal* photographers raced to the scene to take photographs of them.

Mark Fraser examined what they had described as a large print measuring three inches in diameter, and was disappointed to see that it was actually a double print, the back foot having stood in the front print, and that they in fact measured no more than three centimetres, which made them just right for a domestic cat. Mark spoke to Mr Clarke and found him 'a very genuine witness, both puzzled and angry that the physical evidence had seemed to contradict his experience.'

These added anomalies suggest that moggies warp into big cats and back – or seem to – at certain times. The confusion surrounding the size and species of the different kinds of feline was epitomised by a cat-flap in the USA, where a small house cat was implicated in a 'big cat' attack on a housewife.

The encounter happened in Chincoteague, Eastern Virginia, and it presents an array of deliciously baffling features in which a panther-like animal and a domestic cat seemed inextricably confused.

## The Chincoteague Conundrum

For two weeks, the people of Chincoteague reported sightings of a marauding panther, said to be jet-black and bigger than most dogs. The mystery creature made its first appearance at 2 p.m. on 15th January 2003 when Helen White, an island native, left her back door ajar as she answered the phone. 'It was my daughter,' she recalled, 'and as I was talking to her, something came to me – "You'd better look behind you… "'

*Helen White's panther claw-
marks. Were these the work of
a de-clawed moggy?
(Scott Neville/Eastern Shore
News, Eastern Virginia, USA.)*

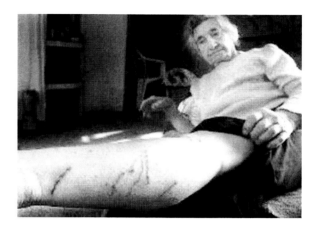

When she did so she saw a panther slipping into her mobile home. It was black and sleek and with large, almond-shaped eyes – 'the greenest eyes I'd ever seen in anything's head. I squealed because, you see, we usually don't get that sort of thing around here. 'When I screamed,' Helen White continued, 'that must have scared him, because that's when he grabbed me by the leg, and he tore the meat of my leg. I grabbed for a plate, and he grabbed my arm.'

Numerous reputable citizens saw the huge, feline animal in the following days and their reports were taken very seriously by the two official bodies concerned, Police Chief Edward Lewis, and Keith Privett of the Accomack County Health Department, who feared that the animal might have rabies, or might even consider children as prey.

They were careful to distinguish it from the native puma, the local newspaper explaining that such animals 'are a variation of leopard native to the tropics.' Even odder was that this panther wore a bright red collar – but, Privett pointed out, 'no-one has claimed the animal and there are no licensed panthers in eastern Virginia.'

More people on the island saw the elusive creature without the police managing to trap or even spot the animal. Just as they were beginning to think a local black Labrador might be the culprit they received a tip that one of Mrs White's neighbours had a big, black domestic cat with a red collar.

The officers checked out the neighbour's cat: they found a green-eyed animal that weighed eighteen to twenty pounds – nowhere near the reported size of the renegade panther, but bulkier than the average house cat. Armed with snapshots of that cat and several others, police visited Mrs White next morning. When she reached the neighbour's cat in the identity parade she said, according to the police, 'That's it. It's got those green eyes, and that's the one.' Police Chief Edward Lewis was indulgent in victory, saying, 'I could see why she could have been confused. It's a big house cat, and it does have a mysterious look about it, when you look at the picture.'

## Mystery solved

'I think we've pretty well solved it,' Lewis announced that afternoon. But Privett and the county health officials were not so sure and organised a face-to-face meeting between Mrs White and the neighbour's cat. Mrs White immediately retracted her identification, saying her attacker had been much larger. Privett's investigators also picked up a second, damning detail which they announced to Police Chief Lewis – the cat had long been de-clawed.

Lewis's victory was therefore short-lived, and he conceded the round to Privett. By the end of the day the search was back on, but with undisguised disagreement about the nature of the quarry. Lewis still claiming the perpetrator was a large house cat and Privett equally sure that the predator was something more worrying, capable of inflicting panther-sized wounds. 'If it is a house cat,' he said, 'it's the biggest house cat there's ever been.'

Only Helen White was in a position to maintain a personal, experiential approach: 'If he'd jumped for my throat, he would have cut my throat, because he had teeth like spike nails,' she said. 'His eyes were shaped like almonds and green as poison. He had murder in his heart. When I go to sleep at night, the last thing I see is the green eyes looking at me.' [25]

The panther was never found. It is appealing to think that the neighbour's moggy might have turned into a panther now and again, or at least the biggest house cat there has ever been, wreaking revenge with restored, daimonic claws. After all the police chief studied the miscreant's mugshot and agreed that 'it does have a mysterious look about it.'

## Out of the corner of my eye…

Once I realised what our household moggies could get up to, so to speak, I found the lens re-aligned on the presence of domestic cats in many ABC encounters. I have already mentioned the suspicious presence of Sylvester, Josh Williams's cat for instance, and Tony Holder's; and that it had occurred to me to wonder how Janet Worsley's moggy spent its nights.

What was I to make of incidents like the one in which the witness was woken by a crying sound and out of the window, he and his wife saw – only ten feet away and clearly visible in the street light – a white domestic cat sitting bolt upright looking at a black cat about four times bigger. The black cat had 'a pear-drop type skull, but no visible ears and a massive tail that looped to the ground and up again.' What was more the ground seemed to be littered with white fur. 'The black cat finally moved off down a side road whereupon the white cat shot off.' He went out to the street and found the white fur was real and therefore backed up the 'unbelievable encounter we had just witnessed.' [26]

Had the white cat been attacked by the black one? A leopard would kill a moggy with one swipe or bite, not engage in the kind of ineffectual scratching match that might leave the ground littered with fur.

Whatever had happened, I was now less inclined to assign to any ABC report which also involved a domestic cat a single, literal interpretation. One case in particular looked quite different when I returned to it after my sojourn in moggy folklore. It was a favourite because it had been long-considered, and rendered into dramatic, anecdotal form by the man to whom it happened.

David Winborn wrote and sent the account to Di Francis in 1984, explaining 'Until I saw you on the TV programme I had never heard of anyone who had seen or heard of these animals, and most people, when I related my incident to them, accused me of exaggerating, or of having had a glass too many at the time... '

Since he took so much trouble to recount the event accurately and interestingly, I have edited it as little as possible:

> 'This incident occurred nearly forty-four years ago. My memory of it is crystal clear; every detail is as though it happened yesterday. As you see I have written an account of the incident in a somewhat dramatic vein, partly because I enjoy writing, and partly because it was undoubtedly a most dramatic happening – I was scared out of my wits! It is also true.

> 'In the middle of August, 1940, some four weeks short of my twentieth birthday, I was posted, an eager young airman, to an RAF station in a remote area a mile or so from the second most southerly tip of Scotland, Burrow Head.

> 'Our station strength totalled fifty-six men, until, early in 1941, a contingent of sixty-six ground defence personnel (they later became the foundations of the RAF Regiment) arrived to take over the security of the station; but until that time we had to guard ourselves and this tedious duty came around every six days or so.

> 'One bitterly cold night in December a chap named Howell-Jones, a great rugby player, and I had been lucky enough to draw the last shift – lucky, because after a couple of hours patrolling the encampment our duty took us into the warmth of the kitchen to light the fires in readiness for the arrival of the cooks. That done we were privileged to brew ourselves a pot of steaming tea, and fry up a breakfast of eggs, bacon and fried bread before we signed off duty and went off for a well-earned morning's sleep.

> 'At the appointed hour we went in through the dining hall, via the servery, to the kitchen. Howell-Jones went straight out through the back door to collect kindling wood and coal for the fire, while I rummaged around for the makings of our breakfast. We had a station mascot, a cheerful, cosy, black moggy which answered to the name of Timmie. As I pottered round the kitchen I thought I caught a sidelong glimpse of him. I turned to greet him. As my lips framed the name 'Timmie' the sound died in my throat.

'The great cat which faced me was every inch of five feet from nose to tail, and as black as Satan. Two great green eyes glared hatred at me. Two pairs of white scimitar fangs gleamed in the red mouth which hissed curses at me. A huge paw, open to display a set of razor claws was raised against me. For an eternity we froze, the cat and I, each in fear of the other. My rifle, with bayonet fixed and loaded with six live rounds of .303 ammunition stood uselessly against the wall behind the animal which threatened me. I didn't give much for my chances of emerging unscathed from a tussle with this huge beast with nothing but my hands and feet for weapons.

'Just then from behind me, returning through the back door I heard the cheerful and very welcome voice of Howell-Jones singing: 'Bless 'em all! Bless 'em all! The long and the short and the tall… '

'The spell was broken and the cat sprang. Not at me, I thank God. He sprang halfway up a black-out curtain, and for a few seconds he hung there, those vicious claws scrabbling at the heavy material. Then the curtain and cat crushed together down to the floor. He sprang again, a magnificent sideways leap which carried him clean over the servery bar into the darkness of the dining hall beyond. My own leap to slam shut the hatch over the bar was almost as agile. I prayed that he would find the open window by which he must have entered.

'Howell-Jones came boisterously into the kitchen with the wood he had chopped and a bucket of coal. 'What on earth is the matter with you?' he asked, 'you look as if you've seen a ghost! And why have you taken down that curtain? It isn't daylight yet! '

'My explanations were greeted with ribald laughter, but after a bit it dawned on my friend that I wasn't play-acting. The black-out curtain was torn and needed mending before we replaced it at the window. The two of us, with rifles ready and bayonets fixed, cautiously opened the servery hatch and ventured into the darkened dining hall. We found the light switches and switched them all on. The hall was empty of all but inanimate tables and chairs. One window was open, with its blackout curtain askew. We rectified that and went back into the kitchen to make our breakfast. My own relief was beyond words. Howell-Jones hadn't seen the cat, and soon began to accuse me, if not of making it all up, at least of exaggerating.

'For a while I often asked people, the fellows on the camp and the local inhabitants, if they had ever heard of such a creature as this huge cat living locally. No one ever had, and nearly all of them at least hinted that they didn't believe my story. After a while I stopped asking – a man can only put up with so much ridicule!'

This was a bizarre animal. Its behaviour was strange, particularly towards the black-out curtain, leaping at it and clawing it down, when it could have either attacked the man or left the way it came, which it subsequently did. It is reminiscent of the emblematic action of a daimon, emphasising the metaphorical nature of a black-out curtain, or the shared element of blackness, rather than the work of a normal, canny, escaped leopard.

But as I re-read the tale an incidental detail for the first time swam into focus: Timmie: the small shadow whose name had just been called. *Could* that have been Timmie after all?

While I could sense in some ways a possible association between Timmie, the regimental mascot, and the snarling ABC, what the actual mechanics of the relationship could be were doubly obscure. Did the daimonic aspect of the little black cat slipping into the room precipitate the appearance of an archetypal black panther? Or did he himself somehow transmute into the ABC? Or did he trigger a glimpse of another reality for the young airman? Or were all these questions too literal-minded – should I simply accept the two black cats as typical of the teasing nature of the daimonic world?

## Cats is faeries

I have gathered this hotchpotch of incidents and beliefs from ancient and modern folklore to suggest that perhaps domestic cats have not wholly abandoned their traditional role as shape-shifters after all.

They remain what Jeremy Harte calls 'vehicles for transformation – for transgressing the critical boundary between people and animals they are already breaking limits of another kind... ' [27]

Cats traditionally mediate between different worlds, the visible/invisible, wilderness/society, natural/ supernatural, animals/men. They are intermediate creatures – what Iamblichus defined as daimons. Perhaps they do – as daimons are apt to – appear at one time big and at another small; at one time as moggies and another time as panthers.

In many cultures this suggestion would not seem as fanciful as it does in ours. Baudelaire described his cat as a daimon – *'Peut-être est-il fée, est-il dieu'*, something between a fairy and a god. Peter Alderson Smith, writing on the Otherworld in Irish literature, notes:

> 'With hares there always remains the possibility that the animal is
> merely natural. According to a Galway informant, no such
> possibility exists with cats. All cats, without exception, are "not
> right... and some have heard them together at night talking Irish;
> for cats is faeries."' [28]

# Chapter 19

# Eyesight *versus* Vision

Once I had pondered the aptitude of moggies for shape-shifting into ABCs, I was drawn to consider the case for the reverse: that perhaps it is people's perceptions that do the shape-shifting – that they somehow mistake one animal for another. This idea had already been considered in the context of apparitions of black dogs by Simon Sherwood, and in his useful chapter 'A psychological approach to apparitions of black dogs' [1] he summarises and evaluates relevant ideas on the subject put forward by various psychologists and parapsychologists. However one of the problems of research in this area, Sherwood notes, is that: 'Although [they] have studied and investigated apparitions, their research has, perhaps understandably, concentrated upon human apparitions and there is very little mention of animal apparitions, even less so apparitions of black dogs.' Inevitably there is even less mention of ABCs.

Sherwood explains that the debate on the nature of apparitions has largely centred on whether they are subjective or objective – to put it simplistically, whether they are inside our heads or out in the world. Again, much of the evidence marshalled for and against the subjective/objective positions is not applicable to ABCs – for instance they do not resemble people's dead loved-ones, they do not fade into invisibility, they do not appear in bedrooms etc.

Nevertheless a few of the commentators on apparitions in general have applied their remarks specifically to ABCs. Each relies to differing degrees on the cultural source hypothesis, according to which: 'The experiences are either fictitious products of tradition or imaginary subjective experiences shaped (or occasionally even caused) by tradition.'

It was no doubt with this hypothesis in mind that the psychologist Christopher French commented: 'Psychological research shows that memory and perception are constructed so that we see what we expect to see.' He continued, 'like the acceptance of the stereotypical alien following the film *Close Encounters*, the repeated reports of big cats have gained sufficient cultural acceptance to become a "contagion".' His implication is that this tradition or 'contagion' might come to the front of people's minds – perhaps at times of fear and uncertainty – and supply the impression of a big cat, where there might have been nothing 'objective' at all. [2]

Following a celebrated shooting of a black Alsatian dog which the farmer in question had intially thought could be a panther, the *Sunday Times* contacted a neuro-psychologist from Bristol University who described a similar mechanism whereby people might see dogs as panthers or pumas. Richard Gregory explained: 'Our visual system is always having to stretch beyond the few clues supplied to it. The nerve channels cannot handle much information anyway, so a whole area of our "seeing" has to do with guessing well, or laying bets. When we follow the same rules in a strange environment, out in the country for example, then we are liable to be tricked by our own over-confidence. So I would say that these sightings of strange creatures often have to do with mis-perception.'[3] Again Gregory implies we may see what we are expecting to see (in the case of this farmer, a panther) rather than the image (in this case a dog) that is actually registering on our retinas.

Cultural 'traditions' or 'contagions' likely to determine the form that apparitions took were also suggested by Susan Blackmore – 'The panthers are a cultural phenomenon,' she says, 'inhabiting a cultural environment.' However she places the 'tradition' more deeply beneath consciousness, in the realm of 'memes' – stories or ideas analogous to genes, replicated by their telling and which take on a successful cultural life of their own. According to Blackmore memes may offer 'evolutionary reasons why our visual systems are honed for survival and interpret images as possible predators.'

In common with Gregory and Blackmore the French folklorist Michel Meurger, in his work on apparitions of lake monsters, suggests an interaction between subjective and objective phenomena in a graphically illustrated version of the cultural source hypothesis.[4] He initially discerned two existing, popular explanations for lake monsters but rejected both of them, writing: 'I must stress that I do not believe that there exists an autonomous phenomenon in these lakes, be it an unknown animal or an occultist's ghost.' The effect, he concluded, lies with the percipient: with the 'power of the human mind, combining an objective phenomenology' (and since he had a practical need to fit in his data, he suggested these might include big fish, bizarre waves and floating tree trunks) 'with a subjective ideology such as that found in legends.' Meurger's 'legends' are directly comparable with the 'traditions' of the cultural source hypothesis – what Christopher French calls 'contagions'.

In his summary Dr Sherwood measured this kind of psychological explanation against both his own research into and personal experience of the black dog phenomenon, concluding: 'Such interactionist theories are not very good at explaining the specific features of the apparitions themselves... Although these theories admit to being only applicable to certain types of apparitions, they do not clearly specify which types they do or do not apply to.'

The problem of applying them was compounded when I held them up against the greater diversity of ABC experiences. Nevertheless it is interesting to look at some occasions where other animals and things have been mistaken for big cats, to see how they match up to the three main interpretations of ABCs, namely:

    1. The witnesses' beliefs that they are purely objective;

    2. French's suggestion that they may be purely subjective;

3. Blackmore's, Gregory's and Meurger's proposal that they are subjective interpretations of existing 'images', for instance objects or animals in the environment.

## David Coe's optical illusion

The following encounter was recorded by David Coe while he was on holiday in Dorset 'a couple of years ago.' He writes:

'Wandering around the little village I glanced over a low fence to see a 'big cat' prowling along the far end of the field about a hundred feet from me. It was bright daylight – perfect "seeing" conditions. I froze and watched it make its way stealthily around the perimeter of the field, I was desperately trying to find some background item to give me a scale, but it was all low shrubs and grass. It turned at the far corner and walked beside the fence towards me – this was too good to be true – I even had a camera! It got closer and I could make out the low slinking, feline walk, the ears pricked up and the eyes, dark but visible... Yet as it got closer and 'the true scale became evident',

Mr Coe realised that, after all, 'It was a domestic moggy, a big bugger but whether it was my preconception of an ABC that made it appear so, or just the lack of background items to show its true size, I don't know; but I shall treat eye-witness reports with caution after this sobering experience.' [5]

David Coe believed that his experience had been an optical illusion, brought on by a lack of background items to give scale, and so perhaps, as Susan Blackmore suggests, his 'visual system' interpreted the image as 'a possible predator.' However the illusion did not last long; as it got closer he saw that it was a domestic cat.

To what extent, therefore, could his experience be an adequate explanation for other ABC sightings? Unfortunately most are not so easily resolved. In fact in the vast majority of cases the opposite situation occurs: ABCs get bigger and more like 'panthers' or 'pumas' as they get closer. It is their inability in the end to make the ABC's appearance fit a more familiar animal – despite determined attempts – that makes witnesses so sure of what they are seeing that they may even call the police.

What about sightings by two or more witnesses over considerable periods of time, or from different angles, such as that of Mrs Bagley and her mother as I quoted in Chapter 1? This is another common occurrence, and witnesses often study the animal closely, note small details of its appearance and confer about what they are looking at. In addition people are generally aware of the unlikelihood of what they are seeing and the concomitant desirability of finding surrounding items against which to judge the size of the ABC, and are at pains to cite the road's width, their car bonnet, the height of the fence and so on as measurements for the animal where possible.

As further support of ABCs as independent, objective phenomena, there are many occasions when the ABC alarms horses, dogs, birds, cattle or other animals, often at some distance from the witnesses.

It is the numerous examples of all the above – many of which I have described in earlier chapters – which seem to release the ABC from confinement inside the head of any one individual.

Moreover if, as apparently happened to David Coe, domestic cats spark misinterpretations, why do they involve mainly black or fawn coloured animals when totally black is an uncommon colour in domestic cats (they more often have white paws or faces) and fawn is unknown except occasionally in exotic breeds such as Abyssinian or Burmese?

## Contagious Labradors

The two colours predominant among ABCs however – black and sandy coloured – predominate among Labrador dogs. Could they, rather than domestic cats, be the animals that provide a rough template on which the witnesses may unwittingly project the picture of a feline predator?

This is where the subjective theories – which I might broadly sum up as French's 'we see what we expect to see' – again run into some trouble, for however 'contagious' the idea of ABCs is likely to become, it will never be as 'contagious' as the idea of Labrador dogs. Anyone researching ABCs will soon lose count of the times witnesses remark that at first they assumed the animal they noticed was someone's black Labrador – only to be at first curious about, and then startled by the progressive revelation of feline characteristics.

Harriet Murray's experience was typical: 'I was out walking my black Labrador in the woods near Dornoch. At first I thought my dog was chasing a larger Labrador and looked for the owner. As I glanced back and called my dog this animal leapt, I should say, about fifteen feet on to a coniferous tree and scaled it in three leaps, like a panther, and was gone.'[6]

It is doubtful that she misinterpreted a black domestic cat because she was able to measure the animal's size and colour directly against her own black Labrador, and it was larger. Despite her initial assumption that the animal was a dog, it promptly climbed a tree – and no dog climbs trees, still less leaps fifteen feet into one. What people expect to see are dogs, or deer, or foxes and of course that is what they usually do see. It is only very occasionally their expectations are upset and they realise they are in fact watching some kind of big cat.

## The black plastic vision

In December 2002 a West Country newspaper, the *Western Morning News*, published some of the local RSPCA's funniest call-outs of the year. Inspectors had attended the report of an injured magpie lying in the motorway, and found a black and white Nike trainer. Another inspector attended the scene of a black swan trapped on the roof of a building, apparently in great distress. He found a black plastic bag flapping in the wind.

I sometimes wondered if the rise of black panthers since the late 1980s could be attributable to the rise in black plastic bin bags over that period; or perhaps black silage wrappers. I myself have been alarmed by what looked like a wounded animal struggling in the road, only to find a piece of silage wrapper, animated by a breeze, performing the pathetic, despairing struggles peculiar to black plastic. I was reminded of the fact that apparitions of the past sometimes took more than one form – in Yorkshire, the Holden Rag was seen 'sometimes in the form of a great black dog, and at other times as a rag of white linen on a thorn.'[7] At any rate there is something so animal in the convulsive movements of black plastic sheeting that I felt it must be a prime candidate for misidentification as an ABC and set about looking for examples.

I unearthed many – but oddly enough the other way around. For, it turned out, black plastic is apparently the 'contagion' from which black panthers emerge.

Gamekeeper Allan Newsham of Freckleton in Lancashire thought he saw a black bin liner lying on the ground, but when he went to pick it up, a black cat leapt to its feet. 'I thought "Oh my God!" It gave me a hell of a shock. It must have leapt about ten feet, like you would expect a deer to and disappeared into the woods.' He had read about other sightings of a big, black feline animal, but this had not predisposed him to assuming this was that creature – on the contrary he added, apparently without irony 'I had thought that was a load of rubbish, but now I know it is really out there.'[8]

Mr John Bragg might have expected to see an ABC, since he had sheep running on land adjacent to Drewstone where the sheep killings attributed to the 'Beast of Exmoor' took place in 1983. But only four years later, in the spring of 1987, his first assumption was that the object he saw moving across the neighbouring field was a plastic bag being blown by the wind. He then realised that it was a large, black cat… It then 'disappeared quite suddenly when it must have become aware of him.' Two people visiting Breedon churchyard, also in Devon, noticed what they also at first thought was a plastic sack on the dry stone wall, overlooking the golf course less than fifty yards ahead. But when they opened the car door a big cat – black, shiny and as big as an Alsatian but with shorter legs – jumped down from the wall and loped off.

Black plastic does not have the exclusive right to provide a first explanation for an anomalous object: other bags, and many other natural objects, also have their chance. Ken Ward, for instance, was out walking near Brockworth, in Gloucestershire, when he noticed what he thought was a brown paper bag by a hedge. When the 'bag' moved its head, Mr Ward realised it was a large cat 'sunning itself.' It was 'three to four feet long, with pointed ears, a small head and a thickish tail. It was light brown in colour, the back half of its body was thick-set' and it quickly escaped through a hole in the hedge.

A former zookeeper, Beverly West, was walking his dog near Pontypool, Wales, when 'I saw what I thought was a boulder in the field: but then it got up, stared at me and just walked away.' A couple driving near Helston, in Cornwall, saw 'what we thought was a black sheep crossing the road about a hundred yards ahead of us. When it was completely in view, we realised it had a long tail and was without doubt a big cat. It filled at least half the width of the narrow road which was about eight feet wide. It stopped, looked at us, then turned and went into the hedge. I have always been a total cynic about these things, but I know what I saw.' Elliott Pemberton was walking on Bangor Mountain, Wales, with a friend, 'when something caught our attention. It was a huge black figure. We decided it must be a tree trunk and we sighed with relief. Then it turned its head and there was no mistaking it – it was no dog, horse, cow or any other native British animal. It had a big cat's snout… '

A striking instance of misinterpretation happened to Mrs P. Champion. She took her golden Labrador dog for a walk up a local valley near Yeovil in Somerset in the spring of 1981. She had started walking through the woods when she happened to look across into the fields on the opposite slope. She noticed a very dark object lying near one of the wooden fences. Believing it to be a piece of felled timber, she continued her walk up into the wood, crossed a small stream and started to return from the fields on the opposite side. As she climbed over the wooden fence, she came upon the 'log'. It suddenly moved, and Mrs Champion realised she was staring at two huge cats, one having been on top of the other. 'They must have been mating as they had been in that position on the hillside for some minutes,' she said, 'then realising we were so close they suddenly ran off in a wide circle to disappear into the bracken.'

One cat – the one she thought was the male – was jet-black, smooth coated and with a long curved tail. It stood about two feet or more at the shoulders. It had a round head and small ears. The second one, she said, was the most beautiful cat she had ever seen. 'It was like a giant Manx cat. I could not see a tail at all and her hair was very long, almost nine inches, and black but with touches of rust colour in it. She was bigger and squarer in build, about three feet at the shoulders, and like one huge bundle of fur'. Both cats were bigger than her own Labrador.[9]

What had initially been a 'log' turned into extraordinary cats – one similar in form to a black panther, the other, while displaying many highly distinctive details, not resembling any known species. It is difficult to see which 'tradition' or 'contagion', or which of Meurger's 'legends' could have prompted this display. And to which or them, or what, was Mrs Champion's dog responding as she struggled to restrain him from racing after them?

**Subject and object**

The polarity of subject and object is firmly entrenched in Michel Meurger's analysis. He opts for a model of distinct 'inner' and 'outer' worlds. These, he suggests, are superimposed one on the other: the outer provides a submerged tree trunk, the inner provides the 'legend' (or 'tradition' or 'contagion') of, say, lake monsters, with which to mistake it. In this he articulates the Cartesian dualism which has determined the Western European world-view since René Descartes divided the world between Mind (subject) and Extension (object) in the seventeenth century.

This same apparent division was further elaborated in the work of the nineteenth century psychologists such as Jung and Freud: indeed Meurger uses a metaphor from depth psychology to explain his proposed movement of an image (his 'subjective ideology') from our minds to the external world – that of 'projection.' This was a mechanism of the psyche by which subjective desires are unconsciously superimposed on the external world where they are taken by the percipient as being objective. The metaphor of 'projection' was in turn derived from the then latest scientific discovery, the magic lantern, which literally threw images from inside itself on to the wall in front.

In the twentieth century dualism – together with its child, scientific materialism – has become so entrenched as to constitute the air we breathe. Its main disadvantage from the point of view of ABC research is that it disables the very tools needed to make anomalous phenomena intelligible – a set of Neoplatonist, or at least pre-Cartesian, perspectives.

Meurger laboured under this disability. Faced with rigidly-differentiated inner and outer worlds, he imposed one on the other, the legend on the tree trunk, hoping that the friction might somehow be able to produce the fire of an unexpected emotional effect – that a frightening creature, such as a lake monster, would emerge.

But looked at in slow motion it is more difficult to see how the mechanism he suggests could really be capable of producing the necessary combustion in the common-sense world in which ABC encounters take place. Here the usual response of the percipient is to check that they are not misinterpreting some natural phenomenon. For instance, Brigid Reilly described what went through her mind when she spotted a black feline shape as she opened her front door one night. She wrote to me describing her experience which took place in Wareham in Dorset in November 2005:

> 'It was late and I was tired, so for a split second my rational mind registered this as a large black domestic cat sitting on the driveway and that a huge black shadow was making it look bigger. But as I opened the door I saw it begin to get up and I realised that there was no shadow and this was no ordinary cat.

> 'I called my dog, who rushed to the door, took one look at the creature and began to leap towards it. The big cat immediately responded by turning and taking one huge leap into the copse on the other side of the driveway. It was then that I saw just how big it was. It was the size of a working Labrador, but with the litheness, confidence and thickness of leg of a panther. My dog chased the cat into the copse and I heard him growl a very cautious warning growl (at least, I assumed at the time that it was him) quite unlike anything I have heard him make before.'

Her initial assumption that a normal domestic cat and its shadow were somehow creating an optical illusion were dispelled when the animal got to its feet and jumped – and her dog clearly shared her resultant conviction that this was indeed some kind of big cat.

In like manner the Welsh farmer who saw an ABC in April 2005 remarked, 'I could not believe my eyes and picked up binoculars to make sure it wasn't an illusion, or that my eyes were not playing tricks.'

Despite his natural caution it seemed that his eyes were not playing tricks: 'What I saw was amazing! The animal was very big, bigger than a dog, black and had a very long tail. It walked across the land like a cat, low down and very stealthy. It was a very impressive creature.'

He then did the next obvious thing – 'I called my wife to take a look – she had no doubts either and we watched it for a few minutes… '[10]

## Jung and Lévy-Bruhl

There are however other models for a relationship between two worlds: ones perhaps more likely to produce the magical flame. Jung spent much of his later work re-casting the idea of subject and object, coming to think less in terms of two worlds, one inside and one outside, and more in terms of two aspects of the same world: a microcosm and a macrocosm. He was helped in this by his experience of a personal daimon, Philemon, who appeared holding, with appropriate daimonic symbolism 'a bunch of four keys, one of which he clutched as if he were about to open a lock… It was he who taught me psychic objectivity, the reality of the psyche' and that 'thoughts were like animals in the forest, or people in a room.'[11]

The anthropologist and philosopher Lucien Lévy-Bruhl postulated an identification with the natural world such as was enjoyed by "primitive" peoples, describing it as *'participation mystique.'* Jung turned to Lévy-Bruhl's work to suggest that the artificial boundaries erected by dualism are pre-dated – either in archaic time or by means of an archaic faculty in ourselves – by a reality both shared and defined by the 'world imagination', the *anima mundi* of the Neoplatonists.

At certain times, Jung came to believe, our own personal imaginations might become one with the continuous creative process of the *anima mundi*. A similar vision – of reunification with an estranged nature – has formed rationalism's animistic undertow: the Romantic movement of eighteenth and nineteenth century Europe, for instance, or the 'Gaia'-based ecology movements of the twentieth and twenty-first centuries.

Difficult as *'participation mystique'* may be to describe adequately it is nevertheless an everyday experience for sections of humanity other than Lévy-Bruhl's 'primitive' peoples. Artists, ascetics such as sportsmen and sportswomen, mystics and poets have often felt reality as an imaginative matrix from which we and the world we know spring as one.

## The Romantic poets

The Romantic poets put forward their own dynamic versions of the same idea. S.T. Coleridge defined the *anima mundi* – the 'Primary Imagination' as he termed it – as reality. It is a reality, he believed, that the individual can know by the same faculty – 'a repetition in the finite mind of the infinite I AM.'

William Blake likened 'Imagination' to seeing 'through, and not just with, the eye.' This faculty may be cultivated, by mystics, or encountered as revelation, by poets. In this way, Blake suggests, the demonically reductive is transformed by the eye of the visionary into the daimonically rich and complex:

'The atoms of Democritus
And Newton's particles of light
Are sands upon the Red Sea shore
Where Israel's tents do shine so bright…'

(From 'Mock on, mock on, Voltaire, Rousseau', 1801)

To Coleridge, Blake and the other proponents of Romanticism Imagination does not mean – as it has come to mean in common usage – a fantasy that is by definition unreal, but a means of perceiving what is *by definition* real.

Through the ever-widening circles of ABC research I, too, gradually came round to this earlier meaning of Imagination as an indispensable tool with which to reconcile what is both real and unbelievable in the individual's ABC experience; and beyond that, as a realm in which we participate, where daimons and their Otherworld are continuous with ours.

## Marching on a bridge

To return to Meurger's experiment in the combustive mechanism of lake monster production: perhaps a more useful metaphor is a not so much that of friction between two worlds, but a quadrille of synchronicity. Perhaps lake monsters and other anomalies such as ABCs occur at the point where our personal Imaginative worlds, either inadvertently or deliberately, find themselves in step with the *anima mundi*. As with the effect of soldiers marching in step, the bridge gives way – all of a sudden we are swimming in the daimonic river.

I was reminded of a vivid illustration of just this kind of experience. The writer Carlos Castaneda describes walking with his friend and mentor Don Juan in the Mexican desert. It was twilight. He writes:

> 'A strong gust of wind jolted me… I stared at him and he looked at me out of the corner of his eye… Another strong gust of wind sent a chill up my spine.' Don Juan then points to an object on the ground ahead of them. Carlos sees a brown shape, shivering, curled up like a dog, yet too big for a dog. He stares at it intently and sees it is an animal that is sleeping or dead, perhaps a brown calf… Then it shivers and he sees it is alive; he can see it breathing. They move nearer to it and he realises it is on its last legs, breathing irregularly, its body shaking spasmodically. Then a spasm lifts it off the ground, he hears an inhuman shriek and it stretches its legs – 'Its claws were more than frightening, they were nauseating… I stared at it in complete and absolute horror… Never in my whole existence had I witnessed anything of that nature – something inconceivable was there in front of my very eyes. I wanted Don Juan to explain that incredible animal. I glanced at him and then at the animal – and then something in me rearranged the world, and I knew at once what the animal was. I walked over to it and picked it up. It was a large branch of a bush.'

Carlos immediately congratulates himself for grasping, as he believes – as David Coe believed – the 'reality' of the situation. However Don Juan takes the opposite, mystical view – William Blake's view – and rebukes him. 'You've wasted a beautiful power,' he explains, 'a power that blew life into that dry twig.'

### 'Out of the corner of my eye...'

In the poem I quoted earlier Blake draws a distinction between eyesight and vision, a distinction confirmed by Castaneda's phrase 'out of the corner of my eye.' The same phrase crops up continually in ABC reports. To my newly attuned ears it sounded like a literalisation of the indirect, altered perspective needed to grasp the daimonic world.

James Bloomfield for instance was packing up his gear after a day's fishing with his brother when, he said, ' I saw something out of the corner of my eye.' The brothers turned to see a black panther-like animal standing in front of them about thirty feet away. 'He took a few steps towards us, looked at us, then went off towards the bridge.' [12]

Teresa Blake was getting her daughter ready for school when she, too 'saw something out of the corner of my eye. At first I thought it was a large dog but what made me look closer was the enormous tail – it was definitely a big cat.' [13]

A sudden change of perspective puzzled John Bagshaw when he saw a puma in a field: 'I first thought it was a fox until my eyes adjusted to what I was looking at,' [14] while Stuart White was driving through Wingfield when 'I saw out of the corner of my eye what looked like a panther.' He stopped the car and watched the cat, 'pure black and about Labrador size', as it stalked across the field only thirty yards away.[15]

In the oblique world of daimons 'the corner of the eye' both provides and symbolises an altered perspective. While our conscious attention is directed elsewhere, the daimonic being enters at the edge of focus.

### Watchers for UFOs

A similar process to that experienced by Castaneda – but inverted – happened to Martin and Louise Jeffrey. As part of a UFO group, Martin wrote:

> 'We used to hold sky watches, generally looking for anything unusual. One particular night, and due to the fact that it was my birthday, we decided to stay late. At 3 a.m. we noticed a strange light approximately two hundred and fifty yards away from us.
>
> 'Louise checked through the binoculars and couldn't decide what it was. I then checked and saw that it was in fact the top of a caravan shining in the moon's light.
>
> 'Suddenly, I noticed something running in front of me. I shouted to Louise to have a look, and we both clearly saw a very large, cat-like creature, nearly twice the size of a sheep, chasing its prey. While this happened the moon had been in full view and had lit

the area in front of us, and we were in no doubt about the creature's size.'

'The "cat" ran out of sight and after about fifteen minutes, seeing nothing more and too nervous to investigate further, we drove off.'[16]

A range of factors had perhaps attuned the couple to the Otherworld, the *anima mundi*, gradually creating a state of *participation mystique*. They had been watching the sky hoping to see anomalous phenomena; the sky was full of stars; it was late; they were alone; it was Martin's birthday; the moon was full – and, sure enough, they then see a strange light.

On the basis of 'we see what we expect to see', the scene is set for a 'misinterpretation' of the light as a UFO. But no, they are commonsensical people and a closer examination reveals the glow is 'only' the moon reflecting off a caravan roof. Yet it is as if their momentary indecision between wonder and rationality – the time they spent in suspense – opened a crack between the two worlds through which a completely unexpected anomaly passed, before racing away into the darkness again.

## Forming from shadows

A graphic example of symbiosis between worlds is illustrated in the ABC encounter of Bruce Sprinkle. He was driving home one night 'when,' he wrote, 'I began to see what appeared to be pools of water lying on the country road. They vanished as I approached, so I knew they were only shadows caused by my headlights in the low-lying areas of the road. Even so, I watched with much interest as the eerie dark shadows came into existence and then faded away.

'Suddenly, out of the corner of my eye, I noticed something moving to the right of the road. So I looked in that direction and saw a large black mass move out on to the road from the right. This mass quickly faded away, leaving something walking on all fours.

> 'I was prepared to put on my brakes to avoid running over a pet dog, but I could soon tell by the demeanour of the animal that it was actually a large, black cat. I saw that the head hung lower than the shoulders as it walked, and the shoulder blades were clearly moving up and down. To be honest, I do not know what kind of cat it was, but it was big enough to be a leopard or puma, and its long tail drooped down with a slight curl on the end as it walked out to the centre of the road.
>
> 'The only thing that kept me from braking at this point – even though the hair was standing up on the back of my neck – was the fact that the cat was receding as I approached, as though the terrain it was standing on was also moving. I have since learnt that this trait occurs in some reports of ghosts. In any case the cat did

have a ghostly appearance, and I kept telling myself that surely all this was an optical illusion of some kind.

'After the cat reached the centre of the road, it turned and began walking in the direction in which I was driving. This continued for about ten seconds, and then it suddenly turned to its right and abruptly stopped, lifted its head up high, and looked in my direction, as if it had heard something from behind. At this moment, optical illusion or not, I put on my brakes a little, and the cat vanished. Shaken, I drove on home.'

It is as if his absorption in the eerie effect of shadows forming and dissolving created a state of *participation mystique*. A bridge to the Otherworld is thereby formed, and, perceivable at first only out of the corner of a human eye, a black panther takes shape at the edge of the road. It is a detailed and fully-formed animal, strolling on with its own agenda – creating a physical effect on Bruce, making his hair stand up; and yet the fact that it defies the laws of physics – stays the same distance from the car – forces Bruce to conclude it is an optical illusion.

However the tale had yet another twist, for when he subsequently told a friend about his 'optical illusion' he discovered that other people, too, had seen a black panther in that area. Bruce then wondered if his 'illusion' had in itself been an illusion – that after all it had been 'something a bit more substantial.' [17]

He is torn between two different world views as the setting for the animal – the material world and the otherworld, whereas perhaps the ABC was a creature whose significance lay in its exact intermediacy: a daimon.

## Shadows congeal

A similar experience shook a witness on the road from Dundee to Cupar in Scotland:

'Before that night my attitude to the reality or otherwise of large, unidentified carnivores was one of healthy, professional scepticism. As a journalist I have come across the ABC phenomenon on several occasions over the years – even interviewed witnesses and written about it – but never been wholly convinced one way or the other.

'But driving home – on a road I use every day – on June 16th 2001 changed that.

'I rounded a bend, came out of a slight dip in the road, and flicked my headlamps to full beam – and did a text-book emergency stop when I saw what I initially took to be other car lights ahead. Only they were the wrong colour – a yellowy amber.

'I could then see a large, and at first indistinct, dark mass on the road just yards in front of my car. As I tried to work out what it was – all this in only a few seconds – what was clearly a very

large, dark cat raised its head to face the car and I realised the
'lights' I had seen were its eyes reflected in my headlamps. The
cat then turned to its right and in one fluid motion jumped out of
my field of vision. It gave the impression of being extremely
powerful and agile.' [18]

Once again a big cat coalesces out of a mass of shadows in the road; once again the
ABC gives the incredulous witness a glance across the chasm between experience
and rationality before disappearing again.

## A Northamptonshire ABC

Not driving this time, but walking home from the bus stop, a Northamptonshire
student also experienced a range of perceptual changes culminating in the
appearance of an acutely observed and distinctively detailed ABC. 'When almost
home,' he writes:

'I remember smelling something musty in the air and was glancing
around thinking that it may be another fox eating from the local
bins as they have often done in the past. Then I looked at my
phone to check the time, and when I was pocketing my phone I
caught a glimpse of a large, black mass in front of me.

'At first, from only glancing at it, I assumed it was a few bin bags.
Then I took a proper look and realised that it was a massive black
cat, about the size of an Afghan dog. It didn't realise I was behind
it – the wind was in my face so it wouldn't have been able to
smell my scent – but after about twenty seconds I made a noise
treading on some leafy material and it stopped and turned around
and eyeballed me. So I also stopped and we both stood still for a
minute or so, then it turned and carried on walking. I continued
following it; then it bounded off and disappeared from view.' [19]

The musty smell, the glancing around in expectation of seeing a fox, the look at the
time, the pocketing of the phone – was this combination of simple actions, involving
heightened sensory awareness, expectation, the shadow of the sundial (well, all right
– the time on the phone) enough to fall suddenly into step with the Otherworld?
Whatever happened the percipient's changing perspective is mirrored in his
vocabulary – a 'glimpse' shows a black mass, a 'glance' shows some bin bags, and a
'proper look' reveals 'a massive black cat.'

The cat was far from formless or vague, but of a distinctive appearance: it was about
four foot long with a two-and-a-half foot long, stocky tail. Its back was matt black,
with blueish-black markings in the sun, but its underside was a patchy, dark grey
with wispy hairs on its legs. Its ears were erect and rounded with wispy hair inside,
and its face had greyish patches on the cheeks. Its eyes were yellow and glowing.

## Jumping over a shadow

Some of the percipients I have quoted above seem themselves to have been semi-
aware of the imaginative state they were in – a state which, deepening perhaps into

*participation mystique*, temporarily opened the window into the real Otherworld. As I have mentioned in a previous chapter this may be combined with physical triggers to precipitate a daimon. Symbolic paraphernalia such as keys, gates, boundaries may – unnoticed by the witness – play a part in setting up the resonance that, like the soldiers falling into step, shivers the bridge's timbers.

As a result I am always interested in what an ABC witness was doing immediately before noticing the animal. They usually cannot remember – the bizarre event having chased the preceding actions out of mind. One child, however, did document very fully the events leading up to an encounter with a daimon:

> 'My mind was full of something my father had just taught me – that when the sun was at its meridian your shadow was directly under you – and as I walked I was jumping around trying to get the better of the sun. Only to find, of course, that my father was right.

> 'Absorbed in this pastime, with my eyes mostly on the ground, I happened to look up when I was about five yards away from the corner of the wall. Something was looking over the wall across the harbour. It was not ten paces away and I could see it only too clearly. It was in the rough shape of a human being, tall and glistening. It began to turn its head very, very slowly towards me. Petrified as I was, I heard a voice in my ear – "If it looks straight at you, Eileen, you will die"... Somehow I managed to turn and run into Mrs Reilly's cottage about fifteen yards away. She said, "You're not the first, nor you won't be the last to see that."' [20]

It is difficult not to infer that Eileen's daimonic endeavour – trying to jump beyond her own shadow – cross its boundary and hers – and her evident absorption in the task, played a part in precipitating the daimon.

However, as with ABC sightings, the all-important relationship is the literal exchange of gaze and by implication the symbolic exchange of perspective.

Eileen is the one who appears, it seems, in the corner of the creature's eye, for it slowly turns as if to look more directly at her. Eileen becomes aware that if their eyes meet a bridge will form, one that she has no business to cross – in her words, that she will die.

## The threshold experience

There used to be a popular quiz game in magazines where you had to identify various everyday objects photographed from odd angles, unusual degrees of magnification and so forth. It was difficult at first to recognise the foreshortened cheese grater, the inside of a cigar lighter, the hugely magnified pores of an orange, or whatever. For a moment you swam pleasurably at sea in, for instance, the orange craters, trying to get your bearings, before you flipped back into your normal perspective on the world and the photo turned into a familiar fruit. In a minor, quotidian way it was like Castaneda's experience: both views of the orange were equally real – it was the slipping from one to the other that provided the imaginative pleasure, the experience of moving over a threshold, the sense that 'the world re-arranged itself.' It could be said that ABCs perform the same trick for us, dislocating our sense of normality, as both the threshold and the experience of the crossing.

Witnesses are sometimes aware of the threshold over which they are looking. Some draw back from it, and may succeed in denying it altogether. The late Auberon Waugh wrote: 'A few years ago I was standing at an upstairs window [of a house in West Somerset] in the late afternoon with about four cricketers and their wives or girlfriends – one of whom was a teetotaller – when we distinctly saw a black panther run across the fields in front of the house.' Waugh suggested writing a letter to the press to record the extraordinary event, but then 'several of the witnesses started to back down, saying that they thought it might after all have been an extremely large, black, domestic cat.' Waugh noticed the threshold implied by the imponderable nature of what they had just seen, for he commented wryly on his friends' denial: 'The modern mind isn't interested in ghosts; it rejects them as unwelcome reminders of some discredited past.' [21]

Yet just as they cannot be termed simple animals, ABCs are clearly not simple ghosts either. They are solidly corporeal, and yet at the same time exceed the limitations of flesh and blood. They straddle a threshold – one which demands that we cultivate the knack of Blake's 'double vision' and enjoy the sensation of seeing both ways simultaneously.

Farmer Mike Sabin was a case in point, looking forward and back over the threshold incredulously: 'I couldn't believe what I was seeing... We must have watched it for at least five minutes. I just couldn't believe it.' [22]

Experiencing something you cannot believe in is, by all accounts, a profound experience.

John Grant 'felt privileged at having seen it and its reaction to me, and the way it seemed to allow me to watch it.' Roy Neville was 'shocked and amazed... astounded and as scared as the animal itself!' [23]

The numinosity of the event is often expressed as an aspect of the ABC itself. 'Magnificent', 'superb', 'beautiful' are frequent descriptions; 'majestic' Sarah Miles called hers, saying 'I stifled a gasp of wonder as the sun rippled its early-morning light right across the sleek and glossy back... shimmering with health.' Two deerstalkers on the Pentland Hills watched what they were certain was a big cat through the scopes on the rifles and they, too, were 'spellbound' by what they saw and said it was 'the most beautiful animal they had ever seen.' [24]

Colin Booth was deeply moved by the animal he saw: 'Its coat was jet-black and shone as it walked... It was a beautiful creature, and had a profound effect on me I will remember it for the rest of my life.' Likewise for Mr Brands of Compton in Devon 'What I saw that evening is something that will live with me for ever.' For Max Dack it was 'one of the worst experiences I've had' and yet at the same time 'a beautiful, beautiful thing.'

## After psychology

One of the drawbacks of those psychological interpretations that I touched on at the beginning at the chapter, is that they seem to imply, however tactfully, that the witnesses' ardent beliefs – that the ABCs they see are objective phenomena – are mistakes; that their eyes have deceived them. In short they seem to devalue what may have struck the percipients as numinous. This is easy enough to do in theory, but in practice the more witnesses I spoke to the less inclined I felt to suggest – even to myself – that, for instance, an 'objective phenomenon' and 'a subjective ideology' had somehow conspired to cheat them.

Besides which this apparent marginalisation of the witnesses' own beliefs is not exchanged for much advance in understanding of apparitions of the ABC type. As I have tried to show such theories have, in any case, a fairly limited application to the ABC experience.

On the other hand the Romantic notions of an *anima mundi* and the primacy of the Imagination at least replace the percipient at the centre of the picture by including their sense of dynamic participation as part of – perhaps fundamental to – the event.

Perhaps there is also a case to be made for the certainty of the ABC witness being the only certainty available to any of us about the world in which we live. As Keats put it, 'I am certain of nothing but… the truth of Imagination – What the imagination seizes as Beauty must be truth – whether it existed before or not.' [25]

# Chapter 20

# Manners

I have been circling the idea that ABCs might belong among those intermediate, indeterminate beings, daimons. But whether or not ABCs are daimons in that traditional sense, the daimonic perspective has much to teach those societies inclined to deny the importance of such notions, of which modern Britain is one.

This was not always so. In the past there were elaborate rules covering the interaction with such beings, and I found plenty of examples of relationships with daimons, nearly all of them contractual to a greater or lesser degree.

The *lares*, the household gods of the Romans, were offered a daily portion of the family's sustenance; the daimons of Britain, the pixies, brownies, and various familiars of families and individuals were also apportioned a bowl of bread, milk, ale, water and so on. 'In 1566 Essex witch Elizabeth Francis described feeding her familiar, in the shape of a cat "with bread and milk"; and in 1582 another Essex witch Elizabeth Bennett claimed to possess two spirits… and that "many times they drank of her milk bowl". In the same region over eighty years later Margaret Moone was accused of feeding her "twelve impes" with "bread and beere".' [1]

### Courtesy

Offerings of cider to the daimons of the orchard, the first beer from the barley field, or a portion of the harvest was customary in rural counties in times past. These physical foodstuffs symbolised the relationship between humans and daimons – the humans reserved for them a part of the feast, and thus metaphorically a place at their table and by extension a place in society. They in turn responded by doing a portion of the housework, finding lost things, helping with the threshing, ensuring a bountiful harvest. I particularly like the helpful daimon John Winnick encountered in Huntingdonshire in about 1646, because it has something of the appearance of an ABC, but in miniature, being only the size of a rabbit. 'On a Friday being in the barne, making hay-bottles for his horses... there appeared unto him a Spirit, blacke and shaggy, and having pawes like a Beare, but in bulk not fully so big as a Coney. The Spirit asked him what he ailed to be so sorrowfull, this Examinate answered that he had lost a purse and money, and knew not how to come by it againe. The Spirit replied "... I will help you".' [2]

I sometimes wonder if those ABCs which inexplicably deign to eat off bird tables – bread not being particularly tempting fare for a leopard – are responding to offerings we make, even though they are for birds, and we do it in the name of a modern deity – the Ecology. There are many reports like that of the Leicestershire man who was woken by his security lights going on and looked out of the conservatory to be confronted, just four feet away, by a 'panther' standing on its hind legs, eating bread from the four foot high bird table.[3] Michael Lefevre was similarly alerted by his security light, scanned his patio for intruders and was astonished to see two 'piercing emerald green eyes' looking straight at him, belonging to a five-foot long cat eating the food he had left out earlier.[4]

But of course it is more complicated than this. Acquaintance with a daimon is a lesson in the subtleties of reciprocity. Thomas Keightly put it like this:

> 'He is, to a certain degree, disinterested; like many great
> personages he is shocked at anything approaching to the name of
> a bribe or douceur, yet, like them, allows his scruples to be
> overcome if the thing be done in a genteel, delicate, and secret
> way.

> 'Thus, offer Brownie a piece of bread, a cup of drink, or a new
> coat and hood, and he flouted at it, and perhaps, in his huff,
> quitted the place for ever; but leave a nice bowl of cream, and
> some fresh honeycomb, in a snug private corner, and they soon
> disappeared, though Brownie, it was to be supposed, never knew
> anything of them.'[5]

Daimons cannot co-exist with the explicit, let alone the ostentatious. A new suit of clothes, offered with the best of intentions, has often been as effective as the sound of church bells in driving away a pixie. 'A good woman had just made a web of linsey-woolsey, and, prompted by her good nature, had manufactured from it a snug mantle and hood for her little Brownie. Not content with laying the gift in one of his favourite spots, she indiscreetly called to tell him it was there. This was too direct, and Brownie quitted the place.'[6]

Ruth Tongue recorded a story from Somerset, about the farmer of Knighton Farm on Exmoor, who was on very friendly terms with a family of pixies. One day, after the Withypool bells were hung, the pixy father met him. 'Wilt gie us the lend of thy plough and tackle?' he said. The farmer was cautious – he'd heard how the pixies ill-used horses. 'What vor do 'ee want'n? he asked. 'I d'want to take my good wife and littlings out of the noise of they ding-dongs.' The farmer trusted the pixies, and lent them his horses, and they moved, lock, stock and barrel over to Windsford Hill; 'and when the old pack-horses trotted home they looked like beautiful two-year-olds.' The reciprocal bond was broken, however, in an unexpected way: "They used to thresh his corn for him and do all manner of odd jobs, until his wife, full of good-will, left suits of clothes for them, and of course they had to leave… '[7]

I found this disdain for new clothes puzzling, until I read about the brownie that had dwelt at Leithin Hall, in Dumfriesshire, for three hundred years. A new heir returning from foreign parts to take possession of the estate, 'ordered that he be given meat and drink, and new livery. Brownie departed, loudly crying', and with him went the luck of Leithin Hall.

To a daimon all clothes are livery, and daimons are not servants. Our kindness becomes acquisitiveness, the bargain unbalanced, disrespectful, if we seek to dress them like ourselves. They are not reducible to the status of humans however long they may have been part of the household; and they cannot be pinned down, even by good intentions.

Their own clothes are ambiguous: either multicoloured or patched. So is their behaviour ambiguous and contrary – helpful and annoying by turns: 'They have in England certain demons, though I know not whether I should call them demons or figures of a secret and unknown generation, which the French call Neptunes, the English Portunes. It is their nature to embrace the simple life of comfortable farmers... They wear little patched coats, and if anything is to be carried into the house, or any laborious work to be done, they lend a hand, and finish it sooner than any man could. It is their nature to have the power to serve, but not to injure. They have, however, one little mode of annoying. When in the uncertain shades of night the English are riding any where alone, the Portune sometimes invisibly joins the horseman; and when he has accompanied him a good while, he at last takes the reins, and leads the horse into a neighbouring slough; and when he is fixed and floundering in it, the Portune goes off with a loud laugh, and by sport of this sort he mocks the simplicity of mankind.' [8]

Our hopeless simplicity in our dealings with the Otherworld is illustrated by the story of two travellers in Ireland who chanced upon some fairies singing (but in Irish of course) 'Monday, Tuesday, Monday, Tuesday.' When one suggested 'Wednesday' as an addition to the song, they were delighted and rewarded him. The other then suggested 'Thursday' – whereupon they were inexplicably furious, and punished him. It is difficult to know exactly how to align our daily lives with the Otherworld – not enough and too much both have their dangers.

Thus the etiquette involved in dealing with the daimonic world needs close attention. The traditional stance towards them of simple acknowledgement – a sacred well or a place near the hearth, a portion of the harvest, or a libation, or the Roman Catholic custom of a holy flame in the hall – is no longer cultural orthodoxy.

Yet on a social or personal level some balance of this kind must be struck if commerce with the Otherworld is to run smoothly. It might be that even a salute to a magpie keeps the conventions intact, and ensures that the daimons will not have to become too importunate in order to be noticed. The one thing we must not do is ignore them because, as Plutarch (died 432) warned, 'he who denies the daimons breaks the chain that unites the world to God.'

Perhaps the more we do ignore them, the more physical and quasi 'scientific' the daimons are forced to become, to attract our attention. Perhaps by closely parodying the fierce felines we see in zoos or in Africa, ABCs answer our modern, 'scientific' requirement for quantifiable effects, and then confound it by disappearing.

## The Lambton Worm again

There is something worse than ignoring daimons, however, and that is denying them altogether. Young Lambton was performing the most daimonic of rituals – linking two mirror-worlds with a strand of silk: he was fishing. He naturally raised a daimon, but did not have any interest in it; he was young and heedless, it was small and insignificant, and his first thought was to throw it back.

If Jung had been a bystander on the river bank he might have had something to say about the folly of repressing aspects of the soul, particularly those you have called to the surface, however small and ugly they look at first. And indeed perhaps he was a bystander, for as Lambton 'wondered what to do with the creature, an old man appeared from behind him, and warned him not to throw the creature back into the river. "It bodes no good for you but you must not cast it back into the river, you must keep it and do with it what you will." At this the old man walked away disappearing as quickly as he had appeared.'

But Lambton neither kept it nor ignored it by throwing it back; he wanted to be even more thoroughly rid of it – so he threw it down the well.

Jung could have told him that after an appropriate gestation period, what is small but denied may return as a monster. As a minor daimon the little worm would have been content with a regular saucer of milk, or the equivalent recognition. Denied that courtesy it perforce took that milk as a terrible beast – the villagers were forced to fill larger and larger troughs for it, but to no avail: 'It took small lambs and sheep and ate them whole, and it tore open cows udders with its razor teeth to get at the milk, which it could smell from miles away.'

It would be possible to make a case for this to have happened with ABCs, were they daimons in the traditional sense. We live in a time when our habits of thought are trained specifically to exclude the sepia, twilit, subtle world of the traditional daimons; therefore it is as muscular, big, alarming, predatory 'escapees' they must return to attract attention.

Perhaps they are obliged to make the point that they are flesh-and-blood explicit, by eating our livestock, before slipping from the physical world without trace as they pass through the hedge. A glance across the divide is enough for them to perform the traditional mediating role of the daimon. Whatever the case, their mere presence as natives, thoroughly at home in our shared countryside, is enough to reveal the limitations of our dualistic, polarised world-view.

## A *volte face*

I was reminded here of one classic ABC encounter I quoted in Chapter 12, that of Martin. It may be recalled he was riding towards a high ridge at dusk, when his mount inexplicably balked. 'Without consciously knowing why, Martin looked upwards to a nearby cliff face and noticed a small cave he had never seen before. Suddenly, an enormous black cat bounded from the opening, landing silently only two metres from where Martin and his horse were now frozen to the spot. The cat looked directly at him for a few seconds that seemed an eternity, then turned, walked off slowly in the opposite direction, and vanished… ' [9]

In the earlier chapter I was concerned with the topography of the event – the cliff-face and the cave. However there were other daimonic signifiers in the encounter. It was at a liminal time, dusk; a nearby presence is sensed first by the frightened horse, though Martin can see nothing. Like his namesake, the Irish Mr Martin, he feels compelled to look in a certain direction, though he does not know why. There he sees 'a small cave he has never seen before.' (I was again reminded of Ireland, where a small cave also appears now and again in the steep side of Ben Bulben, in Sligo, from which the *sidhe* emerge.)

The ABC appears and, with the familiar, gravity-defying bound, lands in the path in front of Martin. Time and motion take on a different aspect for Martin too – he and his horse are 'frozen to the spot', the hair standing up on his neck, while the few seconds of the animal's gaze seem 'like an eternity.'

The creature behaves in the manner of a typical ABC. It glances at him, before walking 'slowly' off. Like many ABCs it appears to be more at home in its surroundings than the startled witness. Like all ABC witnesses Martin was alarmed, troubled and mystified by the encounter – and this is where another story starts.

Paul Ross, who transcribed the story from Martin, had a different reason for relating it. Martin was not his real name – it was Tahiatohiupoko Hita, and he was riding across his home island of Ua Pou, one of the Marquesas Islands of the South Pacific. He was known by his western nickname, Martin, because he was just like most contemporary Marquesans: modern, staunchly Catholic, and thoroughly Westernised. As such he knew that what he had seen was impossible – he 'knew there were no big cats on the island.'

He was still visibly shaken when he arrived home, and his mother asked what had happened. The event that had mystified him did not mystify her at all. The creature was well-known to her, but not to Tahiatohiupoko Hita because, like Lambton, and in the manner of modern youth, he was not interested in local legends and therefore did not know any. His mother sent for a senior family member who told 'Martin' about the ancestral spirits called the *tupapau*.

They are typical daimons in that they are shape-shifters. As well as commonly appearing as ABCs, *tupapau* 'are also said to favour the animal forms of dogs and pigs, all black and very large.' As well as mediating between this world and the Otherworld they are immanent in the landscape. Topography plays a significant part in their appearances: Ross notes 'They are… touchy when it comes to people trespassing on their sites, sites that are *tapu* (sacred). Locals had to zigzag around them as they crossed the island.'

Knowledge of the *tupapau* goes back six thousand years in those islands, yet Western culture is so blinding that Tahiatohiupoko Hita had not noticed it there in the shadows until circumstances plunged him right into what was both literally and figuratively that same shadowy and numinous landscape.

Once acclimatised to it his own culture was revealed to him – he saw a cave for the first time, and, it turned out, not just any cave. His venerable relation explained that the hillside cave 'was an almost forgotten ancient burial site. Foreign archaeologists had never violated it, and so the spirits were still strong.'

Not only was the landscape of his ancestors revealed but he was initiated into it by a direct encounter with one of its inhabitants – a creature directly analogous with one of our British ABCs.

Tahiatohiupoko Hita was of the first generation of islanders to have ignored the daimonic world, but his experience changed him. Twenty years later he is intent on reclaiming and continuing that tradition that was so nearly lost to him, and those like him, at the time his initiation occurred, in the 1980s.

Can parallels be drawn with the situation in our small island? Just when we too had stopped believing in fairies, or to put it another way, just as the daimonic perspective had become most thoroughly discredited, would it benefit us – as it did Tahiatohiupoko Hita – to look more closely at our own culture, from a different standpoint? Are the lessons we can learn from the Beast of Gloucester and the Pedmore Panther, similar to those the Dragon of Mordiford and the Lambton Worm may have taught our ancestors?

# Chapter 21

# Summary: traps and bait, hope and expectation

I ended the previous chapter with a stream of questions, but of course there are no ready answers to them. I was halfway into my research before realising that ABCs could not easily be contained within any single framework of explanations.

I have been the first researcher to write in depth about the ABC phenomenon in Britain since the 1980s. The intervening decades had produced such a profusion of additional data that the practical, if unproven explanations for ABCs of the early days – for instance that they might be feral zoo animals or pets – now had to exclude most of this data to remain viable.

Psychological explanations suffered from the same drawback – the range of conditions surrounding ABC experiences, and the wealth of 'objective' evidence for the animals, disqualified them, in the main, from significantly productive examination by this method.

Instead I turned to a daimonic approach, drawn loosely from the Neoplatonic tradition. It allowed me the kind of treatment of the data I hoped would be at worst inclusive and at best richly suggestive.

However its disadvantage – or advantage – was that it offered no prospect of 'explaining' the presence of ABCs, or 'solving' the mystery; the words themselves belong to a methodology inimical to the daimonic approach. In fact far from 'solving' anything it shows how the mystery of ABCs may be but one fruiting body of an invisible mycelium running beneath 'normal' existence and implicated in other inexplicable aspects of our world, from showers of frogs to consciousness itself.

The mystery extends well beyond our shores too. Australia, which has no native felines, also has some of the most impressive evidence for the existence of big cats; so has New Zealand. American GIs were held responsible for sightings of a 'panther' in Afghanistan two years ago, just as British urban legend claims they released 'mascots' in wartime Britain. A mysterious black panther put in an appearance in the French Alps last winter, and panther-like animals have been reported in Holland and Germany. In the August of 2004 a friend driving to an airport early one morning in a remote part of Sweden saw a black panther crossing a meadow. All these animals apparently disappeared without trace. This week black panther-like animals are

*This trap, baited with heart and liver, still awaits an ABC*

causing cat-flaps in Hertfordshire, Yorkshire, Cambridgeshire and Venice – the latter was apparently caught indistinctly on film, so – who knows – perhaps that one will be the first ABC to be caught by a trap, a bullet or a documentary-maker.

Times have changed since the marines staked out Exmoor in a bid to shoot the Beast. Despite becoming more numerous and widespread Beasts have become less ravenous – the odd sheep is taken but not the scores that distinguished that predator. Time has passed too for those who hoped then to shoot or capture alive an ABC. The traps set for the Surrey Puma rusted away empty but their pattern has been repeated continually since – for notwithstanding their forty years of failure there is a constantly replenishing pool of enthusiasts who feel they are but a whisker away from catching an ABC in a cage, or on film, for the world to see.

Yet it sometimes seems that the failure of these traps may be telling us that it is just when we regard ABCs as prey, even metaphorically speaking, that we are – ironically enough – least likely to encounter them. Could it be that the traps we make tend, instead, to confine us in a literal mode of thinking? This idea was illustrated by my favourite allegory: hunter Pete Bailey had been trying to catch the Beast of Exmoor for fifteen years. He had set a steel cage-trap on the remote moor, but as he was changing the bait the door slammed shut. He was stuck in his own coffin-sized cage for two freezing nights, eating the raw pheasant he had meant for the ABC, before being freed by a passing shepherd.

It was a trap which had sprung on me too, for looking up from my research I found that instead of the five months I had thought it would take, five years had passed. It seemed I, at least, had encountered as Yeats did, 'the daimon who would ever set us to the hardest work.'

But perhaps these were less traps than portals – simply the kind of enforced discomfort and unpredictability through which we need to pass in order to change our customary perspective? Certainly as I emerged blinking I found myself – in company with Pete Bailey and all the other initiates who had started out so determined to get to the bottom of the subject – in a world much less familiar than the one I had supposed it to be.

Wherever they choose to turn up ABCs perform this change of perspective. They invigorate our relationship with the landscape. Emerging from the familiar contours of everyday life they pause to dazzle and mystify us before disappearing into the hedges and ditches we had thought we knew so well. Perhaps this is the point of them and that, as the American fortean Jim Boyd succinctly put it, 'they exist to be noticed.'

Moreover it seems they are here to stay, stalking not just the landscape as big cats but the newspaper headlines as folklore. The countryside is no longer home simply to the Surrey Puma and the Exmoor Beast, but now also the Beast of Bodmin, the Fen Tiger, the Beast of Ongar, the Pedmore Panther, the Beast of Gloucester, the Thing from the Ling, the Beast of Borehamwood, the Wrangaton Lion, the Beast of Shap, the Beast of Brentwood, the Lyndsey Leopard, the Lincolnshire Lynx, the Wildcat of the Wolds, the Beast of Roslin, the Kilmacolm Big Cat, the Beast of Burford, the Chilterns Lion, the Beast of Castor, the Beast of Sydenham, the Shooters Hill Cheetah, the Beast of Bucks, the Plumstead Panther, the Beast of Bexley, the Beast of Barnet, the Nottingham Lion, the Durham Puma, the Hornden Panther, the Beast of Cricklewood, the Beast of Bont, the Beast of Gobowen, the Harpenden Panther… and many, many more.

Have you seen an ABC or another anomalous creature? If so I would like to hear from you. Email sighting@harpur.org or write to me at Reagh, Strokestown, Co. Roscommon, Ireland.

# Select bibliography

Alderson Smith, Peter. *W. B. Yeats and the tribes of Danu,* Colin Smythe 1987.

Beer, Trevor. *The Beast of Exmoor: Fact or Legend?* Countryside Productions, Barnstable, Devon, 1983.

Bord, Janet and Colin. *Alien Animals,* Panther books 1985.

Bord, Janet and Colin. *The Bigfoot Casebook,* Granada 1982.

Brierly, Nigel. *They Stalk by Night: the Big Cats of Exmoor and the South-West,* Yeo Valley Productions, Bishops Nympton, Devon, 1989.

Briggs, K.M.. *The Fairies in Tradition and Literature,* Routledge and Kegan Paul 1967

Briggs, Katharine M.. *A Dictionary of Fairies,* Penguin 1976.

Briggs, Katharine M.. *The Anatomy of Puck,* Routledge and Keegan Paul 1959.

Campbell, J.G. *Superstitions of the Highlands and Islands of Scotland,* James MacLehose, Glasgow, 1900.

Clark, Jerome. *Unexplained!* Visible Ink Press, Washington DC, 1993.

Cohn, Norman. *Europe's Inner Demons,* Sussex University Press 1975.

Coleman, Loren. *Bigfoot!* Paraview Pocket Books, New York, 2003.

Coleman, Loren. *Mysterious America,* Paraview, New York, 1983.

Collins, Andrew. 'Earthquest News' Nos. 9, 10, Spring 1984.

Croker, T. Crofton. *Fairy Legends and Traditions of the South of Ireland,* John Murray 1825.

Crowe, Catherine. *The Night Side of Nature,* George Routledge and Sons 1848.

Dash, Mike. *Borderlands,* Arrow Books 1997.

David-Neel, A.. *Magic and Mystery in Tibet,* Picador 1976.

Dennis, Bardens. *Psychic Animals,* Robert Hale 1987.

Downes, Jonathan and Wright, Nigel. *The Rising of the Moon: UFOs and High Strangeness in South Devon,* CFZ publications 1999.

Dunne, John J.. *Haunted Ireland,* Appletree Press 1989.

Eitel, Ernest J.. *Feng Shui, The Science of Sacred Landscape in Old China,* Synergetic Press 1984.

Evans Wentz, W.Y.. *The Fairy Faith in Celtic Countries.* Colin Smythe 1981.

Fort, Charles. *Lo!* first published USA 1931; Fortean Times/ John Brown Publishing 1996.

Fort, Charles. *New Lands*; first published USA 1923; Fortean Times/ John Brown Publishing 1996.

Fort, Charles. *The Book of the Damned*; first published USA 1919; Fortean Times/John Brown Publishing 1995

Fort, Charles. *The Complete Books of Charles Fort,* Dover, New York, 1974.

Fort, Charles. *Wild Talents*; first published USA 1932; Ace Books, New York, 1972.

Francis, Di. *Cat Country: the quest for the British big cat,* David and Charles 1983

Francis, Di. *The Beast of Exmoor,* Cape 1993.

Glassie, Henry. *Irish Folk-Tales,* Penguin 1985.

Gregory, Augusta. *Gods and Fighting Men*, Colin Smythe 1970.

Gregory, Augusta. *Visions and Beliefs in the West of Ireland*, Colin Smythe 1979.

Guggisberg, C.A.W.. *Wild Cats of the World*, David and Charles 1975.

Harpur, Patrick. *Daimonic Reality: A Field Guide to the Otherworld*, UK Penguin 1995; USA Idyll Arbor 2000.

Harpur, Patrick. *The Philosophers' Secret Fire: A History of the Imagination*, UK Penguin 2000; USA Ivan R. Dee Inc. 2003.

Heuvelmans, Bernard. *On the Track of Unknown Animals*, Kegan Paul International Limited 1995.

Jung, C.G.. *The Collected Works*, vol 8: 'The Structure and Dynamics of the Psyche', trans. R.F.C. Hull, Routledge and Kegan Paul 1971.

Jung, C.G.. *The Collected Works*, vol 9, 'The Archetypes and the Collective Unconscious', trans. R.F.C. Hull, Routledge and Kegan Paul 1971.

Keel, John A.. *The Complete Guide to Mysterious Beings*, Tor, New York, 2002.

Keightley, Thomas. *The Fairy Mythology: Illustrative of the Romance and Superstition of Various Countries*, 1870; online at http://www.sacred-texts.com/neu/celt/tfm/index.htm 2005.

Kirk, Robert. *The Secret Common-Wealth of Elves, Fauns and Fairies*, D.S. Brewer for the Folklore Society 1976.

Lévy-Bruhl, Lucien. *How Natives Think*, trans. Lilian A. Clare, Allen & Unwin 1926.

Mac Manus, Dermot. *Between Two Worlds*, Colin Smythe 1979.

Mac Manus, Dermot. *The Middle Kingdom*, Colin Smythe 1973.

MacRitchie, David. *Fians, Fairies and Picts*, Kegan Paul, Trench, Trubner and Co. 1893.

McEwan, Graham J.. *Mystery Animals of Britain and Ireland*, Robert Hale 1986.

Meurger, Michel and Gagnon, Claude. *Lake Monster Traditions: A Cross-cultural Analysis*, Fortean Tomes 1988.

Michell John. *The Earth Spirit: its Ways, Shrines and Mysteries*, Thames and Hudson 1975.

Michell, John and Rickard, Robert. *Phenomena: a book of wonders*, Thames and Hudson 1977.

Moiser, Chris. *Mystery Cats of Devon and Cornwall*, Bossiney Books 2001.

O'Reilly, David. *Savage Shadow: The Search for the Australian Cougar*. Creative Research, Perth, 1981.

Randles, Jenny. *MIB: Investigating the Truth Behind the Men in Black Phenomenon*, Piatkus 1997.

Scot, Reginald. *The Discoverie of Witchcraft*, London, 1584; Reprinted with an introduction by Montague Summers: Dover Publications, New York, 1972.

Shuker, Karl P. N.. *Mystery Cats Of The World*, Robert Hale 1989.

Tongue, Ruth L.. *Somerset Folklore*, The Folk-lore Society 1965.

Trubshaw, Bob (ed.). *Explore Phantom Black Dogs*, Explore Books 2005.

Van Vechten, Carl. *The Tiger in the House*, A. A. Knopf, USA, 1922; online at www.bartleby.com 2000.

Williams, Charles. *The Place of the Lion*, Faber 1931.

Wood-Martin, W. G.. *Traces of the Elder Faiths of Ireland; a Handbook of Irish Pre-Christian Traditions*, Longmans, Green and Co. 1902.

Yeats, W.B.. *Mythologies*, Macmillan 1959.

Yeats, W.B.. *The Secret Rose*, Macmillan 1998.

# End notes

## Chapter 1 Big cats in Britain

1    Dorset police force and personal communication.
2    May 2003, *The Shropshire Star*, and personal communication.
3    thisisGloucestershire Web site archive.
4    Letter to Di Francis, and personal communication.
5    Letter to Di Francis, dated 10 October 1983
6    *Fortean Times*, April 2001
7    Sighting on 23 October 1981. Letter to Di Francis.
8    From the *Eastern Daily Press Magazine*, 4–11 May 2001.
9    Personal communication, 27 June 2004.
10   The controversy in America about the existence or not of native black pumas is succinctly summed up by the cryptozoologist Loren Coleman: 'Scientific proof does not exist for melanistic *Puma concolor*, to date.' Email, 5 May 2005, www.lorencoleman.com
11   *Daily Telegraph*, 26 October 1998, p14
12   Archive of Mark Fraser, www.scottishbigcats.co.uk
13   Near Arne, Dorset, in April 2004. personal communication.

## Chapter 2 Witnesses: the big cat experience

1    Sighting near Mylor Bridge, Cornwall, Friday 4 February 2000; personal communication.
2    Personal communication. My thanks to Nigel Brierly for putting me in touch with Claire Blick.
3    Stourhead, Wiltshire, 15 June 2005; personal communication.
4    Personal communication.
5    21 June 1998, Co. Roscommon, Ireland; personal communication.
6    On the Skene to Garlogie road, Aberdeenshire, in February 2004; archive of Mark Fraser.
7    Near Seckington, 5th February 2005; archive of Mark Fraser
8    Personal communication.
9    Sighting was in September 2004; personal communication.
10   Marshwood vale, 2003; personal communication.
11   Gloucester Citizen via *www.thisisgloucestershire.co.uk* 14 March 2002
12   March 2004; personal communication.
13   Friday 11 July 2003; personal communication.

## Chapter 3 The hunt for the British big cat

1    Nigel Brierly, *They Stalk by Night: the big cats of Exmoor and the South-West.* Yeo Valley Productions, Devon, 1989.
2    BBC News Online – 13 November 1999
3    *Daily Express,* 18 May 1983
4    *Daily Express,* 18 May 1983
5    Trevor Beer, *The Beast of Exmoor. Fact or Legend?* Countryside Productions, 1985
6    *The Beast of Exmoor* p17.
7    *The Daily Post* (Wales), 5 Apr 2004
8    *The Belfast Telegraph.* 2 October 2003
9    *They Stalk by Night*
10   Clive Moulding.
11   There is actually one exception, the capture of Felicity, a tame puma, which I discuss in a later chapter.
12   *They Stalk by Night* p68
13   *They Stalk by Night*

## Chapter 4 Where have they come from?

1    *The Yorkshire Post,* 29 Jan 2000
2    Chris Moiser, contribution to 'The Beast of Bodmin – a Debate', Plymouth CFE Online.
3    Chris Moiser, ibid.
4    Terry Dye writes in a biographical note: 'My father used to collect regimental badges from his customers in his gents haircutting shop. Some were USAAF personnel based in Cambridgeshire – i.e. Duxford, Fowlmere (where the Fen Tiger has been seen several times), Alconbury and Lakenheath/Mildenhall. I also remember the USAAF base at Milton Road where the Cambridge Science Park now is. On Sundays we used to visit Gran and stop to see the tanks in the base (thousands of them) waiting to be scrapped. This was in the early 1950s. When Dad died in 1973 I scraped the badges off the wall of the shop and cleaned them.'
5    Events which happen to a 'friend-of-a-friend', or 'foaf'.
6    www.bigcats.org.uk/sightings2001.html
7    *Daily Record,* 4 Nov 1980
8    *Aberdeen Press and Journal,* 11 December 1980
9    *The Scotsman,* 6 Nov 1980
10   *The Scotsman,* 11 Nov 1980
11   *Aberdeen Evening Express,* 31 October 1980
12   James Smith, personal communication.

## Chapter 5 Escapes: early explanations for ABCs

1   *The Scotsman*, 2 February 2002, via Detective Sergeant John Cathcart of Inverness, who has kept a dossier of big cat sightings since the end of the 1970s.

2   Graham J. McEwan, *Mystery Animals of Britain and Ireland.* Robert Hale, 1986; p41

3   Sighting 1963. Letter to Di Francis, 5 June 1984

4   William Cobbett: *Rural Rides* (1830), p204 in Penguin 2001 edition.

5   Personal communication

6   Personal communication

7   Ronnie Patterson, 'Diary of a big cat hunter / Part 1, October 1997' in *Scottish Mystery Cat Sightings,* from www.scottishbigcats.co.uk

8   Trevor Beer, *The Beast of Exmoor. Fact or Legend?* Countryside Productions,1985, p17

9   Andy Roberts, *Cat Flaps! Northern Mystery Cats*, Brigantia Books, 1986

10  Marcus Matthews, 'Historical Mystery Beasts of Great Britain' in *Talking Stick Magazine*, London, 1995

11  Chris Moiser, contribution to 'The Beast of Bodmin – a Debate', Plymouth CFE Online.

12  Chris Moiser, contribution to 'The Beast of Bodmin – a Debate', Plymouth CFE Online. appendix 6.

13  Chris Moiser, contribution to 'The Beast of Bodmin – a Debate', Plymouth CFE Online.

14  Chris Moiser, contribution to 'The Beast of Bodmin – a Debate', Plymouth CFE Online.

15  The original cross was replaced in Victorian times.

16  Recounted by Mr Gittus on BBC Radio 4's *Home Truths* programme, 23 July 2005.

17  4 May 1975 at Medstead, Hampshire. *Fortean Times 167* February 2003, citing Dr Karl Shuker, *Fortean Studies* Vol. 2 1995

18  October 1976. *Fortean Times 167* February 2003, citing Dr Karl Shuker, *Fortean Studies* Vol. 2 1995

19  January 1977. *Fortean Times 167* February 2003, citing Dr Karl Shuker, *Fortean Studies* Vol. 2 1995

20  2000. *Fortean Times 167* February 2003, citing Dr Karl Shuker, *Fortean Studies* Vol. 2 1995

21  August 1975. Bord, Janet and Colin: *Alien Animals* p 60–1

22  *Torquay Herald Express*, 21 June 2001

23  *Hendon Times*, 3 October 2001

24  Letter to Di Francis, 1985.

25  Archive of Mark Fraser, www.scottishbigcats.co.uk

26  Name and address supplied. *Round & About*: (Mull Newsletter) January 2003.

27  'British Big Cat Society' report.

28  Di Francis: *Cat Country: the quest for the British big cat*, David and Charles, 1983. p49

29  *Cat Country* p55

30   *The Farnham Herald,* 19 March 1982
31   *The Farnham Herald,* 26 July 1991
32   Personal communication, 2003.

## Chapter 6 Creatures which can't be caught

1    *Explore Phantom Black Dogs,* ed. Bob Trubshaw, Heart of Albion Press, 2005
2    Sledmere, north-east Yorkshire. Personal communication, February 16, 2004
3    *Scunthorpe News,* 10 January 2004
4    Nigel Brierly, *They Stalk by Night: The big cats of Exmoor and the South-West.* Yeo Valley Productions, 1989, p40
5    Trevor Beer, *The Beast of Exmoor. Fact or legend?* Countryside Productions, 1985, p19
6    Archive of Mark Fraser. 25 July 2003; Melrose, Scotland.
7    W.H. Auden, *Collected Poems,* Faber and Faber, 1972, p160
8    A term coined by the anthropologist Victor Turner. A useful introduction to liminality is Bob Trubshaw's online article 'the metaphors and rituals of place and time' at www.indigogroup.co.uk/foamycustard/fc009.htm
9    Bruton in Somerset in the October of 1995. Personal communication.
10   Archive of Andy Williams, May 2003
11   Bob and Lyn Engledow, via www.scottishbigcats.org
12   Dermot Mac Manus, *The Middle Kingdom,* Colin Smythe, 1973
13   Email from C. E. De Rosett, September 2002, via www.indigogroup.co.uk/edge/bdemails.htm
14   Introduction to *Explore Phantom Black Dogs,* ed. Bob Trubshaw, Heart of Albion Press, 2005
15   Archive of Mark Fraser, 15 August 1995
16   *The Westmorland Gazette* 21 Jan 2003
17   Personal communication.
18   Archive of Mark Fraser. Scottish borders, 29 July 1983
19   Archive of Mark Fraser. Kilmarnock, 23 September, 1996
20   Email to Mark Fraser, following an article in the *Harborough Mail,* Leicestershire, 9 March 1999
21   *The Farnham Herald,* 26 July 1991
22   *Shropshire Star,* 29 May 2003
23   October 1999, personal communication.
24   *They Stalk by Night*
25   Archive of Mark Fraser. Near Dalrymple, Ayrshire, Scotland, 6 June 2004
26   Durness, Scotland, 11 May 2004
27   Personal communication.
28   Wooler, *Northumberland Gazette,* 22 October 2004
29   *Western Gazette,* Yeovil, 5 July 2001
30   *The Beast of Exmoor* p21.
31   Adam Edwards, *The Sunday Telegraph,* 15 January 2000
32   *North Devon Journal,* 13 February 2002
33   *Hampshire Chronicle,* 27 December 2000

## Chapter 7 Hard evidence: Kills, footprints, bodies, skulls

1    This is Somerset online news digest, www.thisissomerset.co.uk 2 August 2002
2    This is Somerset, online news digest, 3 October 2002
3    www.bigcats.org.uk
4    *Yorkshire Evening Post*, 24 January 2001
5    *Somerset Guardian* 12 August 2004
6    Nigel Brierly, *They Stalk by Night: the big cats of Exmoor and the South-West.* Yeo Valley Productions, 1989
7    Nigel Brierly, personal communication
8    Professor Alayne Street-Perrott, University of Swansea, Wales – her own horse suffered such wounds
9    *Norwich Evening News,* 1990s
10   Near Bridport, Dorset. Personal communication
11   *They Stalk by Night* p28
12   *Daily Telegraph* 21 November 1998
13   Ferne Park, Berwick St John, Wiltshire. August 2003. Archive of Marcus Matthews
14   Dr Karl Shuker, email to Mark Fraser, October 2004
15   For the technical differences between big and small cats see Appendix 1
16   www.transact.org/library/factsheets/biodiversity.asp
17   Archive of Mark Fraser
18   Reported to Chris Johnson, July 2004
19   *Western Daily Press*, 14 August 2002
20   The M11 near Junction 12. Archive of Terry Dye, Cambridge.
21   9 November 2004. Archive of Mark Fraser
22   *The Scottish Press and Journal*, 15 December 1977
23   *Oldham Evening Chronicle,* 2 December 2003
24   Aberdeenshire 1995. Personal communication
25   Chris Moiser, *Mystery Cats of Devon and Cornwall*, Bossiney Books, 2001
26   Bridport, Dorset. Personal communication. June 2003
27   Karl P.N. Shuker, *Mystery Cats of the World.* Robert Hale, 1989, p48
28   Archive of Mark Fraser

## Chapter 8 Photos and films, roars, screams and growls

1    *Huddersfield Daily Examiner*, 20 May 2005
2    Sighting took place at 1 p.m. on 25 January 2000; personal communication
3    Archive of Terry Dye
4    Personal communication
5    *Animals and Men*, journal of the Centre for Fortean Zoology, issue 3 p7
6    Archive of Mark Fraser, 14 October 2003
7    *Mercury News*, 1 October 1998
8    Co. Durham
9    Personal communication
10   At the time of writing the best collection may be viewed on the website of the British Big Cats Research Group, www.britishbigcatgroup.com

11   Nigel Brierly, *They Stalk by Night: the big cats of Exmoor and the South-West.* Yeo Valley Productions, 1989

12   Graham J. McEwan, *Mystery Animals of Britain and Ireland.* Robert Hale, 1986, p31; McEwan is citing an example, I think, from Trevor Beer's book

13   Archive of Mark Fraser

14   Personal communication

15   Near Wareham, Dorset, April 2004, personal communication

16   Cambridgeshire 1985, personal communication

17   Archive of Chris Moiser, 3 April 2005

18   *Westmorland Gazette,* 27 October 2000

19   *Hertfordshire Mercury,* 30 October 2003

## Chapter 9 Accounting for the anomalies: the hybrid theory

1    Pat O'Halloran, www.danu.co.uk, Big cat sightings in Scarborough and Ryedale

2    Archive of Mark Fraser, Yorkshire big cats.

3    Mark Fraser, www.scottishbigcats.co.uk

4    Paul Sieveking, *Sunday Telegraph,* 11 February 2001

5    Yeovil, May 2004; personal communication

6    Personal communication

7    Sighting was in 1984 near Paignton, Devon. Nigel Brierly, *They Stalk by Night: The big cats of Exmoor and the South-West.* Yeo Valley Productions, 1989. p60

8    Trevor Beer, *The Beast of Exmoor. Fact or legend?* Barnstable, 1985

9    Pat O'Halloran, www.danu.co.uk, Big cat sightings in Scarborough & Ryedale

10   Ronnie Patterson, 'Diary of a big cat hunter / Part 1, October 1997' in *Scottish Mystery Cat Sightings,* from www.scottishbigcats.co.uk

11   *Evening News*, Norwich, 26 April 1996

12   Archive of Mark Fraser, Yorkshire big cats, 1999 sightings

13   Nigel Spencer's archive, Rutland sightings 2001

14   *This is Wiltshire* online news, 27 December 2002

15   *North Devon Journal,* 13 February 2002

16   Archive of Mark Fraser, Yorkshire big cats, 1999 sightings.

17   Archive of Mark Fraser; sighting in June 2005

18   Archive of Clive Moulding, 30 March 2002

19   Karl P.N. Shuker, *Mystery Cats of the World,* Robert Hale, 1989

20   *They Stalk by Night* p40

21   4 September 2002

22   *The Beast of Exmoor* p19

23   Witness interviewed by David Spencer, March 1999

24   In 1982, investigated by Di Francis, *Cat Country*

25   J.S. Hartwell, www.messybeast.com

26   J.S. Hartwell, www.messybeast.com

27   R. Tabor, *The Wildlife of the Domestic Cat,* Arrow Books, 1983; quoted by K.P.N. Shuker, *Mystery Cats Of The World.* Robert Hale, 1989

28   Alan Fleming, personal communication

29  Scripps Howard News Service, USA, 6 July 2005
30  The convoluted subject of the genetics of big cats is well covered in J.S. Hartwell's Messybeast Cat Resource Archive Web site, www.messybeast.com

## Chapter 10 Accounting for the anomalies: the hide-out theory

1   The term 'cryptozoology', meaning hidden animals, was reputedly coined by another cryptozoologist, Ivan T. Sanderson
2   Karl P.N. Shuker, *Mystery Cats of the World*. Robert Hale, 1989
3   Raphael Holinshed, *Description of England* Vol 1 p225
4   Graham J. McEwan, *Mystery Animals of Britain and Ireland*. Robert Hale, 1986.
5   Paul Sieveking, *Fortean Times*, No.167, February 2003
6   Andy Roberts, *Cat Flaps: Northern mystery cats*. Brigantia Books, 1986
7   Loren Coleman, *Mysterious America*. Paraview Press, 2001, p153
8   *Daily Mail*, 21 September 1994
9   *Daily Telegraph*, 21 November 1998
10  Archive of Mark Fraser, Great Wakering, Essex, February 1999
11  16–22 June 1999, reported in local and national press, quoted in Paul Sieveking, '1999 Big Cat Roundup', *Fortean Times* No.133, April 2000,
12  Web site of the Quaternary Research Association, www.interscience.wiley.com/journal/jqs. 10 October 2005
13  http//cal.man.ac.uk/student_projects/2002/MNBF9ALS/default.htm
4   *Sunday Post* (Scotland), 15 August 1976
5   Archive of Mark Fraser, December 1996
6   Archive of Mark Fraser, January 1997
7   Archive of Mark Fraser, 17 January 2000
8   Personal communication
9   The event happened at 7.30 a.m. in September 1990, personal communication
20  John Michell and R.J.M. Rickard, *Phenomena*: *A book of wonders*; Thames and Hudson, 1977

## Chapter 11 Other theories

1   Archive of Mark Fraser, Emailed report, 13 September 2003
2   Email from 'Phebe' in 2002 to non-nativecats@yahoogroups.com
3   Personal communication
4   Graham J. McEwan, *Mystery Animals of Britain and Ireland*. Robert Hale, 1986, p49
5   *Daily Express* 14 January 1927
6   Charles Fort, *Lo!* (1931), Chapter 7, from *The Complete Books of Charles Fort*, Dover Publications, 1974
7   Charles Fort, *The Complete Books of Charles Fort*. Dover Publications, 1974

## Chapter 12 The Earth tiger

1   Michell, John. *The Earth Spirit: Its Ways, Shrines and Mysteries.* Thames and Hudson, 1975. p14.
2   Moore, Steve: 'Notes on Greenwich Phenomena, Part three of a Taoist interpretation of fortean phenomenology', *Fortean Times* No. 16, June 1976, p8
3   Brown, Theo, 'The Black Dogs', *Folklore,* Sept 1958 p175-192.
4   Monday 5th May 2003. Archive of Nigel and David Spencer, Leicestershire and Rutland Panther Watch. website: http://www.bigcats.org.uk
5   December 2001. Archive of Nigel and David Spencer
6   9pm on Friday 11 February 2000
7   2000. Archive of Nigel and David Spencer
8   Nigel Spencer, 25 April 2005
9   Ethel Rudkin 'The Black Dog' *Folk-lore*, Vol. 49, 1938
10  Archive of Mark Fraser, near Darvel in Ayrshire, the last Monday of August 2001
11  *Dorset Echo* 4 March 2002
12  Sighting from the 1980s, personal communication
13  *South Wales Echo* 3 September 1999
14  Near Brayford, Devon. *North Devon Journal,* 18 January 2001
15  Nigel Spencer
16  Paul Ross, *Fortean Times,* No. 181, March 2004
17  Archive of Mark Fraser, www.scottishbigcats.co.uk
18  Steve Moore, 'Notes on Greenwich Phenomena, Part three of a Taoist interpretation of fortean phenomenology', *Fortean Times* No. 16, June 1976, p8
19  Nigel Brierly, *They Stalk by Night: The big cats of Exmoor and the South-West.* Yeo Valley Productions, 1989, p42
20  Archive of Mark Fraser, latest sighting 4 April 2005
21  Thomas Keightley. 1870. *The Fairy Mythology: Illustrative of the Romance and Superstition of Various Countries.* http://www.sacred-texts.com/neu/celt/tfm/index.htm 2005, in a footnote citing Hugh Miller, *The Old Red Sandstone*, p. 251.
22  *Worcester Evening News*, 24 February 2001
23  *They Stalk by Night*
24  Early 1980s, near Heathfield, Sussex. Personal communication
25  Ernest J. Eitel, *Feng Shui, The science of sacred landscape in old China.*
26  *Aberdeen Press and Journal*, 17 January 2003
27  *Aberdeen Press and Journal*, 9 January 2002
28  August 2003
29  In 1995 by Chris Moiser.
30  At Pease Pottage Golf Club, near Crawley in Surrey. *Crawley News*, 10 October 2001
31  Archive of Mark Fraser, Scottish Big Cat Society, www.scottishbigcats.co.uk
32  *Aberdeen Press and Journal*, 31 July 2003

## Chapter 13 Daimons and their slippery nature

1   Patrick Harpur. *Daimonic Reality: A Field Guide to the Otherworld*, Penguin, 1995; and *The Philosophers' Secret Fire: A History of the Imagination*, Penguin 2000

2   Aniela Jaffé, *Apparitions* University of Dallas 1979

3   W.B. Yeats, *Mythologies*, Macmillan, 1959

4   Iamblichus, *On the Mysteries of the Egyptians, Chaldeans and Assyrians...* trans. Thomas Taylor 1821

5   Account by Brian Murphy for archive of Mark Fraser. 30 March 2002, Galston, Ayrshire

6   Wiltshire local press, 2 May 2002

7   Local press, Spring 1994

8   25 January 2003, Stourbridge. Mark Fraser, ABC round-up 2003, *Journal of the Centre for Fortean Zoology*

9   *Southern Evening Echo,* 19 October 1983

10  Nigel Spencer, Rutland and Leicester Panther Watch,  www.bigcats.org.uk January 1999

11  *Daily Mail*, 8 January 1985

12  *Northampton Chronicle and Echo*, 4 September 2002

13  www.thisisderbyshire.co.uk 6 August 2002

14  Letter to Di Francis, 1983

15  Letter to Di Francis, 1983

16  Archive of Mark Fraser, 15 June 2002

17  *Guardian* 7 April 1999, Near Gobowen, Shropshire, on a bright, sunny morning.

18  Letter to Di Francis, 1983, sighting in 1978

19  Archive of Mark Fraser, 11 October 2003, Cornwall

20  Email report from witness, Thetford, Norfolk, 4 July 2003

21  Archive of Nigel Spencer, Rutland 21 June 2001

22  *Devon Express and Echo,* 16 March 1983

23  Archive of Alan White, email to bigcatsnews group, 1 December 2004

24  Trevor Beer, *The Beast of Exmoor. Fact or legend?* Barnstable, 1985

25  Archive of Mark Fraser

26  Archive of Mark Fraser, Ayrshire, December 2000

27  *Shropshire Star*, 8 August 2002

28  2004, personal communication

29  Iamblichus, *On the Mysteries of the Egyptians, Chaldeans and Assyrians... ,* trans. Thomas Taylor 1821

## Chapter 14 A dragon as big as a kitten

1   Iamblichus, *On the Mysteries of the Egyptians, Chaldeans and Assyrians... ,* trans. Thomas Taylor 1821

2   Archive of Di Francis, Redruth, Cornwall. 31 October 1983

3   'One can measure a circle beginning anywhere... ', *The Complete Books of Charles Fort,*   Dover Publications 1974

4   *Waltham Forest Guardian* 25 January 2001
5   Rutland 2 April 2002, archive of Nigel Spencer
6   *Black Isle North Star* 26 September 2003
7   *The Cornishman* 8 July 1999
8   Rutland 21 June 2001, archive of Nigel Spencer
9   Archive of Mark Fraser.
10  July 2003. personal communication
11  Ruth L. Tongue, *Somerset Folklore*: County Series VIII, FLS 1965, p128–9
12  Katherine Briggs, *The Fairies in Tradition and Literature*. Routledge and Keegan Paul, 1967, p64–5
13  The Lambtons are a longstanding family in the area and Lambton Castle and large parts of the estate are nearby. Lord Lambton is the patron of St George's Church. Local belief is that the real 'worm hill' is small hillock on the north bank of the Wear by Fatfield Bridge within the St George's parish.
14  W.Y. Evans Wentz, *The Fairy Faith in Celtic Countries*. Colin Smythe, 1981, p47

## Chapter 15 Traditional daimons and ABCs

1   In a letter written to his brothers George and Thomas on the 21st December, 1817
2   Dermot Mac Manus, *The Middle Kingdom*, Colin Smythe 1973
3   E.Œ. Somerville and Martin Ross, *The Smile and the Tear*, Methuen, 1933. The event happened in July 1921 and is recorded in the chapter entitled 'Lakes and Monsters.' I am grateful to David Ainslie for drawing my attention to this passage
4   Archive of Mark Fraser
5   Nigel Brierly, *They Stalk by Night: The big cats of Exmoor and the South-West*. Yeo Valley Productions, 1989, p49
6   Andrew Collins, 'The Hornden black panther, and theories regarding the nature of mystery beasts', *Earthquest News* Nos. 9 and 10, Spring 1984
7   January 1995, personal communication
8   I describe Mr Windsor's sighting in Chapter 7
9   1.30 p.m. 4 September 2002, near Woodhouse Eaves, Leicestershire. Archive of Nigel Spencer
10  Personal communication, 1989
11  Title taken from a traditional Scottish song, in *Collected Ghost Stories of M.R. James* Edward Arnold & Co., 1931
12  Emma Wilby, 'The Witch's Familiar and the Fairy in Early Modern England and Scotland', *Folklore* 111, 2000
13  *Rutland Times*, 8 June 2001
14  In the December of 1977 at about 9.30 p.m.
15  Paul Ross, 'Spirits of the South Pacific', *Fortean Times* No.181, March 2004
16  W.Y. Evans Wentz, *The Fairy Faith in Celtic Countries*. Colin Smythe, 1981. Patrick Waters told this to Evans Wentz in September 1909.
17  Kathleen Murray, personal communication
18  Memphis, Tennessee, USA; *Fortean Times* online message board, 2002

19   Karl P.N. Shuker, *Mystery Cats of The World.* Robert Hale, 1989
20   *Norwich Evening News,* 3 July 1997
21   Archive of Christopher Johnston, 8 August 2004
22   *The Times,* 31 May 1983
23   *Western Morning News,* 30 December 1997
24   *Western Morning News,* 30 January 2003
25   Cited by Graham J. McEwan in *Mystery Animals of Britain and Ireland,* Robert Hale, 1986
26   12 April 2003, personal communication
27   A character in the television series *Star Trek*
28   11 August 1995, Banff, personal communication
29   Inverness-Shire, Mark Fraser, Scottish Big Cat Society, www.scottishbigcats.co.uk
30   Archive of Mark Fraser, 9 November 2003
31   *Daily Telegraph,* 26 October 1998
32   Shipham on the Mendips, 11 October 2002
33   January 1995, near Staxton. Scarborough and Ryedale archive of Pat O'Halloran, www.danu.co.uk 2002
34   8 June 2003, Bramhall, Cheshire
35   *Ripley News* via *Ripley Today* 2 October 2003
36   Correspondence with Di Francis, 5 June 1984
37   Near Ferndown, Dorset, in October 2001; personal communication
38   Near Enfield, 21 September 2003; archive of Andy Williams
39   M.R. James, 'Oh, whistle and I'll come to you, my lad', *Collected Ghost Stories,* Edward Arnold & Co., 1931
40   February 2004, personal communication
41   *Shropshire Star* 24 May 2003
42   *Ormskirk Advertiser* 2 October 2003

## Chapter 16 Blackness and shine

1    Cited by Mike Dash in *Borderlands,* Arrow Books, 1997, p161
2    January 2001 Archive of Nigel Spencer, Rutland and Leicestershire Panther Watch, www.bigcats.org.uk
3    *Gloucestershire Echo,* 24 November 2000
4    October 2004, personal communication
5    *Eastern Daily Press,* 10 May 2002
6    *Hexham Courant,* 19 July 2005
7    16 January 2003, personal communication
8    Nigel Brierly, *They Stalk by Night: The big cats of Exmoor and the South-West.* Yeo Valley Productions, 1989.
9    Archive of Mark Fraser, 12 April 2003
10   Tixover, South Rutland. Rutland and Leicester Panther Watch, www.bigcats.org.uk
11   Sighting occurred in April 1987
12   David Colman, 'Pussy Galore', article on website www.scottishbigcats.org
13   *Mercury News,* 1 October 1998

14   3 September 2002 at about 10.30 a.m.
15   Katherine Briggs, *The Fairies in Tradition and Literature.* Routledge and Kegan Paul, 1967, p135
16   Dermot MacManus; *The Middle Kingdom,* Max Parrish, 1959, p33
17   Nigel Spencer, Rutland and Leicester Panther Watch, www.bigcats.org.uk:
18   *Birmingham Post* 16 January 2003
19   North Ayrshire. *Sunday Express,* 16 June 1974
20   *The Evening Telegraph,* Dundee, 4 November 2002
21   Archive of Mark Fraser, Okehampton, 17 October 1999
22   Bowthorpe Road, Norwich. *Norwich Evening News,* 26 July 1997
23   November 2002. Nigel Spencer, personal communication
24   *Evening Standard* 24 January 2003
25   Archive of Mark Fraser, May 1997 Fintry, Stirlingshire
26   A term coined by UFOlogist Jenny Randles, referring to *The Wizard of Oz*
27   1983, personal communication
28   March 2003, personal communication
29   Celia Green, cited in
     www.sawka.com/spiritwatch/interview_with_celia_green.htm,
     accessed 13 October 2005
30   Early summer 2004, personal communication
31   November 2003, personal communication
32   Reginald Scot, *Discoverie of Witchcraft* (vii, xv) 1584
33   John Campbell-Kease (ed.). *'Tribute to an Armorist', Essays for John Brooke-Little,* 2000 p 90
34   Personal communication
35   Dennis Bardens, *Psychic Animals,* Robert Hale, 1987, p96, citing contributors to the London *Daily News* in the 1920s

## Chapter 17 Physical encounters and half-hearted attacks

1    In December 1992
2    www.thisisworcestershire.co.uk 10 October 2001
3    Early afternoon 9 January 2002, personal communication
4    Report by Mark Fraser
5    Hayfield, near Chapel-en-le-Frith, Derbyshire Peak District. *Daily Telegraph,* 3 April 1992
6    *The Scotsman,* 23 March 2005
7    *The Sun,* 21 April 1994
8    *The Sun,* 20 October 1993
9    Archive of W. Ritchie Benedict. *The Cincinnati Enquirer,* 'Liberty, Indiana, Tuesday December 25th, 1877'
10   Thomas Crofton Croker, *Fairy Legends and Traditions of the South of Ireland.* John Murray, 1834
11   Event occurred on 17 March 1996. Marcus Matthews, 'Wiltshire Wildcats', www.dorsetbigcats/matthews.htm September 2005
12   Personal communication
13   www.dalesman.co.uk

14    Norman Cohn *Europe's Inner Demons*, Sussex Univ. Press, 1975
15    Long Island, New York, 2000. Submitted to www.unexplained-mysteries.com/sightings.htm

**Chapter 18 'I never sleep if one is near... '**

1     Sir Algernon Blackwood, *A Psychical Invasion*, London, 1908.
2     *Westmorland Gazette* 13 March 2003
3     Near Chudleigh Knighton, Devon. *Herald Express*, Devon, 1 March 1983.
4     June 2005, personal communication
5     Archive of Mark Fraser, Ayrshire, December 2000
6     Archive of Mark Fraser, Ayrshire, December 2000
7     G. Markie email to non-nativecats@yahoogroups.com 27 January 2003
8     Henry Glassie, *Irish Folk-Tales,* Penguin, 1985, p178
9     Emma Wilby, 'The Witch's Familiar and the Fairy in Early Modern England and Scotland', *Folklore*, Vol. 111 October 2000
10    Jeremy Harte, 'Pussycat, pussycat, where have you been?' Originally published in *At the Edge* No. 6 1997; online at www.indigogroup.co.uk/edge/pussycat.htm
11    Graham J. McEwan, *Mystery Animals of Britain and Ireland,* Robert Hale, 1986
12    General Sir Thomas Edward Gordon, *A Varied Life,* 1906
13    Kathleen Briggs, *The Fairies in Tradition and Literature*, Routledge and Kegan Paul, 1967, p71–2; citing *Folk-Lore Journal* Vol. 2, p22
14    Carl Van Vechten, *The Tiger in the House*, A. A. Knopf, 1922, Chapter 4, 'The Cat and the Occult', published online November 2000 by www.bartleby.com
15    *Fortean Times* online notice board, April 2003
16    *Fortean Times* No. 171, June, 2003. Email from Jason Hanrahan
17    *The Tiger in the House*
18    *The Tiger in the House*
19    *The Tiger in the House*
20    *Nigel Brierly, They Stalk by Night: The big cats of Exmoor and the South-West.* Yeo , Valley Productions, 1989
21    Personal communication
22    *Independent,* 4 September 2002
23    *Basingstoke Gazette*, 23 July 1976
24    Archive of Mark Fraser, March 2005, Aberdeenshire
25    Earl Swift, article in local paper *The Virginian-Pilot*, 1 February 2003 www.pilotonline.com/news/nw0201cat.html
26    Archive of Mark Fraser, Market Weighton, Yorkshire, July 1999
27    Jeremy Harte, 'Pussycat, pussycat, where have you been?' Originally published in *At the Edge* No. 6 1997; online at www.indigogroup.co.uk/edge/pussycat.htm
28    Peter Alderson Smith, *W B Yeats and the tribes of Danu*, Colin Smythe, 1987, p124

## Chapter 19 Eyesight *versus* vision

1   Simon J. Sherwood, 'A psychological approach to apparitions of black dogs', in *Explore Phantom Black Dogs*, ed. Bob Trubshaw, Explore Books, 2005
2   Paul Evans, *Guardian*, 7 April 1999
3   *Sunday Times*, 2 November 1980
4   Michel Meurger and Claude Gagnon, *Lake Monster Traditions : A cross-cultural analysis*, Fortean Tomes, 1988
5   *Fortean Times* notice board, July 2001
6   Dornoch, Sutherland, Scotland. Letter to Di Francis, 1984
7   Jeremy Harte, 'Black dog studies', in *Explore Phantom Black Dogs*, ed. Bob Trubshaw, Explore Books, 2005
8   *Blackpool Gazette*, 29 August 2003
9   Trevor Beer, *The Beast of Exmoor. Fact or legend?* Countryside Productions, 1985, p36
10  Archive of Mark Fraser, Gwynned, Wales, 24 April 2005
11  C.G. Jung, and A. Jaffe, *Memories, Dreams, Reflections*. Collins, 1967 p208–9
12  Bungay, Suffolk. BBC News, 2 August 2004
13  *Norwich Evening News*, 3 July 1997
14  Archive of Mark Fraser. Sighting 15 April 2004
15  West Wiltshire local press, 30 March 2001
16  Martin and Louise Jeffrey, 'Who's Stalking Who?', article on Mark Fraser's website, www.scottishbigcats.co.uk
17  Bruce Allen Sprinkle, the *INFO Journal*, (publ. Arlington, Va. USA), January 1994, p29. The event was in the fall of 1977. From the archive of W. Ritchie Benedict
18  Report sent to Mark Fraser
19  Archive of Mark Fraser, 6.10 p.m. March 2003
20  Dermot Mac Manus *The Middle Kingdom*, Colin Smythe 1973, p142–4
21  *New Statesman*, 26 December 1975
22  *Worcester Evening News*, 24 February 2001
23  Roy Neville, letter to Di Francis, 7 January 1982. The encounter took place in October 1981
24  Reported to Ronald Black, November 2004
25  John Keats, letter to Benjamin Bailey, 22 November 1817

## Chapter 20 Manners

1   Emma Wilby, 'The Witch's Familiar and the Fairy in Early Modern England and Scotland', *Folklore* Vol. 111, No. 2, October 2000
2   Emma Wilby, citing John Davenport, *The Witches of Huntingdon*. London, 1646
3   Archive of Nigel Spencer, 20 October 2004
4   *Evening Echo*, Colchester, 10 January 2002
5   Thomas Keightley, *The Fairy Mythology: Illustrative of the romance and superstition of various countries*, 1870

6   *The Fairy Mythology*
7   Ruth L. Tongue, *Somerset Folklore*. The Folk-lore Society 1965.
8   *The Fairy Mythology*
9   Paul Ross, 'Spirits of the South Pacific', *Fortean Times,* No.181, March 2004

# Index

Places are listed under name of country (e.g. France, Italy, Scotland, Wales) except for English places which are listed under name of county.

# Explore Phantom

# Black Dogs

## edited by Bob Trubshaw

Contributors: Jeremy Harte, Simon Sherwood, Alby Stone, Bob Trubshaw and Jennifer Westwood.

The folklore of phantom black dogs is known throughout the British Isles. From the Black Shuck of East Anglia to the Moody Dhoo of the Isle of Man there are tales of huge spectral hounds 'darker than the night sky' with eyes 'glowing red as burning coals'.

The phantom black dog of British and Irish folklore, which often forewarns of death, is part of a world-wide belief that dogs are sensitive to spirits and the approach of death, and keep watch over the dead and dying. North European and Scandinavian myths dating back to the Iron Age depict dogs as corpse eaters and the guardians of the roads to Hell. Medieval folklore includes a variety of 'Devil dogs' and spectral hounds. Above all, the way people have thought about such ghostly creatures has steadily evolved.

This book will appeal to all those interested in folklore, the paranormal and fortean phenomena.

> 'I think this must be the best entry in the Explore series I have seen so far... ' **Aeronwy Dafies** *Monomyth Supplement*

> 'This is an excellent work and is very highly recommended.' **Michael Howard** *The Cauldron*

ISBN 1 872883 78 8. Published 2005. Demy 8vo (215 x 138 mm), 152 + viii pages, 10 b&w half-tones, paperback. **£12.95**

# Explore Dragons

## Richard Freeman

The dragon is the most ancient and widespread of all monsters. Dragon legends are told in every culture and in every continent on Earth. Its breath condenses and forms rain in China. It slithers across the heavens in Mexico as Quetzalcoatl. In Scandinavian lore its coils encircled the whole earth. No other monster is so universal in its occurrence or so varied.

But the Britain Isles are the homeland of the dragon. Although a small country, it is seething with dragon legends. Explore Dragons puts British dragon stories into their international context and attempts to fathom out what really lurks behind these fanciful tales. Could dragons once have been real creatures? Are such creatures still alive?

**Richard Freeman** is a former zookeeper and has a degree in zoology. He is the zoological director of the Centre for Fortean Zoology in Exeter. A full-time cryptozoologist, he has searched for monsters and mystery animals in Indo-China, Sumatra, and Mongolia as well as in the UK.

Published by Explore Books, an imprint of Heart of Albion Press.
EAN 978-1-872883-939. ISBN 1 872883 93 1. May 2006
Demy 8vo (215 x 138 mm), paperback.
£12.95

# A Bestiary of Brass

## Peter Heseltine

From antelopes to wyverns, with over fifty species in between, *A Bestiary of Brass* looks the animals, birds, insects, fish – even shellfish – which have been depicted on medieval memorial brasses in Britain. Some are native, others – such as elephants and panthers – were exotic, while dragons and unicorns were as mythical then as they are today.

At the time they were engraved these creatures evoked a wide range of folklore and legends. This rich symbolism is brought to life by the author. But enigmas remain – why would anyone want to be associated with a fox when they were more noted for cunning and slyness, or a hedgehog, or even a whelk? We also find out about the lives of the people commemorated and share the author's detailed knowledge of their heraldic emblems. Practical advice is provided to help make brass rubbings and to learn more about these memorials.

The illustrations show a wide range of the memorials, with detailed views of the creatures they incorporate. *A Bestiary of Brass* will appeal to anyone interested in folklore, art and medieval history. Above all, these masterpieces of craftsmanship reveal that our deep fascination with animals was shared by our ancestors many hundreds of years ago.

EAN 978 1872 883 908. ISBN 1 872883 90 7. March 2006.
Demy 8vo (215 x 138 mm), over 280 illustrations, paperback
£12.95

# The Princess Who Ate People

## The psychology of Celtic myths

### Brendan McMahon

Childhood, adolescence, courtship and death. Personal identity and madness. These are the key themes of many myths in traditional Celtic literatures. Although written many centuries ago, their narratives still reflect and define our essential humanity.

Many Celtic tales of exile and loss anticipate modem dilemmas of alienation but offer ways of understanding such difficulties without pathologising them. Individuals are seen in their social context and, in contrast, madness is identified with loneliness and isolation. The traditional stories describe how appropriate narratives help restore integrity and identity. These life-cycle narratives and concepts of identity are more complex and less fixed than psychoanalytic narratives which, by comparison, seem contrived or impoverished.

Psychotherapy assists people to construct a narrative which makes sense of their lives. However psychoanalysis too often relies on outdated and limited assumptions. By learning from the poets who created the Celtic myths, therapists can help their patients develop more appropriate personal narratives.

However this is not a book written only for psychotherapists. The stories considered here speak to all of us. McMahon helps us to fully understand these life cycle narratives and thereby helps us to understand ourselves. We need these myths now more than ever before.

**Brendan McMahon** is a practicing psychotherapist in Derbyshire who has written many articles and papers on therapy and Celtic myth. He is also a poet and university teacher.

ISBN 1 872883 88 5. January 2006. Demy 8vo (215 x 138 mm), 102 + viii pages, 5 specially commissioned illustrations from Ian Brown, paperback  **£9.95**

# Taliesin's Travels

## A demi-god at large

## Michael Dames

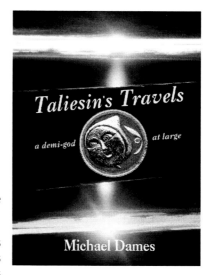

*Taliesin's Travels* brings fresh significance to one of Britain's best-loved tales.

For over a thousand years the impish Taliesin has enthralled and enlightened people. As a farmer's son, he is grounded in the land. Yet, because his mother is the goddess Nature, he can travel, free as a demi-god, throughout time and space.

Thanks to his intimate contact with spirits of place, sun and underworld, Taliesin reveals and portrays the interconnecting, ever-transforming essence of life. His often painful and sometimes ludicrous adventures engage with creation in its entirety. Transcending history, he invites us to see our own millennium as a cyclical, mythic journey so that, like him, each individual comes to identify with the whole of creation.

With a keen sense of enjoyment, Michael Dames provides a deep and imaginative account of the tales and poetry associated with Taliesin. Prehistoric, Romano-British and Christian aspects of Taliesin's persona are brought together in a magical synthesis.

**Michael Dames** is well-known for his pioneering studies of the myths and legends of the British Isles. His previous books include *The Silbury Treasure, The Avebury Cycle, Mythic Ireland* and *Merlin and Wales.*

EAN 978 1872 883 892. ISBN 1 872883 89 3. February 2006.
245 x 175 mm, over 200 illustrations, paperback
£16.95

# The Enchanted Land

## Myths and Legends of Britain's Landscape

Revised, fully illustrated edition

## Janet and Colin Bord

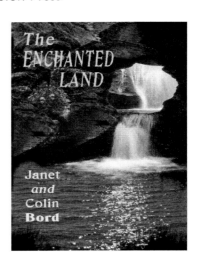

Britain's landscape is overlain by a magic carpet of folklore and folktales, myths and legends. Enchantment and legend still lurk in places as diverse as hills and mountains, rivers and streams, caves and hollows, springs and wells, cliffs and coasts, pools and lakes, and rocks and stones.

The dramatic stories woven around these places tell of sleeping knights, beheaded saints, giants, dragons and monsters, ghosts, King Arthur, mermaids, witches, hidden treasure, drowned towns, giant missiles, mysterious footprints, visits to Fairyland, underground passages, human sacrifices, and much more.

The 'Places to Visit' section locates and describes in detail more than 50 sites.

This revised edition is fully illustrated, with around 130 photographs and illustrations.

**Janet and Colin Bord** live in North Wales, where they run the Fortean Picture Library. They have written more than 20 books since their first successful joint venture, *Mysterious Britain* in 1972.

### From reviews of the first edition:

'Janet's own enthusiasm for a number of the sites is conveyed vividly and lends credibility to the notion that Britain is still an enchanted land.' *Mercian Mysteries*

ISBN 1 872883 91 5. March 2006. 245 x 175 mm, over 200 illustrations, paperback **£16.95**

# Sacred Places
## Prehistory and popular imagination
### Bob Trubshaw

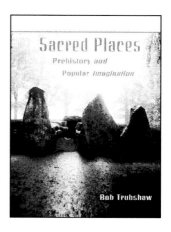

*Sacred Places* asks why certain types of prehistoric places are thought of as sacred, and explores how the physical presence of such sacred sites is less important than what these places signify. So this is not another guide book to sacred places but instead provides a unique and thought-provoking guide to the mental worlds – the mindscapes – in which we have created the idea of prehistoric sacred places.

Recurring throughout this book is the idea that we continually create and re-create our ideas about the past, about landscapes, and the places within those landscapes that we regard as sacred. For example, although such concepts as 'nature', 'landscape', 'countryside', 'rural' and the contrast between profane and sacred are all part of our everyday thinking, in this book Bob Trubshaw shows they are all modern cultural constructions which act as the 'unseen' foundations on which we construct more complex myths about places.

Key chapters look at how earth mysteries, modern paganism and other alternative approaches to sacred places developed in recent decades, and also outline the recent dramatic changes within academic archaeology. Is there now a 'middle way' between academic and alternative approaches which recognises that what we know about the past is far less significant than what we believe about the past?

**Bob Trubshaw** has been actively involved with academic and alternative approaches to archaeology for most of the last twenty years. In 1996 he founded *At the Edge* magazine to popularise new interpretations of past and place.

> '*Sacred Places...* is a very valuable addition to the small body of thoughtful work on the spiritual landscapes of Great Britain and therefore recommended reading.' Nigel Pennick *Silver Wheel*

> 'One of the best books in the field I have ever read.'
> D J Tyrer *Monomyth Supplement*

ISBN 1 872883 67 2. 2005. 245 x 175 mm, 203 + xiv pages, 43 b&w illustrations and 7 line drawings, paperback. **£16.95**

# Stonehenge:
## Celebration and Subversion

## Andy Worthington

This innovative social history looks in detail at how the summer solstice celebrations at Stonehenge have brought together different aspects of British counter-culture to make the monument a 'living temple' and an icon of alternative Britain. The history of the celebrants and counter-cultural leaders is interwoven with the viewpoints of the land-owners, custodians and archaeologists who have generally attempted to impose order on the shifting patterns of these modern-day mythologies.

The story of the Stonehenge summer solstice celebrations begins with the Druid revival of the 18th century and the earliest public gatherings of the 19th and early 20th centuries. In the social upheavals of the 1960s and early 70s, these trailblazers were superseded by the Stonehenge Free Festival. This evolved from a small gathering to an anarchic free state the size of a small city, before its brutal suppression at the Battle of the Beanfield in 1985.

In the aftermath of the Beanfield, the author examines how the political and spiritual aspirations of the free festivals evolved into both the rave scene and the road protest movement, and how the prevailing trends in the counter-culture provided a fertile breeding ground for the development of new Druid groups, the growth of paganism in general, and the adoption of other sacred sites, in particular Stonehenge's gargantuan neighbour at Avebury.

The account is brought up to date with the reopening of Stonehenge on the summer solstice in 2000, the unprecedented crowds drawn by the new access arrangements, and the latest source of conflict, centred on a bitterly-contested road improvement scheme.

> '*Stonehenge Celebration and Subversion* contains an extraordinary story. Anyone who imagines Stonehenge to be nothing but an old fossil should read this and worry. [This book is] ... the most complete, well-illustrated analysis of Stonehenge's mysterious world of Druids, travellers, pagans and party-goers'. Mike Pitts *History Today*

ISBN 1 872883 76 1. 2004. Perfect bound, 245 x 175 mm, 281 + xviii pages, 147 b&w photos, **£14.95**

*Winner of the Folklore Society Katherine Briggs Award 2005*

# Explore Fairy Traditions

## Jeremy Harte

We are not alone. In the shadows of our countryside there lives a fairy race, older than humans, and not necessarily friendly to them. For hundreds of years, men and women have told stories about the strange people, beautiful as starlight, fierce as wolves, and heartless as ice. These are not tales for children. They reveal the fairies as a passionate, proud, brutal people.

*Explore Fairy Traditions* draws on legends, ballads and testimony from throughout Britain and Ireland to reveal what the fairies were really like. It looks at changelings, brownies, demon lovers, the fairy host, and abduction into the Otherworld. Stories and motifs are followed down the centuries to reveal the changing nature of fairy lore, as it was told to famous figures like W.B. Yeats and Sir Walter Scott. All the research is based on primary sources and many errors about fairy tradition are laid to rest.

Jeremy Harte combines folklore scholarship with a lively style to show what the presence of fairies meant to people's lives. Like their human counterparts, the secret people could kill as well as heal. They knew marriage, seduction, rape and divorce; they adored some children and rejected others. If we are frightened of the fairies, it may be because their world offers an uncomfortable mirror of our own.

> '... this is the best and most insightful book on fairies generally available... ' John Billingsley *Northern Earth*

> '*Explore Fairy Traditions* is an excellent introduction to the folklore of fairies, and I would highly recommend it.' Paul Mason *Silver Wheel*

ISBN 1 872883 61 3. Published 2004. Demy 8vo (215 x 138 mm), 171 + vi pages, 6 line drawings, paperback. **£9.95**

*'Highly recommended'*
*Folklore Society Katherine Briggs*
*Award 2003*

# Explore Folklore

## Bob Trubshaw

**'A howling success, which plugs
a big and obvious gap'**

Professor Ronald Hutton

There have been fascinating developments in the study of folklore in the last twenty-or-so years, but few books about British folklore and folk customs reflect these exciting new approaches. As a result there is a huge gap between scholarly approaches to folklore studies and 'popular beliefs' about the character and history of British folklore. *Explore Folklore* is the first book to bridge that gap, and to show how much 'folklore' there is in modern day Britain.

*Explore Folklore* shows there is much more to folklore than morris dancing and fifty-something folksingers! The rituals of 'what we do on our holidays', funerals, stag nights and 'lingerie parties' are all full of 'unselfconscious' folk customs. Indeed, folklore is something that is integral to all our lives – it is so intrinsic we do not think of it as being 'folklore'.

The implicit ideas underlying folk lore and customs are also explored. There might appear to be little in common between people who touch wood for luck (a 'tradition' invented in the last 200 years) and legends about people who believe they have been abducted and subjected to intimate body examinations by aliens. Yet, in their varying ways, these and other 'folk beliefs' reflect the wide spectrum of belief and disbelief in what is easily dismissed as 'superstition'.

*Explore Folklore* provides a lively introduction to the study of most genres of British folklore, presenting the more contentious and profound ideas in a readily accessible manner.

ISBN 1 872883 60 5. Published 2002. Demy 8vo (215x138 mm), 200 pages, illustrated, paperback **£9.95**

*Also from Heart of Albion Press*

# Explore Mythology

## Bob Trubshaw

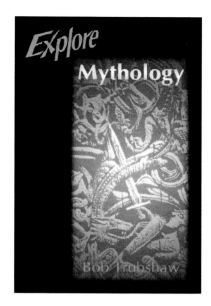

Myths are usually thought of as something to do with 'traditional cultures'. The study of such 'traditional' myths emphasises their importance in religion, national identity, hero-figures, understanding the origin of the universe, and predictions of an apocalyptic demise. The academic study of myths has done much to fit these ideas into the preconceived ideas of the relevant academics.

Only in recent years have such long-standing assumptions about myths begun to be questioned, opening up whole new ways of thinking about the way such myths define and structure how a society thinks about itself and the 'real world'.

These new approaches to the study of myth reveal that, to an astonishing extent, modern day thinking is every bit as 'mythological' as the world-views of, say, the Classical Greeks or obscure Polynesian tribes. Politics, religions, science, advertising and the mass media are all deeply implicated in the creation and use of myths.

*Explore Mythology* provides a lively introduction to the way myths have been studied, together with discussion of some of the most important 'mythic motifs' – such as heroes, national identity, and 'central places' – followed by a discussion of how these ideas permeate modern society. These sometimes contentious and profound ideas are presented in an easily readable style of writing.

> 'Here's another brilliant volume, an account of mythology such as you are unlikely ever to have seen before. This is no mere collection of mythological stories. It's a thoughtful, well researched exposition which really gets down to the deep structure of the narratives which encode the consciousness of groups and societies.... Buy it! If you follow up even a fraction of the leads, there's enough here to keep you occupied for many a month to come.' Francis Cameron *Pentacle*

> '... this book is... a useful introduction to literature that many would find hard to come by, and offers a challenging perspective that does not let assumptions rest easy.' John Billingsley *Northern Earth*

ISBN 1 872883 62 1. Perfect bound. Demi 8vo (215 x 138 mm), 220 + xx pages, 17 line drawings. **£9.95**

# Heart of Albion

The UK's leading publisher of
folklore, mythology and cultural studies.

Further details of all Heart of Albion titles online at
**www.hoap.co.uk**

All titles available direct from Heart of Albion Press.
Please add 80p p&p (UK only; email
**albion@indigogroup.co.uk** for overseas postage).

To order books or request our current catalogue
please contact

## Heart of Albion Press

2 Cross Hill Close, Wymeswold
Loughborough, LE12 6UJ

Phone: 01509 880725
Fax: 01509 881715
email: albion@indigogroup.co.uk
Web site: www.hoap.co.uk